Saint Peter's University Library
Withdrawn

Computing Methods in Optimization Problems - 2

Computing Methods in Optimization Problems - 2

Edited by

Lotfi A. Zadeh
University of California,
Berkeley

Lucien W. Neustadt
University of Southern California,
Los Angeles

A. V. Balakrishnan
University of California,
Los Angeles

Papers Presented at a Conference held at San Remo, Italy September 9-13, 1968

Academic Press
New York • London
1969

ACADEMIC PRESS, INC.
111 Fifth Avenue, New York, New York 10003

United Kingdom Edition published by
ACADEMIC PRESS, INC. (LONDON) LTD.
Berkeley Square House, London W.1

LIBRARY OF CONGRESS CATALOG CARD NUMBER: 72-84161

PRINTED IN THE UNITED STATES OF AMERICA

PREFACE

This volume is based on papers presented at the Second International Conference on Computing Methods in Optimization Problems held in San Remo, Italy, September 9–13, 1968. The Conference was sponsored by the Society for Industrial and Applied Mathematics (SIAM), with the cooperation of the University of California and the University of Southern California, and was hosted by the Consiglio Nazionale Delle Ricerche, Italy. The Conference focused on recent advances in computational methods for optimization problems in diverse areas including: optimal control and trajectory problems; mathematical programming; economics, meteorology, biomedicine, and related areas; identification and inverse problems; computational aspects of decoding and information retrieval problems; and pattern recognition problems.

The Organizing Committee of the Conference consisted of: A. V. Balakrishnan (USA) Chairman, L. W. Neustadt (USA) Co-Chairman, L. A. Zadeh (USA) Co-Chairman, G. Debreu (USA), E. Gilbert (USA), H. Kelley (USA), J. Rosen (USA), J. Lions (France), A. Ruberti (Italy), A. Lepschy (Italy), E. Biondi (Italy), G. Marchuk (USSR), N. Moiseev (USSR), and B. Pschenichniy (USSR).

Lotfi A. Zadeh
Lucien W. Neustadt
A. V. Balakrishnan

May 1969

ERRATA

COMPUTING METHODS IN OPTIMIZATION PROBLEMS - 2

Edited by

Lotfi A. Zadeh,
Lucien W. Neustadt,
A. V. Balakrishnan

The material on page incorrectly numbered *222* should follow page *223.*

The material on pages incorrectly numbered *371-375* should follow page *393.*

CONTENTS

SOME COMPUTATIONAL CONSIDERATIONS IN INPUT SIGNAL SYNTHESIS PROBLEMS

M. Aoki* and R. M. Staley*
University of California, Los Angeles, California

This paper discusses some of the numerical techniques which have proved useful in the problem of input signal synthesis for system parameter identification. The system considered is a scalar input, scalar output discrete linear system with Gaussian additive noise on the observations. The identification problem is that of estimating the k-dimensional parameter vector $\underline{\phi}$ from the noisy observations. The input signal synthesis problem is that of determining the input signal $\{u_i\}$ which will minimize some functional related to the estimation error, subject to an energy constraint on the signal. It is assumed that the system is being operating off-line during the identification procedure, so that the input signal is open to choice.

The system equation is assumed to be of the form

$$x_{j+1}-a_1x_j-a_2x_{j-1} \cdots -a_kx_{j-k+1} = u_j \qquad (j = 0,1, \ldots ,n)$$

with known initial conditions

$$x_o = x_{-1} = \cdots = x_{-(k-1)} = 0$$

The measurements are taken to be of the form

$$y_j = x_j+n_j \quad (j = 1, \ldots ,n+1)$$

where $\{n_j\}$ is uncorrelated Gaussian noise with zero mean and standard deviation v.

The identification problem is that of estimating the (kx1) parameter vector defined by

$$\underline{\phi} = (a_1, \ldots ,a_k)^T$$

---

* Supported in part by AFOSR Grant 1328-67A

from the (n+1)x1 observation vector defined by

$$\underline{y} = (y_1, y_2, \ldots, y_{n+1})^T$$

It is quite difficult to obtain a closed form expression for the covariance matrix of the estimation error in a non-linear estimation problem of this kind. Hence, cost functionals which are defined directly on the covariance matrix of the estimation error are not easily minimized. An alternative procedure is to maximize the amount of information contained in the output about the unknown parameters, i.e. to maximize the objective function

$$J = tr[M_c]$$

where M_c is the (kxk) Fisher information matrix (1), defined by

$$M_c = \int_Y p(\underline{y}|\underline{\phi})[\nabla_{\underline{\phi}} \ln p(\underline{y}|\underline{\phi})][\nabla_{\underline{\phi}} \ln p(\underline{y}|\underline{\phi})]^T d\underline{y}$$

where for any scalar S the gradient is defined as

$$\nabla_{\underline{\phi}} S = (\frac{\partial S}{\partial a_1}, \ldots, \frac{\partial S}{\partial a_k})^T$$

This procedure is, of course, equivalent to minimizing the cost functional

$$J' = \frac{1}{tr[M_c]}$$

which takes on additional significance in light of the well known Cramer-Rao inequality (2), i.e.

$$E_{\underline{y}|\underline{\phi}} \{[\underline{\gamma}_c(\underline{y})-\underline{\phi}][\underline{\gamma}_c(\underline{y})-\underline{\phi}]^T\} \geq M_c^{-1}$$

where $\underline{\gamma}_c(\underline{y})$ is any unbiased conditional estimate of $\underline{\phi}$.

If the vector $\underline{v}$ is defined by

$$\underline{v} = (u_o, u_1, \ldots, u_n)^T$$

then it can be shown that the objective function J is given by the quadratic form

$$J = \underline{v}^T \mathcal{S}_u \underline{v}$$

where $\mathcal{S}_u$ is an (n+1)x(n+1) matrix of the form

$$\mathcal{S}_u = S_1^T G^T G^T G G S_1 + \dots + S_k^T G^T G^T G G S_k$$

The S_i matrix appearing in this expression is an (n+1)x(n+1) shift matrix of the form

$$S_i = \begin{bmatrix} 0 & \cdot & \cdot & \cdot & \cdot & \cdot & \cdot & \cdot & \cdot & 0 \\ \cdot & & & & & & & & & \cdot \\ \cdot & & & & & & & & & \cdot \\ \cdot & & & & & & & & & \cdot \\ 0 & & & & & & & & & \cdot \\ 1 & \ddots & & & & & & & & \cdot \\ 0 & & \ddots & & & & & & & \cdot \\ \cdot & & & \ddots & & & & & & \cdot \\ \cdot & & & & \ddots & & & & & \cdot \\ 0 & \cdot & \cdot & 0 & 1 & 0 & \cdot & \cdot & \cdot & 0 \end{bmatrix} \quad \leftarrow i^{th} \text{ row at the } 1$$

and the (n+1)x(n+1) G matrix is given by

$$G = g_1 I + g_2 S_1 + \dots g_{n+1} S_n$$

where $\{g_i\}$ represents the impulse response of the system, i.e. the solution to the equation

$$g_{j+1} - a_1 g_j - a_2 g_{j-1} \dots - a_k g_{j-k+1} = \delta_{j,o}$$

$$(j = 0, \dots, n)$$

with initial conditions

$$g_o = g_{-1} = \dots = g_{-(k-1)} = 0$$

where $\delta_{j,o}$ is the Kronecker delta function.

If the energy constraint

$$\underline{v}^T \underline{v} \leq K_1$$

is applied then it is clear that the objective function J will be maximized if $\underline{v}$ is an eigenvector of the matrix $\mathcal{S}_u$ corresponding to its largest eigenvalue. A typical solution for the eigenvector is presented in Fig. (1) for the case k=3, n=40.

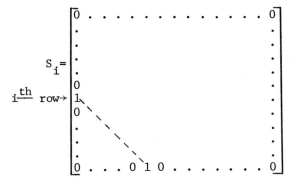

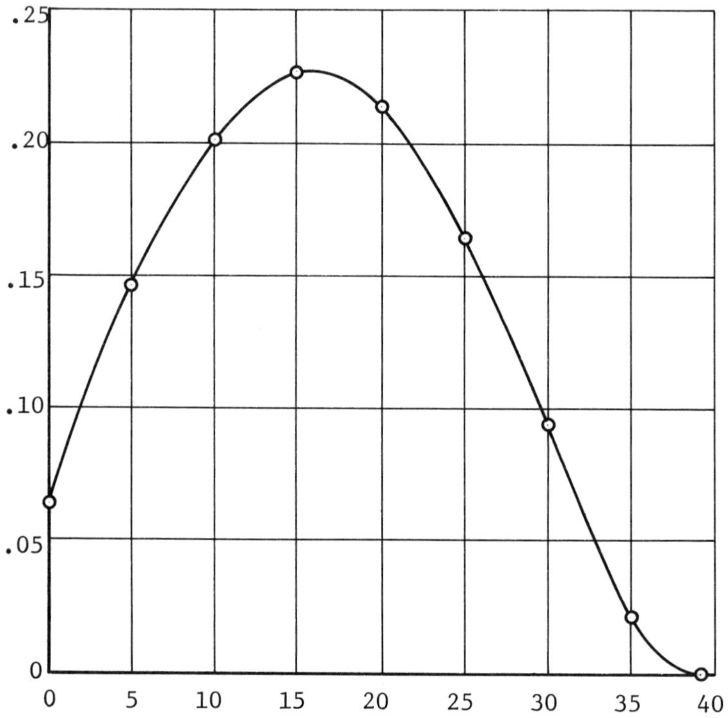

Fig. (1) - Eigenvector of the Matrix $\mathcal{S}_u$
Corresponding to λ_{max}, for $k = 3$

$a_1 = 1.5$

$a_2 = -0.74$

$a_3 = 0.12$

It has been shown that the matrix $\mathcal{S}_u$ can also be written in the form

$$\mathcal{S}_u = \left[\begin{array}{c|c} \mathcal{G}_u & 0 \\ \hline 0 & 0 \end{array}\right]$$

where $\mathcal{G}_u$ is a non-singular (nxn) matrix. Hence, if the vector $\underline{u}$ is defined as

$$\underline{u} = (u_o, u_1, \ldots, u_{n-1})^T$$

then the objective function can be rewritten as

$$J = \underline{u}^T \mathcal{G}_u \underline{u}$$

and the energy constraint becomes

$$\underline{u}^T \underline{u} + u_n^2 \leq K_1$$

Therefore, the vector $\underline{u}$ should be chosen to be an eigenvector of the matrix $\mathcal{G}_u$ corresponding to its largest eigenvalue, and u_n should be set to zero. Equivalently, $\underline{u}$ should be an eigenvector of the matrix $\mathcal{G}_u^{-1}$ corresponding to its smallest eigenvalue.

It has also been shown that $\mathcal{G}_u^{-1}$ can be approximated by a Toeplitz matrix (3) with elements $c_{ij} = c_{|i-j|}$, with $c_{ij} = 0$ for $|i-j| > 2k$. The approximation is valid in the sense that as n becomes large the eigenvector of C corresponding to its smallest eigenvalue approaches the eigenvector of $\mathcal{G}_u^{-1}$ corresponding to its smallest eigenvalue. A solution for the eigenvector of the matrix C corresponding to its smallest eigenvalue is shown in Fig. (2) for the same set of numbers employed in Fig. (1). A comparison of the two curves shows that they are quite similar.

All of these techniques require the determination of the eigenvector of an (nxn) matrix. For large values of n these methods become computationally unfeasible. A gradient technique has been developed to perform the input signal synthesis which avoids this problem of dealing with large matrices. The procedure differs from the usual steepest ascent method in that a modification is made to handle the energy constraint.

Using superscripts to differentiate vectors from differ-

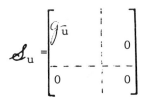

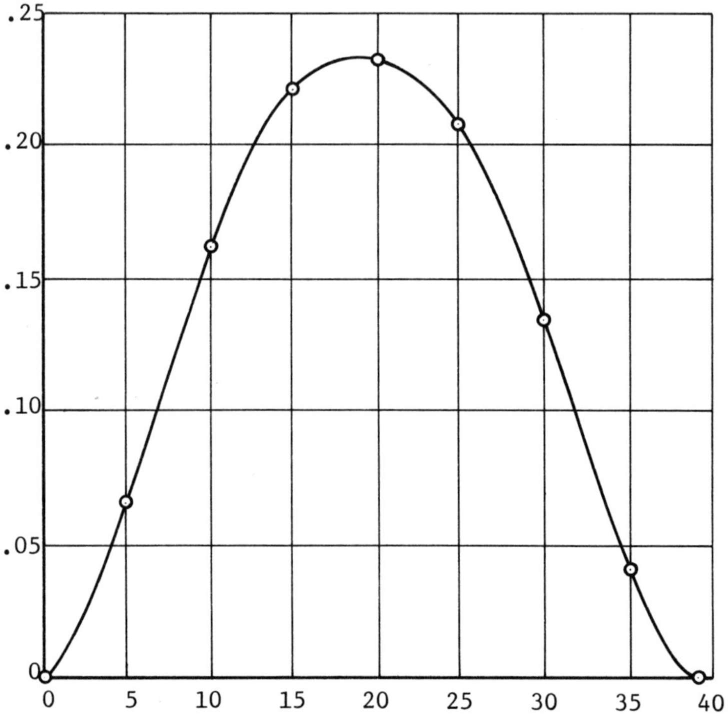

Fig. (2) - Eigenvector of the Toeplitz Matrix C Corresponding to λ_{min} for k = 3

$a_1 = 1.5$

$a_2 = -0.74$

$a_3 = 0.12$

ent steepest ascent passes, the resulting equations are of the form

$$\underline{w}^{j+1} = \underline{u}^{j} + K_j(\nabla_{\underline{u}} J)^{j}$$

and

$$\underline{u}^{j+1} = \frac{\underline{w}^{j+1}}{||\underline{w}^{j+1}||}\sqrt{K_1}$$

where $\nabla_{\underline{u}}J$ is the gradient of the objective function with respect to the vector $\underline{u}$, and K_j is a pre-set number. The gradient, $\nabla_{\underline{u}}J$, can be found by solving a set of forwards and backwards difference equations.

Some control vectors resulting from this procedure are shown in Fig. (3) for the case where $\underline{u}^{o}$ is a step function. After about three steepest ascent iterations there is very little change in the control vector, $\underline{u}$, or in the objective function.

The methods discussed so far have simply assumed that $\underline{\phi}$ was an unknown parameter vector. The resulting input signal synthesis procedures are somewhat unrealistic in that they require a knowledge of $\underline{\phi}$ to design the signal. They are presented only because they give some insight into the problem. A more realistic procedure is to assume that $\underline{\phi}$ is a random variable with an a priori density function $p(\underline{\phi})$. In this case the objective function is defined to be

$$J = tr\{E_{\underline{\phi}}[M_c]\}$$

where $E_{\underline{\phi}}$ represents expectation with respect to the random variable $\underline{\phi}$.

It is easily shown that the objective function is again a quadratic form in $\underline{v}$, and is given by

$$J = \underline{v}^T E_{\underline{\phi}}[\mathcal{S}_u]\underline{v}$$

where $\mathcal{S}_u$ was defined previously. Hence, the optimal input is an eigenvector of the matrix $E_{\underline{\phi}}[\mathcal{S}_u]$ corresponding to its largest eigenvalue. The other synthesis methods discussed above carry over in a similar manner.

A Monte Carlo simulation was devised to test the effectiveness of the input signals synthesized by the above techniques, and also to determine whether the use of feedback could further improve the accuracy of identification. It was assumed that an a priori density function $p(\underline{\phi})$ was available. The minimum variance unbiased estimate, or Bayes estimate, for

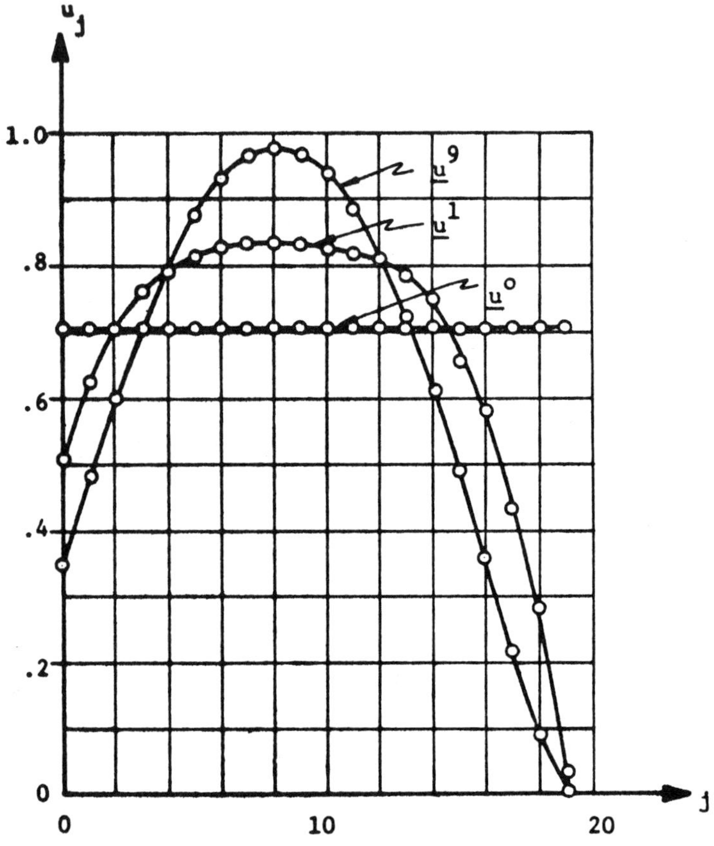

Fig. (3) - Some Control Vectors From the Steepest Ascent Procedure

a = 0.5

n = 19

$\underline{\phi}$ requires the evaluation of two rather difficult integrals after each observation. It has been suggested previously (4) that the computing load could be considerably reduced by representing the continuous distribution on $\underline{\phi}$ by a discrete distribution. In this case the required equations reduce to

$$p(\underline{y}^j) = \sum_{i=1}^{K_a} p(\underline{y}^j | \underline{\phi}_i) p(\underline{\phi}_i)$$

$$p(\underline{\phi}_i | \underline{y}^j) = \frac{p(\underline{y}^j | \underline{\phi}_i) p(\underline{\phi}_i)}{p(\underline{y}^j)}$$

and

$$\hat{\underline{\phi}} = \sum_{i=1}^{K_a} \underline{\phi}_i p(\underline{\phi}_i | \underline{y}^j)$$

where

$$\underline{y}^j = (y_1, \ldots, y_j)^T$$

These equations are considerably simpler to mechanize on the computer. However, it has been found that the estimate $\hat{\underline{\phi}}$ usually converges to one of the discrete $\underline{\phi}_i$ values as n becomes large. This effect can lead to sizeable errors if the original grid on the discrete points is very coarse. For this reason a procedure has been developed to re-select the $\underline{\phi}_i$ values on the basis of the observed data. The subroutine which performs this procedure is referred to as "Thresh" in the sequel.

The Thresh subroutine checks the a posteriori probability, i.e. $p(\underline{\phi}_i | \underline{y}^j)$ at each time step j. If this probability exceeds the threshold, T, for $\underline{\phi}_i = \underline{\phi}_T$ then a new set of $\underline{\phi}_i$ values is selected which are centered around $\underline{\phi}_T$ with reduced spacing. The effectiveness of this routine is demonstrated in Fig. (4) for the one parameter case with a step input. These results were obtained by making 200 Monte Carlo runs. Note that in the limit the two curves reach the same lower bound, which represents the performance which would have been obtained with the true Bayes estimate.

If an open loop feedback procedure (5) is used then the input signal is redesigned after each new observation. The same procedure is used as in the open loop case, except $p(\underline{\phi})$ is replaced by $p(\underline{\phi} | \underline{y}^j)$. Only the first component of the resulting control sequence is actually applied to the system. The true closed loop feedback control can only be obtained by

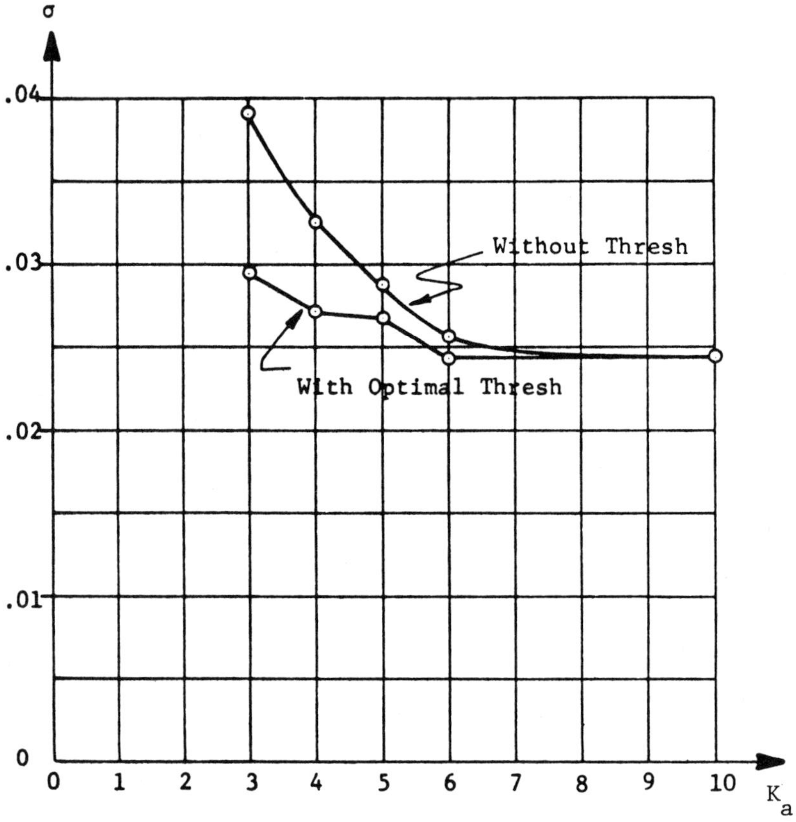

Fig. (4) - Standard Deviation of Estimation Error for a Step Input

$n = 10 \qquad M = 200$

$v = 0.25$

dynamic programming arguments, and is much more cumbersome to mechanize on the computer.

The results of the Monte Carlo studies for various inputs of equal energy are shown in Table 1.

It is evident from this table that the optimal open loop signal does give significant improvement over the other inputs, but that the open loop feedback procedure does not give enough further improvement to justify the increased complexity.

Table 1. - Standard Deviation of Estimation Error for Various Inputs in the One Parameter Case

Input	Standard Deviation
1. Worst Input (Impulse at n)	0.115
2. Impulse at j = 0	0.0387
3. Step Input	0.0242
4. Optimal Open Loop	0.0229
5. Open Loop Feedback	0.0228

References

1. Kullback, S., "Information Theory and Statistics", Wiley and Sons, New York, 1959.

2. Middleton, D., "An Introduction to Statistical Communication Theory", McGraw Hill Book Co., Inc., New York, 1960.

3. Grenander, M., and G. Szego, "Toeplitz Forms and Their Applications", University of Calif. Press, Berkeley and Los Angeles, 1958.

4. Mortensen, R. E., "Bayesian Identification of Nonlinear Systems", Proceedings of the Hawaii International Conference on System Sciences, Jan. 1968.

5. Dreyfus, S. E., "Some Types of Optimal Control of Stochastic Processes", SIAM Journal on Control, No. 1, pps. 120-134, 1964.

NUCLEAR REACTOR SYSTEMS AND THEIR ASSOCIATED VARIATIONAL AND OPTIMIZATION PROBLEMS

Martin Becker
Rensselaer Polytechnic Institute
Division of Nuclear Engineering and Science
Troy, New York

In the past several years there has been increasing interest in the use of optimization techniques in nuclear engineering. Even greater, however, has been the degree of development and implementation of variational methods as analytical tools. Much of the optimization and optimal control work has involved the application of general techniques (such as the maximum principle) to specific problems. Weaver has discussed the optimal control work in a recent text (1). (One interesting innovation has been the input-output concept suggested by Kyong and Gyftopoulos (2) and utilized by Stacey (3). This concept really falls under the heading of a direct variational method applied to an optimal control problem). Actually, most of the variational method work in nuclear engineering has not been associated directly with optimization problems. However, because of the close relation of the calculus of variations to optimization theory and of the interesting developments in variational methods made in connection with nuclear engineering problems, I shall devote this paper primarily to discussing these developments in the hope that these developments may be of some potential use to people working in optimization.

There have been two principal departures from conventional methods-least squares variational methods (LSV) (4) and discontinuous trial function variational methods (DVM) (5). The LSV are similar in philosophy to the approaches to optimization problems described at this conference by Kenneth, et.al. and DeJulio. While the LSV have been applied to several problems, (4,6-10) the DVM currently appear to hold greater immediate potential and therefore will be emphasized in this paper.

Let us begin by reviewing conventional variational methods. We assume that we are faced with an equation of either of the following types

$$H\phi - f = 0 \tag{1}$$

$$H\phi - \lambda M\phi = 0 \tag{2}$$

i.e., that we may be concerned with either a homogeneous or an inhomogeneous problem. We also assume that we have reason to believe that we can describe the solution in terms of certain trial functions ϕ_i

$$\phi = \sum_{i=1}^{N} a_i \phi_i \tag{3}$$

The unknown parameters a_i may be algebraic numbers (in which case we call the overall procedure a direct method) or they may be functions of some, though not all, of the independent variables (semidirect method). While the direct methods have been useful in nuclear engineering, the semidirect methods are of greater current and potential interest. This is because the nuclear engineer must solve multidimensional problems of great size and complexity. He therefore has much incentive for attempting to develop approximate techniques aimed at reducing the number of dimensions in the equations he must solve.

Upon making the expansion of Eq. (3), one must invoke a procedure for determining the coefficients a_i . A variational method will select the coefficients in such a way as to give an especially accurate value of some functional

$$J = \int_a^b dx\, F(x,\phi) \tag{4}$$

for which the equation of interest is the Euler equation. One then substitutes Eq. (3) into Eq. (4) and requires that the functional be insensitive to variations in the a_i , i.e., that the following equations be satisfied

$$\frac{\partial J}{\partial a_i} = 0 \qquad i = 1, \ldots, N \tag{5}$$

If a suitable functional of the form of Eq. (4) cannot be found, one can construct a functional upon the introduction of an auxiliary or adjoint function ϕ^* The variation of the functional with respect to ϕ^* should yield the equation of interest as the Euler equation, i.e.,

$$\delta J = \int_a^b dx\, \delta\phi^*(H\phi - f) \tag{6}$$

Integration with respect to ϕ^* yields the functional

$$J = \int_a^b dx \left[\phi^*(H\phi - f) - h(\phi, x) \right] \tag{7}$$

where $h(\phi, x)$ is a "constant of integration." Making the functional insensitive to variations in ϕ implies

$$H^*\phi^* - \frac{\partial h}{\partial \phi} = 0 \tag{8}$$

where H* is the adjoint operator. One chooses the term $h(\phi, x)$ in accordance with the significance one wishes to attach to the parameter that is calculated accurately, i.e., to the value of J. Procedurally, one expands

$$\phi^* = \sum_{i=1}^{N} a_i^* \phi_i^* \tag{9}$$

and requires

$$\frac{\partial J}{\partial a_i^*} = 0 \tag{10}$$

Variational methods have been applied to a wide variety of nuclear engineering problems including multidimensional neutron diffusion problems, space-energy problems, space-time problems and resonance absorption problems. Several of these applications are described in Volume 1 of the Naval Reactors Physics Handbook (11).

Because of the expense of generating trial functions (for example, a two dimensional diffusion problem with a small eigenvalue separation and about twenty thousand mesh points might take up to a few hours on even a very fast modern computer), there was incentive to try to handle even relatively non-separable problems with only a few trial functions. One might therefore wish to get greater capability from a few trial functions, rather than from addition of more trial functions. One way to get this capability is to break up the trial function into several components, each of which varies independently, i.e., by making the trial solution discontinuous. Thus, given a set of trial functions ϕ_i, we might write, instead of Eq. (3),

$$\phi^j(x) \approx \sum_{i=1}^{N} a_i^j \phi_i(x) \qquad j = 1, \ldots, J \tag{11}$$

where the j superscript denotes individual regions. One difficulty that existed, though, was that the variational principles used previously (11) for solving diffusion problems did not admit discontinuities of the type shown in Eq. (11). Selengut (12) pointed out that if one expressed the diffusion equation for neutron flux as two first-order equations, then the types of variational procedures used above would admit discontinuous trial functions. Wachspress and Becker (5,13) then implemented the suggestion in a manner to be described below.

It is interesting to note that the possibility of utilizing discontinuous trial functions with first-order equations had been recognized previously. Federighi (14) had formulated a variational principle for the Boltzmann transport equation with explicit accounting for spatially-discontinuous trial functions and utilized this principle in the derivation of interface conditions to be used in certain approximate procedures (the spherical harmonics method and Yvon's method). However, this contribution of Federighi did not receive wide recognition and the idea of utilizing discontinuities had to be presented again before this idea would have a significant impact on the nuclear engineering field.

The diffusion equation usually is written in the form

$$-D \frac{d^2\phi}{dx^2} + \Lambda\phi = 0 \tag{12}$$

where D is a diffusion coefficient and where Λ represents fission and absorption processes. To put this in first-order form, we write

$$\frac{dj}{dx} + \Lambda\phi = 0 \tag{13}$$

$$j + D\frac{d\phi}{dx} = 0 \tag{14}$$

where Eq. (13) is the equation of continuity and Eq. (14) is Fick's law of diffusion. Substitution of Eq. (14) into Eq. (13) yields Eq. (12). We now introduce adjoint flux and current variables and write the variational principle

$$F = \int_a^b \left[\phi^* \Lambda \phi + \phi^* \frac{dj}{dx} - j^* \frac{d\phi}{dx} - j^* D^{-1} j \right] dx \tag{15}$$

Let us consider a simple type of trial function

$$\phi(x) = a_1 \phi_1(x) \left[1 - u(x - x_0) \right] + a_2 \phi_2(x) u(x - x_0) \tag{16}$$

where u(y) is the unit step function. Using similar trial functions for all variables and assuming a "symmetric" discontinuity, i.e.,

$$\int_a^b u(x - x_0) \delta(x - x_0) dx = \frac{1}{2} \tag{17}$$

where $\delta(y)$ is the Dirac delta function, it follows that terms involving derivatives yield finite contributions at discontinuities

$$\int_{x_0-}^{x_0+} dx \, \phi^* \frac{dj}{dx} = \frac{1}{2} \left[\phi^*(x_0^+) + \phi^*(x_0^-) \right] \left[j(x_0^+) - j(x_0^-) \right] \tag{18}$$

The same results, Eq. (19), would be obtained if one were to use a more sophisticated mathematical limiting process in the vicinity of the discontinuity (15).

If we consider the variation of the functional Eq. (15) with respect to the adjoint flux using the simple type of trial function of Eq. (16), we obtain, upon making use of Eq. (18)

$$0 = \int_a^{x_0} dx \, \delta\phi_1^* \left(\frac{dj}{dx} + \Lambda \phi \right) + \int_{x_0}^b dx \, \delta\phi_2^* \left(\frac{dj}{dx} + \Lambda \phi \right)$$

$$+ \frac{1}{2} \left[\delta\phi_1^*(x_0) + \delta\phi_2^*(x_0) \right] \left[j_2(x_0) - j_1(x_0) \right] \tag{19}$$

If the variations are arbitrary, the continuity equation, Eq. (13), must be satisfied within regions. At the interface x_0, Eq. (19) implies continuity of current

$$j_2(x_0) = j_1(x_0) \tag{20}$$

However, no relation is implied between the variations of the adjoint flux on the two sides of the interface. When variations with respect to all variables are taken, continuity is implied for flux, adjoint flux, and adjoint current, but no relation is implied between variations of adjoint current, flux, and current on the two sides of the interface. Thus, while the variational principle implies that the exact solutions will be continuous, it does not imply that approximations need be continuous.

Several authors (13,16-20) have generated numerical results using discontinuous principles, but space does not permit discussion of many of these results here. One problem which illustrates well the potential gain that can be realized from discontinuous methods will be given here (19). A one-dimensional reactor governed by the diffusion equation is perturbed by changing the absorption on one side. The trial functions are "Green's function" modes (21) given by

$$-D\frac{d^2\phi_i}{dx^2} + \Sigma_a\phi_i = \Delta_i\,\nu\Sigma_f\phi_0 \tag{21}$$

$$\Lambda = \Sigma_a - \nu\Sigma_f \tag{22}$$

$$\Delta_i = \begin{cases} 1 & \text{in Region } i \\ 0 & \text{elsewhere} \end{cases} \tag{23}$$

where Λ has been broken up into absorption and fission terms. Two regions were used, one corresponding to each side of the reactor. The trial solutions for the DVM were

$$\phi^k = a_1^k\phi_1^k + a_2^k\phi_2^k \tag{24}$$

$$j^k = b^k - C_1^k D_1\frac{d\phi_1^k}{dx} - C_2^k D_2\frac{d\phi_2^k}{dx} \tag{25}$$

where k denotes region number and subscripts denote trial function numbers. The reason for using the constant term b^k in the current trial function will be explained below. Table 1 shows the tilt factors

$$T = 1 - \frac{\int\phi_L\,dx}{\int\phi_H\,dx} \tag{26}$$

(k and H denote low-flux and high-flux regions of the reactor) from exact, standard continuous variational (STD) and DVM calculations for various reactor sizes. The improvement is striking.

The ability to use a constant term in Eq. (25) is important. It has been shown (15), for example, that one can admit discontinuous trial functions with a variational principle based on the second order form of the diffusion equation. The principle is

$$F = \frac{1}{2}\left(\int_a^{x_0} dx + \int_{x_0}^{b} dx\right)\left[-\left(\frac{d\phi}{dx}\right) + \lambda\phi^2\right] + \frac{1}{2}\left[\frac{d\phi}{dx}(x_0^+) + \frac{d\phi}{dx}(x_0^-)\right]\left[\phi(x_0^-) - \phi(x_0^+)\right] \tag{27}$$

For a simple trial function of the form Eq. (16), one obtains as one of the algebraic equations

$$\frac{1}{2}\, a_2 D(x_0^-)\, \frac{d\phi_1}{dx}(x_0^-)\phi_2(x_0^+) = a_1 \int_a^{x_0} dx\, \phi_1\left(D\frac{d^2\phi_1}{dx^2} + \lambda\phi_1\right) \tag{28}$$

If a trial function has a zero gradient at the discontinuity, then there is no solution. However, use of the first order form and the constant term permits a solution. An example with a zero gradient at an interface is given in Reference (13).

In semidirect applications, there is a restriction on the flexibility available for allowing discontinuities (22). With a second variable E (which could denote neutron energy), one obtains terms such as

$$\int dE\left[\delta\Phi_1^*(x_0,E) + \delta\Phi_2^*(x_0,E)\right]\left[J_2(x_0,E) - J_1(x_0,E)\right] = 0 \tag{29}$$

If one assumes simple trial functions, such as

$$J(x,E) = \begin{cases} j_1(x)\, f_1(E) & x < x_0 \\ j_2(x)\, f_2(E) & x > x_0 \end{cases} \tag{30}$$

for all variables, the vanishing of coefficients of arbitrary variations implies the equations

$$\int dx\, \phi_2^*(E) \left[j_2(x_0)\, f_2(E) - j_1(x_0)\, f_1(E) \right] = 0 \tag{31}$$

$$\int dx\, \phi_1^*(E) \left[j_2(x_0)\, f_2(E) - j_1(x_0)\, f_1(E) \right] = 0 \tag{32}$$

These equations can be inconsistent. The response to this problem has been to utilize "staggered discontinuities" (5). If the flux and current quantities (or the direct and adjoint quantities) are not discontinuous at the same location, then Eqs. (31) and (32) can be satisfied.

Buslik (22) has suggested a method of avoiding the problem. He introduces additional "multiplier" functions at the interfaces and expands these in trial functions. While the inconsistency problem is avoided, one must provide additional trial functions, possibly at positions where one may have little insight into how those trial functions should be selected.

Other approaches are possible in specific types of problems (23-25). In initial-value problems, for example, one can take advantage of the forward-bias of the time-like variable and utilize an asymmetric discontinuity. One could use a functional (15)

$$F = \sum_k F_k + \sum_i \int dx \left\{ \phi^*(x,\tau_i^-) \left[1 - \beta_i(x) \right] + \beta_i(x)\, \phi^*(x,\tau_i^+) \right\} \cdot \left[\phi(x,\tau^-) - \phi(x,\tau^+) \right] \tag{33}$$

where F_k is an integral over time interval k. A discontinuity is permitted at time τ_i for arbitrary $\beta_i(x)$. However, if

$$\beta_i(x) = 1 \tag{34}$$

the inconsistency problem is eliminated. (If β_i were zero, there still would be a problem (24)).

Another common situation (23,25) is the expansion of a function near an interface in terms of asymptotic solutions far from the interface. For example, one might assume that the neutron energy distribution near an interface between two media can be represented by an interpolation between the asymptotic energy distributions far from the interface. If there are many media and interfaces, one would like to use different trial functions in different regions, since a distribution appropriate near one interface may not be appropriate several media away. It turns out that at the logical locations for switching trial functions, the amplitudes of some trial functions will be very small compared to the rest. It can be shown (23) that one can take advantage of the disparity in magnitudes to eliminate the inconsistency problem.

As was mentioned earlier, one important incentive toward using the DVM is that it appears to be more economical, at least in some important nuclear engineering applications, to add to the number of undetermined coefficients per trial function than to add to the number of trial functions. Even so, the effective number of additional coefficients is not as great as one might suspect at first glance. In the trial function expansions of Eqs. (24) and (25) for two trial functions and two regions, there are ten undetermined coefficients, five for each region. However, the matrices obtained are reducible, and the coefficients associated with Eq. (25) can be expressed in terms of those for Eq. (24). Thus, in effect, one must solve for four coefficients. (In the continuous approach, of course, there are two coefficients). This reducibility appears in the general formulation (5), and is not restricted to the example chosen.

In summary, the use of discontinuous trial function variational methods provides the potential for increased flexibility in the use of variational methods as an analytical tool. Numerical results obtained to date by various investigators on a variety of problems have been quite promising. While useful results are being generated, the theoretical development is still at an early stage. Although the developments to date have not been oriented toward optimization problems, the importance of the calculus of variations in optimization leads me to believe that improvements in variational techniques should have implications for computing methods in optimization problems.

Table 1. Comparison of Tilt Calculations

Size (cm)	STD	DVM	EXACT
260	.0492	.1080	.1211
240	.0524	.1086	.1212
220	.0557	.1094	.1214
200	.0596	.1103	.1216
180	.0643	.1114	.1219
160	.0697	.1127	.1224
140	.0765	.1145	.1231

REFERENCES

1. L. Weaver, Reactor Dynamics and Control, American Elsevier, New York, 1968.
2. S. Kyong and E. P. Gyftopoulos, "Input-Output Approach to Optimal Control," Trans. Am. Nuc. Soc. 8, 479 (1965).
3. W. M. Stacey, "Application A Variational Synthesis to the Optimal Control of a Point Reactor Model," Nucl. Sci. Eng. 33, 257 (1968).
4. M. Becker, The Principles and Applications of Variational Methods, MIT Press, Cambridge, Mass., 1964; M. Becker, "Semidirect Least Squares Variational Methods and Initial-Value Problems," Trans. Am. Nuc. Soc. 10, 550 (1967).
5. E. L. Wachspress, and M. Becker, "Variational Synthesis with Discontinuous Trial Functions," Proc. Conf. Application of Computer Methods to Reactor Problems, AEC Report ANL-7105, p. 191, 1965.
6. T. E. Murley and I. Kaplan, "A Modal Representation of Fast Reactor Spectra," Trans. Am. Nuc. Soc. 8, 238 (1965).
7. H. Fenech, A. Goodjohn and A. D. McWhirter, "A Useful Approximation for the Spatial and Energy Dependence of the Scalar Flux in Heterogeneous Media," Trans. Am. Nuc. Soc. 8, 227 (1965).
8. R. Bobone, "The Method of Solution Functions: A Computer-Oriented Solution of Boundary Value Problems as Applied to Nuclear Reactors-Part 1. Cylindrical Reactors in ρ-θ Geometry," Nucl. Sci. Eng. 29, 337 (1967).
9. J. D. Jenkins and P. B. Daitch, "Analysis of Pulsed Fast-Neutron Spectra in Multiplying Assemblies," Nucl. Sci. Eng. 31, 222 (1968).
10. P. F. Gast, "Criteria for the Density of Monitoring Points in Large Reactors," Proc. Conf. Safety, Fuels and Core Design in Large Fast Power Reactors, AEC Report ANL-7120, 1965.
11. A. Radkowsky, ed. Naval Reactors Physics Handbook, Vol. I, USAEC, Washington, 1964.
12. D. S. Selengut, unpublished work, 1964.
13. E. L. Wachspress and M. Becker, "Variational Multichannel Synthesis with Discontinuous Trial Functions", AEC Report KAPL-3095, 1965.
14. F. D. Federighi, "Variational Methods in Nuclear Reactor Physics," Ph.D. Thesis, Harvard University, 1961.

15. G. C. Pomraning, "A Variational Description of Dissipative Processes," J. Nucl. Energy, Parts A & B 20, 617 (1966).
16. E. L. Wachspress, "Some Mathematical Properties of the Multichannel Variational Synthesis Equations and Two-Dimensional Synthesis Numerical Studies," AEC Report KAPL-M-6588 (ELW-13), 1966.
17. J. B. Yasinsky and S. Kaplan, "Synthesis of Three-Dimensional Flux Shapes Using Discontinuous Sets of Trial Functions," Nucl. Sci. Eng. 28, 426 (1967).
18. J. B. Yasinsky, "The Solution of the Space-Time Neutron Group Diffusion Equations by a Time-Discontinuous Synthesis Method," Nucl. Sci. Eng. 29, 381 (1967).
19. P. C. Rohr and M. Becker, "Modal Analysis of Power Tilting," Trans. Am. Nuc. Soc. 11, 169 (1968).
20. W. M. Stacey, "A Variational Multichannel Space-Time Synthesis Method for Nonseparable Reactor Transients," Nucl. Sci. Eng. 34, 45 (1968).
21. D. E. Dougherty and C. N. Shen, "The Space-Time Neutron Kinetics Equation Obtained by the Semidirect Variational Method," Nucl. Sci. Eng. 13, 143 (1962).
22. A. J. Buslik, "A Variational Principle for the Neutron-Diffusion Equation Using Discontinuous Trial Functions," Trans. Am. Nuc. Soc. 9, 199 (1966).
23. M. Becker, "Overlapping Group Methods with Discontinuous Trial Functions," Nucl. Sci. Eng., in press.
24. M. Becker, "Asymmetric Discontinuities in Synthesis Techniques for Initial-Value Problems," Nucl. Sci. Eng., in press.
25. M. Becker, "Methods of Resolving Interface Ambiguities in Discontinuous Variational Methods," Trans. Am. Nuc. Soc., Vol. II, No. 2, 1968.

IDENTIFICATION DE SYSTEMES GOUVERNES
PAR DES EQUATIONS AUX DERIVEES PARTIELLES

A. BENSOUSSAN

Institut de Recherche d'Informatique et d'Automatique (I.R.I.A.),
78 - Rocquencourt, France.

I - UN EXEMPLE

On considère le système

$$(1)\quad \begin{cases} \dfrac{\partial y}{\partial t} - u\Delta y = f + B\xi(t,x) & x \in \Omega \quad t \in]0,T[. \\ \left.\dfrac{\partial y}{\partial n}\right|_{\Sigma} = 0 \ , \ \Sigma = \partial(\Omega \times]0,T[) \ , \Gamma = \partial\Omega \\ y(0) = \zeta(x) . \end{cases}$$

On peut supposer que $\xi(t,x)$ et $\zeta(x)$ sont des fonctions aléatoires dont les caractéristiques stochastiques sont connues. Le paramètre u est inconnu et à identifier.

On fait fonctionner le système et on fait des observations : Par exemple, une observation naturelle est la suivante :

$$(2)\quad z(t,x) = y(t,x)|_{\Gamma} + \eta(t,x)|_{\Gamma} \qquad t \in]0,T[;$$

$y(t,x)$ étant une erreur de mesure, fonction aléatoire dont on connaît les caractéristiques stochastiques.

Le problème consiste alors à définir le meilleur estimateur de u. Bien entendu, il faut expliciter ce qu'on entend par "meilleur". On examine ici un critère de type Bayésien.

II - DIFFICULTES

1. Difficultés de nature probabiliste :

Dans les systèmes physiques les fonctions aléatoires intervenant sont généralement des bruits blancs.

2. Difficultés de calcul :

S'il est possible de définir un estimateur, il n'en reste pas moins que le calcul exact est généralement impossible, d'où la nécessité de trouver des algorithmes d'approximation.

III - NOTIONS SUR LES PROCESSUS LINEAIRES

Soit Φ un Hilbert identifié à son dual. On considère une famille $X_\varphi(\omega)$ de variables aléatoires réelles, telle que la fonction

$$\varphi \longrightarrow X_\varphi(\omega) \quad \text{soit linéaire (de } V \text{ dans } R \text{ ; } \omega \text{ fixé) .}$$

On suppose que

$EX\varphi$ et $E[X\varphi X\psi]$ existent $\forall \varphi, \psi \in V$;

Les applications

$\varphi \longrightarrow EX\varphi$

et

$\varphi, \psi \longrightarrow E[X\varphi X\psi]$,

sont respectivement linéaire et bilinéaire , mais en général non continues. Nous ferons l'hypothèse supplémentaire qu'elles sont continues. Dans ces conditions, il existe $m \in \Phi$ et $\Lambda \in \mathcal{L}(\Phi, \Phi)$ tels que

(3) $EX\varphi = (m, \varphi)$. $, \forall \varphi \in \Phi$

(4) $EX_\varphi X_\psi - EX_\varphi EX_\psi = (\Lambda\varphi, \psi)$ $, \forall \varphi, \psi \in \Phi$;

Λ étant par définition > 0 et auto adjoint.

Si m et Λ existent, nous les appellerons respectivement, Espérance Mathématique et Opérateur de Covariance du processus $X\varphi(\omega)$. Nous dirons que $X\varphi(\omega)$ est un processus Gaussien, si $\forall \varphi$ la variable aléatoire $X\varphi(\omega)$ est une variable aléatoire Gaussienne (de moyenne (m, φ) et de variance $(\Lambda\varphi, \varphi)$) .

Cette notion de processus linéaire est une généralisation de la notion de variable aléatoire à valeur dans un Hilbert. En effet, une variable aléatoire à valeur dans Φ est une application mesurable d'un espace d'épreuves $\underline{\omega}$ dans Φ , soit $X(\omega)$.

Dans ces conditions $(\varphi, X(\omega))$ est un processus linéaire .

Réciproquement, étant donné un processus Gaussien, défini par une espérance mathématique m et un opérateur de covariance Λ, un problème important est de savoir s'il correspond à une variable aléatoire $X(\omega)$ à valeur dans un Hilbert.

La réponse à ce problème est fournie par le théorème de Minlos [1]

La C.N.S. pour que

(5) $$X\varphi(\omega) = (\varphi, X(\omega))$$

est que Λ soit un opérateur nucléaire.

Nous appellerons propriété P la propriété

P : Λ est un opérateur nucléaire.

IV - LE PROBLEME D'ESTIMATION DANS LE CAS OU LA PROPRIETE P A LIEU :

Soit $\mathcal{U}$ un espace de Hilbert (en général de dimension finie), espace des paramètres u . Nous nous donnons sur $\mathcal{U}$ une loi de probabilité μ , concentrée sur un convexe fermé borné U_0 de $\mathcal{U}$.

Soit K un Hilbert, espace des observations.

Nous nous donnons sur K , une famille dépendant de u , de processus Gaussiens $Y_k(\omega ; u)$ ($\omega \in \bar{\omega}$ espace d'épreuves, $k \in K$) d'espérance mathématique $\bar{Y}(u)$ et d'opérateur de covariance $\Lambda(u)$.

Nous supposons que

(6) $u \longrightarrow \bar{Y}(u)$ est μ-mesurable de U dans K ,

(7) $u \longrightarrow (\Lambda(u)\varphi, \psi)$ est μ-mesurable ,

(8) $\forall u$, $\Lambda(u) \in \mathcal{L}(K;K)$ est auto-adjoint défini positif ou nul,

(9) $\forall u$, $\Lambda(u)$ possède la propriété P .

En raison de (9) on a

(10) $Y_k(\omega;u) = (k\ ,\ Y(\omega;u))$.
Soit G_u la loi de probabilité (u étant fixé) de la variable aléatoire $Y(\omega;u)$ à valeur dans K ;
g_u est en fait une fonction de transition, i.e. $g_u(f)$ dépend mesurablement de u (par rapport à la mesure μ) $\forall f \in \mathcal{B}(K)$, ($\mathcal{B}(K)$= ensemble des fonctions continues et bornées sur K ; pour la définition des mesures de Radon sur un espace topologique arbitraire cf [1]).
Il existe donc une <u>loi de probabilité</u> $\rho = \mu \otimes g_u$ sur l'espace produit $U \times K$.
Soit $L^2_U(\rho)$ l'espace de Hilbert des variables aléatoires définies sur $U \times K$ à valeur dans $\mathcal{U}$ dont le carré de la norme est ρ-sommable. Soit W le sous-espace fermé dans $L^2_U(\rho)$, des variables aléatoires ρ- p.s. indépendantes de u .

<u>Définition</u> : On appelle <u>estimateur de Bayes</u> du paramètre u, la projection sur W de la fonction de $L^2_U(\rho)$, identique à u .

<u>Remarque</u> : ρ est la loi de probabilité du couple (u,Y) paramètre à identifier, observation ; $L^2_U(\rho)$ est l'espace des fonctions de (u,Y) de carré ρ - sommable. Un estimateur de u est une fonction $\in L^2_U(\rho)$, qui ne dépend que de Y.

V - <u>ALGORITHME D'APPROXIMATION DE L'ESTIMATEUR DE BAYES</u>

En général, on ne peut calculer exactement les fonctions $\bar{Y}(u)$ et $\Lambda(u)$. On est obligé de passer par une discrétisation. Nous ferons les hypothèses suivantes :
Soit ξ un paramètre de dimension finie, destiné à tendre vers 0 .
Nous supposons données des familles $\bar{Y}_\xi(u)$ et $\Lambda_\xi(u)$ telles que

(11) $(\bar{Y}_\xi(u), \varphi)_K \longrightarrow (\bar{Y}(u), \varphi)_K \ \forall u\ ;\ \forall \varphi$ lorsque $\xi \longrightarrow 0$,

(12) $(\Lambda_\xi(u)\varphi, \psi)_K \longrightarrow (\Lambda(u)\varphi, \psi)_K \ \forall u\ ; \forall \varphi; \forall \psi$ lorsque $\xi \rightarrow 0$.

Nous nous donnons également, h étant un paramètre de dimension finie, destiné à tendre vers 0 , une famille K_h de sous espaces vectoriels fermés de K(dimension de $K_h = N(h))^h$.
Soit e_h^j , j = 1 ... N(h) une base de K_h . Nous désignons par τ_h l'application $\in \mathcal{L}(K; R^{N(h)})$ définie par

(13) $(\tau_h \varphi)^i = (\varphi, e_h^i) \quad i = 1 \dots N(h) \ , \ \varphi \in K$,

et par $\Lambda_{h\xi}(u)$ la famille de matrices

(14) $(\Lambda_{h\xi}(u))_{ij} = (\Lambda_\xi(u)\, e_h^i\ ,\ e_h^j) \qquad i, j = 1 \dots N(h)$;

$\hat{u}(Y)$ désignant l'estimateur de Bayes, nous appellerons <u>estimateur de Bayes approché</u> l'élément $\hat{u}_{h\xi}(Y)$ de W défini par

$$(15)\quad \hat{u}_{h\xi}(Y) = \frac{\displaystyle\int_U d\mu(u)u \frac{e^{\frac{1}{2}(\Lambda^{-1}_{h\xi}(u)(\tau_h Y - \tau_h \overline{Y}_\xi(u)), \tau_h Y - \tau_h \overline{Y}_\xi(u))_{R^{N(h)}}}}{\sqrt{|\Lambda_{h\xi}(u)|}}}{\displaystyle\int_U d\mu(u) \frac{e^{-\frac{1}{2}(\Lambda^{-1}_{h\xi}(u)(\tau_h Y - \tau_h \overline{Y}_\xi(u)), \tau_h Y - \tau_h \overline{Y}(u))_{R^{N(h)}}}}{\sqrt{|\Lambda_{h\xi}(u)|}}}$$

Nous avons

<u>Théorème</u> 1 : Sous les hypothèses et notations de V , la suite $\hat{u}_{h\xi}(Y)$ converge fortement dans $L^2_U(\rho)$ vers l'estimateur de Bayes $\hat{u}(Y)$, lorsque $h, \xi \longrightarrow 0$.

Pour la démonstration du théorème 1, nous renvoyons à [2] .

VI - <u>EXEMPLE</u>

Considérons le système

$$(16)\quad \begin{cases} \dfrac{\partial y}{\partial t} - \dfrac{u\partial^2 y}{\partial x^2} = 0 . & x \in]0,1[\qquad t \in]0,T[\\ \dfrac{\partial y}{\partial x}(t,0) = \dfrac{\partial y}{\partial x}(t,1) = 0 \\ y(0,x) = y_0(x) ; \end{cases}$$

<u>Observation</u>

$$z(t) = y(t,0) + \eta(t) .$$

Alors K espace des observations est $L^2(0,T)$. On considère un découpage de $[0,T]$

$$0,\ h,\ 2h \ldots \qquad rh = T .$$

Soit $w_m(t)$ la fonction caractéristique de $[m\,h, (m+1)h[$;

K_h est l'espace des $\varphi_h(t)$ définies par

$$(17)\quad \varphi_h(t) = \sum_{m=0}^{r-1} w_m(t)\, \varphi_h(mh) ,$$

$$(18)\quad e_h^i = \frac{w_i(t)}{\sqrt{h}} ,$$

$$(19)\quad \tau_h \varphi = \left[\frac{1}{\sqrt{h}} \int_0^h \varphi(t)dt, \ldots, \frac{1}{\sqrt{h}} \int_{mh}^{(m+1)h} \varphi(t)dt, \ldots, \frac{1}{\sqrt{h}} \int_{(r-1)h}^{rh} \varphi(t)dt\right]$$

L'observation Y est alors définie par $Y = z(t),\ t \in [0,T]$.

Nous avons

$$(20)\quad Y(u) \equiv y(t,0;u) .$$

En analyse numérique, il existe des procédés d'approximation de la solution de (16). Soit $y_\xi(t,0;u)$ une telle approximation (ξ désignant un indice de discrétisation, ici en x et t). Remarquons que d'après l'hypothèse (11) seule la convergence faible dans $L^2(0,T)$ de $y_\xi(t,0;u)$ vers $y(t,0;u)$ est nécessaire. On peut employer indifféremment les schémas de CEA ou RAVIART ([3] [4]).

Si Λ désigne l'opérateur de covariance du bruit $\eta(t)$, considéré comme un élément de $L^2(0,T)$, nous avons ici

(21) $\Lambda(u) = \Lambda$,

relation qui résulte du fait que le système étudié est non stochastique.

Remarquons que si $\Gamma(t_1,t_2)$ désigne la fonction de corrélation du bruit $\eta(t)$, dire que Λ est nucléaire signifie que

$$\int_0^T \Gamma(t,t)dt < +\infty .$$

VII - ESTIMATION DANS LE CAS OU LA PROPRIETE P N'A PAS LIEU

Nous ne supposons plus que P a lieu, mais par contre, nous supposons qu'a lieu la propriété P' suivante

(22) P' : Λ est un opérateur inversible.

Cette hypothèse est faite très couramment dans la pratique, lorsqu'on admet par exemple que l'erreur de mesure est un bruit blanc.

En effet, prenons le cas de $K = L^2(0,T)$ et $\Lambda =$ identité.

Un processus Gaussien sur K est donc une famille $\xi_\varphi(\omega)$ de variables aléatoires réelles ($\varphi \in L^2(0,T)$) et nous avons

$$(23) \qquad E\{\xi_\varphi(\omega)\,\xi_\psi(\omega)\} = (\Lambda\varphi,\psi)_{L^2(0,T)} = \int_0^T \varphi(t)\psi(t)dt .$$

Si on pose formellement

$$(24) \qquad \xi_\varphi(\omega) = \int_0^T \xi(t,\omega)\varphi(t)dt .$$

Il est clair que, pour que la formule (23) soit valable, on doit définir la fonction de corrélation de la fonction aléatoire $\xi(t,\omega)$ par

$$(25) \qquad E\{\xi(t_1,\omega)\,\xi(t_2,\omega)\} = \delta(t_1-t_2) .$$

Nous ferons maintenant sur l'observation $Y_k(\omega;u)$ l'hypothèse

$$(26) \qquad Y_k(\omega;u) = (\bar{Y}(u),\varphi) + \eta_k(\omega) ,$$

où $\eta_k(\omega)$ est un processus Gaussien d'espérance mathématique 0 et d'opérateur de covariance Λ inversible.

D'après la réciproque du théorème de Minlos, il est clair que $Y_k(\omega,u)$ ne peut être associé à une variable aléatoire à valeur dans K. Par conséquent, il n'est pas possible de définir l'estimateur de Bayes comme précédemment. Cependant pour $Y = Y_d$ fixé dans K , nous pouvons toujours considérer la formule (15) de l'estimateur de Bayes approché, qui est, elle, parfaitement définie. Si nous posons

(27) $$(\Lambda_h)_{ij} = (\Lambda e_h^i , e_h^j) ,$$

la formule (15) prend la forme pour $Y = Y_d$ fixé

(28) $$\hat{u}_{h\xi}(Y_d) = \frac{\int_U d\mu(u) u e^{-\frac{1}{2}(\Lambda_h^{-1}(\tau_h Y_d - \tau_h \bar{Y}_\xi(u)), \tau_h Y_d - \tau_h \bar{Y}_\xi(u))}}{\int_U d\mu(u)\, e^{-\frac{1}{2}(\Lambda_h^{-1}(\tau_h Y_d - \tau_h \bar{Y}_\xi(u)), \tau_h Y_d - \tau_h \bar{Y}_\xi(u))}} .$$

Nous avons alors

Théorème 2 : Sous les hypothèses et notations de VII la suite $\hat{u}_{h\xi}(Y_d)$ converge, lorsque $h,\xi \to 0$, fortement dans U et $\forall Y_d \in K$, vers $\hat{u}(Yd)$ défini par

(29) $$\hat{u}(Y_d) = \frac{\int_U d\mu(u) u e^{-\frac{1}{2}(\Lambda^{-1}(Y_d - \bar{Y}(u)), Y_d - \bar{Y}(u))}}{\int_U d\mu(u)\, e^{-\frac{1}{2}(\Lambda^{-1}(Y_d - \bar{Y}(u)), Y_d - \bar{Y}(u))}}$$

Remarque : Seules possèdent un sens du point de vue probabiliste les formules discrétisées (28) donnant $\hat{u}_{h\xi}(Y_d)$. Le théorème 2 montre alors la stabilité et la convergence de ces formules La limite (29) peut donc, de façon naturelle, être appelée estimateur de Bayes dans le cas considéré (où la propriété P' a lieu).

VIII - EXEMPLE NUMERIQUE

On a considéré le problème

(30) $$\begin{cases} \dfrac{\partial y}{\partial t} - \dfrac{u\partial^2 y}{\partial x^2} = f & x \in]0,1[\quad t \in]0,T[. \\ \dfrac{\partial y}{\partial x}(t,0) = \dfrac{y}{x}(t,1) = 0 \\ y(0,x) = y_o \end{cases}$$

avec

(31) $$f(x,t) = \gamma \cos \pi x \, e^{\beta \pi^2 t}$$

(32) $$y_o(x) = 0 .$$

L'observation est définie par

$$z(t) = y(t,0) + \eta(t) \quad ,$$

$\eta(t)$ est un <u>bruit blanc</u> d'écart type σ, i.e,

$$(33) \qquad E\left\{\eta(t_1)\eta(t_2)\right\} = \sigma\delta(t_1 - t_2) \; .$$

Nous avons traité le problème par <u>simulation</u>. En effet avec le choix de la fonction f en (31) on peut définir exactement la solution de (30) soit

$$(34) \quad y(t,x) = \left\{\gamma\left(-\frac{1}{(u+\beta)\pi^2}\right)e^{-u\pi^2 t} + \frac{\gamma e^{\beta\pi^2 t}}{(u+\beta)\pi^2}\right\}\cos\pi x$$

Nous nous sommes donné la valeur vraie u_o de u, ce qui permet de calculer exactement

$$(35) \quad y(t,x) = \gamma\left(-\frac{1}{(u_o+\beta)\pi^2}\right)e^{-u_o\pi^2 t} + \frac{\gamma e^{\beta\pi^2 t}}{(u_o+\beta)\pi^2} \; .$$

La formule à appliquer est alors la formule (28) avec $\Lambda_h = \sigma^2 I$ soit

$$(36) \quad \hat{u}_{h\xi}(Y_d) = \frac{\int_U d\mu(u)\, u\, e^{-\frac{1}{2\sigma^2}\left\|\tau_h Y_d - \tau_h \bar{Y}_\xi(u)\right\|^2}}{\int_U d\mu(u)\, e^{-\frac{1}{2\sigma^2}\left\|\tau_h Y_d - \tau_h \bar{Y}_\xi(u)\right\|^2}} ,$$

avec pour $m = 0 \ldots r-1$

$$(37) \left[\tau_h Y_d\right]_m = \frac{1}{\sqrt{h}}\int_{mh}^{(m+1)h}\left\{\frac{-\gamma e^{-u_o\pi^2 t}}{(u_o+\beta)\pi^2} + \frac{\gamma e^{\beta\pi^2 t}}{(u_o+\beta)\pi^2}\right\}dt + \zeta_m ,$$

ζ_m <u>variable aléatoire Gaussienne</u> de moyenne nulle, d'écart type σ .

Nous avons pris pour μ une distribution uniforme sur un intervalle borné.

<u>Application numérique</u> :

$\gamma = 10$, $\beta = 0{,}5$, $\sigma = 0{,}1$.

θ_0 valeur vraie du paramètre = 7 .

<u>1er essai</u> : valeurs possibles de θ à priori 1,2,... 51 avec une <u>probabilité égale</u>

- <u>nombre de Runs</u> : 60

<u>moyenne expérimentale de l'estimateur optimal</u>: 7,76

<u>variance expérimentale de l'estimateur optimal</u>: 0,03

cf. figure 1.

Figure 1

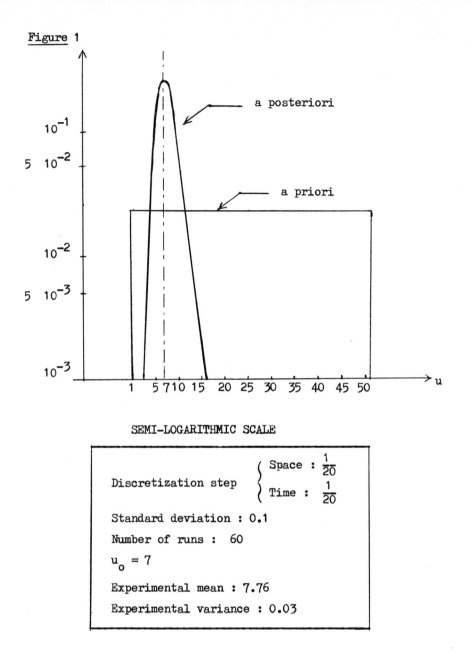

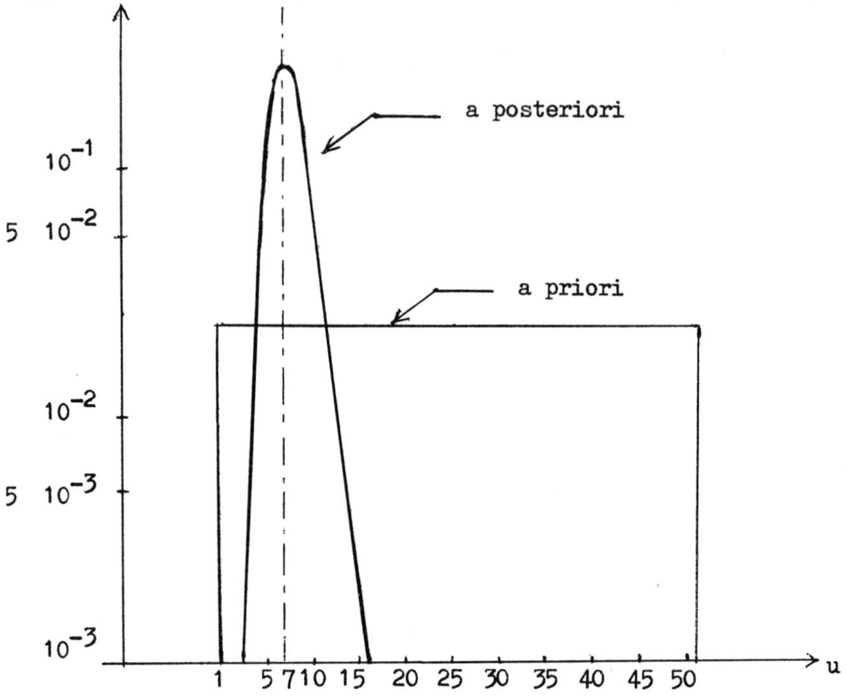

SEMI-LOGARITHMIC SCALE

Discretization step: Space : $\frac{1}{20}$, Time : $\frac{1}{20}$

Standard deviation : 0.1

Number of runs : 60

$u_o = 7$

Experimental mean : 7.76

Experimental variance : 0.03

Figure 2

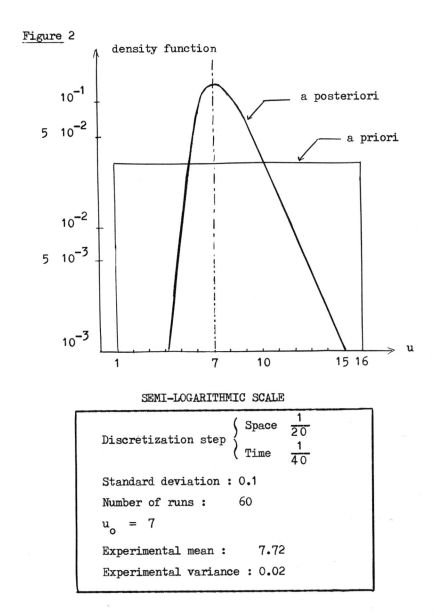

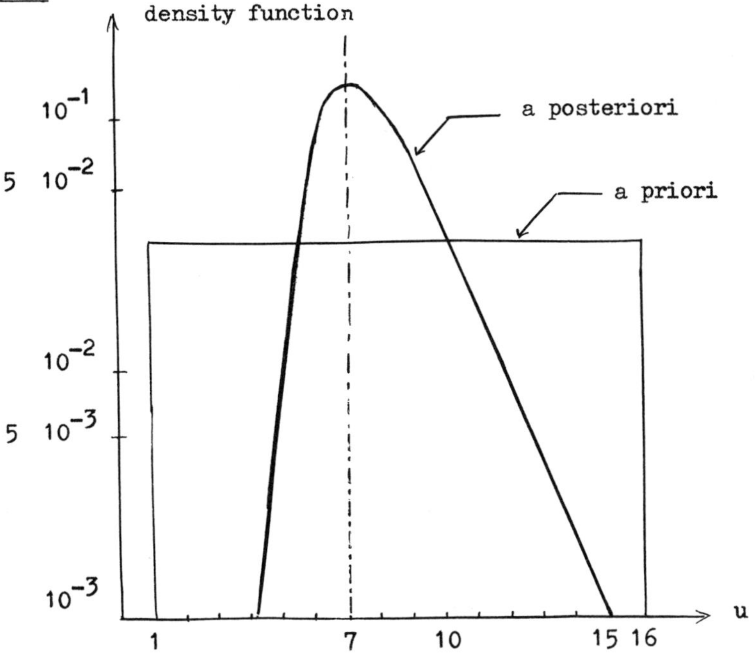

SEMI-LOGARITHMIC SCALE

Discretization step { Space $\frac{1}{20}$; Time $\frac{1}{40}$ }

Standard deviation : 0.1

Number of runs : 60

$u_o = 7$

Experimental mean : 7.72

Experimental variance : 0.02

2e essai : valeurs possibles de θ a priori 1, 1.5, 2, 2.5, ... 16

- nombre de Runs : 60
  moyenne expérimentale : 7,72
  Variance expérimentale : 0,002

cf. figure 2.

REFERENCES

[1] L. SCHWARTZ Mesures de Radon sur des Espaces Topologiques (Tata Institute.Bombay)

[2] A. BENSOUSSAN Thèse (à paraître, Cahiers de l'IRIA)

[3] J. CEA Thèse Paris (1964)

[4] P.A.RAVIART These Paris (1965)

"OPTIMAL SOLUTION FOR A CLASS OF ASSIGNMENT AND TRANSPORTATION PROBLEMS" (*)

E. Biondi - L. Divieti - C. Roveda - R. Schmid
Istituto di Elettrotecnica ed Elettronica
Politecnico di Milano - Italy

1. INTRODUCTION

In the last years graph theory has represented a powerful tool for approaching many problems arising in different fields of the applied science. In fact, many problems, apparently very different in nature, may be formulated in terms of graph theory exactly in the same way.

In this paper an algorithm is presented for finding the optimal solution of a problem related to some particular acyclic graphs. Actually, this problem arose from the study of the optimal implementation of multivariable discrete linear systems (1). Because of the particular form of the performance index considered, the optimization problem, formulated in terms of graph theory, led to the search of the minimal cost arborescence in a particular acyclic graph. Removing some constraints on the graph structure inherent to the nature of the original problem, it has been possible to define a larger class of acyclic graphs and formulate the general optimization problem that will be discussed in this paper. This generalization of the problem makes it fitting many important assignment and transportation problems, as shown in the next section.

In the third section the optimization problem is approached and solved via Dynamic Programming. The computing algorithm is described in the fourth section and it is illustrated by a numerical example given in the last section.

(*) The present research has been supported by C.N.R. (Consiglio Nazionale delle Ricerche) Rome, Italy.

2. PROBLEM STATEMENT

Let $\mathbf{X} = \{X_1, \ldots, X_n\}$ and $\mathbf{Y} = \{Y_1, \ldots, Y_m\}$ be two finite non-empty disjoint sets of vertices, and R_0 an isolated vertex. Let Γ_0 be a multivalued mapping of R_0 into $\mathbf{X}$ such that

$$\left| \Gamma_0^{-1} X_i \right| = 1 \ ; \ \forall \ X_i \in \mathbf{X} \tag{1}$$

and Γ_1 be a multivalued mapping of $\mathbf{X}$ into $\mathbf{Y}$.

Let G be the acyclic graph defined by:

$$G = (R_0, \mathbf{X}, \mathbf{Y}, \Gamma_0, \Gamma_1)$$

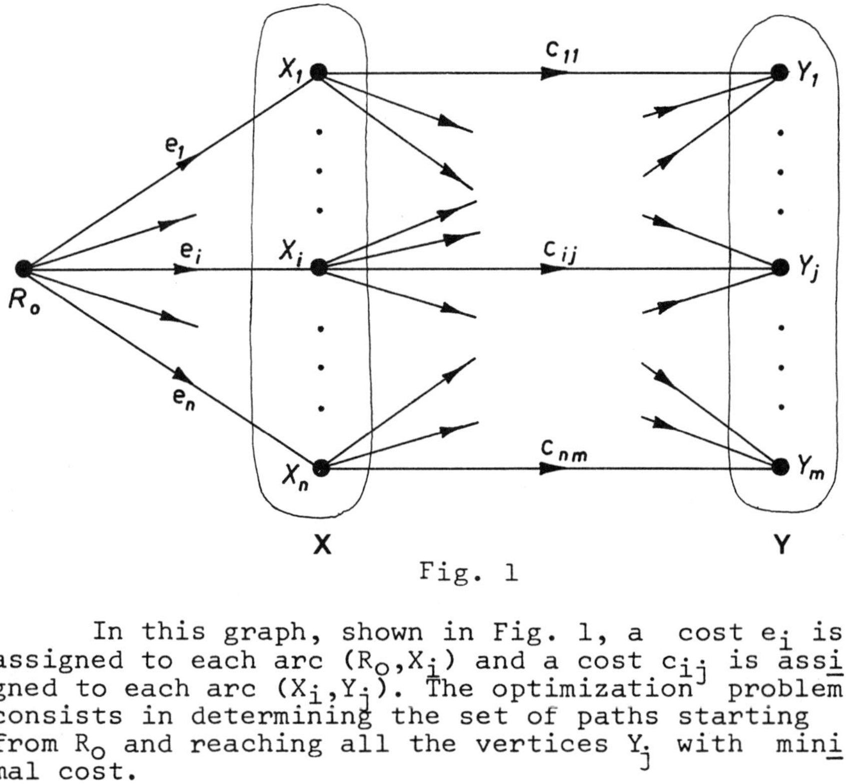

Fig. 1

In this graph, shown in Fig. 1, a cost e_i is assigned to each arc (R_0, X_i) and a cost c_{ij} is assigned to each arc (X_i, Y_j). The optimization problem consists in determining the set of paths starting from R_0 and reaching all the vertices Y_j with minimal cost.

This formulation is typical of some transportation problems dealing with distribution networks, which consist of a source, a certain number of stor ehouses and some terminals. If the cost of the transport from the source to the storehouses has a fixed charge, while the cost of the transport from the storehouses to the terminals (customers) depends on the amount of commodities transported, the distribution network can be described by the graph G. In order to satisfy customers' demands and minimize the transportation cost, we must solve the above stated problem.

The classical assignment problems are generally formulated in a different way (2). Actually, these problems can be described by means of bipartite graphs, consisting of two finite disjoint sets $\mathbf{X}$ and $\mathbf{Y}$ of vertices and a mapping Γ_1 of $\mathbf{X}$ into $\mathbf{Y}$. In these graphs the costs are associated only to the arcs (X_i, Y_j), and they represent, for instance, the costs of assigning the men X_i to the jobs Y_j. The optimization problem consists in finding the minimal cost matching of these graphs, and there are many algorithms for doing it.

However, we can consider a different and in some way more general class of assignment problems, in which fixed and unfixed charges (e.g. hiring costs and man hour costs) are both involved. These problems can be described by means of the same bipartite graphs, but there are now two different types of costs: costs e_i (e.g. hiring costs) associated to the vertices of $\mathbf{X}$ and costs c_{ij} (e.g. man hour costs) associated to the arcs (X_i, Y_j). The optimization problem consists in finding the partial subgraph $S = (\mathbf{A}, \mathbf{Y}, \Gamma)$ of the graph $G = (\mathbf{X}, \mathbf{Y}, \Gamma_1)$ such that

$$\mathbf{A} \subseteq \mathbf{X}$$

$$\left| \Gamma^{-1} y_j \right| = 1 \; ; \quad \forall\, Y_j \in \mathbf{Y}$$

and minimizes the cost

$$C = \sum_{X_i \in \mathbf{A}} \sum_{j=1}^{m} c_{ij} + \sum_{X_i \in \mathbf{A}} e_i$$

Obviously, the graph G' can be easily transformed into the graph G, in which the costs are associated only to arcs. The assignment problem can be reformulated as the general optimization problem stated at the beginning of this section.

3. PROBLEM SOLUTION VIA DYNAMIC PROGRAMMING

According to some structural approaches of optimization problems (3),(4) and (5), the problem stated in the proceeding section can be structured and described in terms of block diagrams in many different ways. The simplest structure we can give to the problem is that of a straight foreward chain; each block of this chain corresponds to a vertex $Y \in \mathbf{Y}$. In fact, let us define the elementary block (Fig. 2) in the following way.

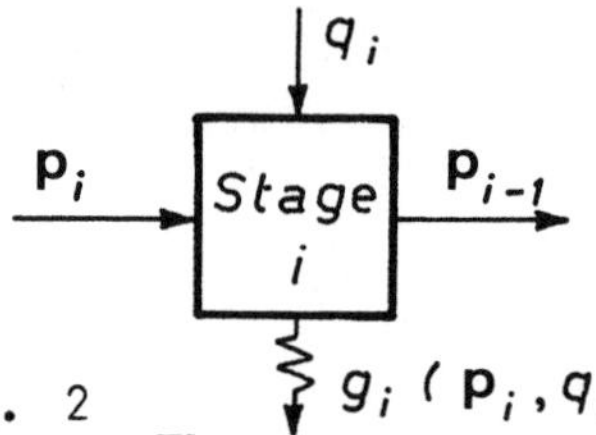

Fig. 2

i) State $\mathbf{p}_i$ - The state $\mathbf{p}_i$ is the set of vertices $X_k \in \mathbf{X}$ through which the paths starting from R_o and reaching $Y_m,\ldots,Y_{i+1}$ go. It is worth noting that no more than m-i vertices of $\mathbf{X}$ could have been chosen for reaching the vertices $Y_m,\ldots,Y_{i+1}$. Then, we can define the set $\mathbf{P}_i = \{\mathbf{p}_i^j\}$ of all possible input states for the i-th block as follows

$$\mathbf{P}_i = \{\mathbf{p}_i^j\} \;\Big|\; \Gamma_1 \mathbf{p}_i^j \supseteq \{Y_m \ldots\ldots Y_{i+1}\}\,;\; |\mathbf{p}_i^j| \leq m-i \qquad (2)$$

ii) Decision q_i - The decision q_i is the vertex $X_k \in \mathbf{X}$ through which the path starting from R_o and reaching Y_i should go. The set $\mathbf{Q}_i = \{q_i^j\}$ of all possible decisions for the i-th block is defined by

$$\mathbf{Q}_i = \Gamma_1^{-1} Y_i \qquad (3)$$

iii) Transformation function $\mathfrak{F}(\mathbf{p}_i, q_i)$. The transition from the input state $\mathbf{p}_i$ to the output state $\mathbf{p}_{i-1}$ is obtained by means of the following relation

$$\mathbf{p}_{i-1} = \mathcal{F}(\mathbf{p}_i, q_i) = \mathbf{p}_i \cup q_i \qquad (4)$$

iv) Cost $g_i(\mathbf{p}_i, q_i)$- The cost of the i-th stage is given by

$$g_i(\mathbf{p}_i, q_i) = \delta(q_i) + \rho(q_i)\,\varphi(\mathbf{p}_i, q_i) \qquad (5)$$

where

$$\delta(q_i) = c_{ki} \quad if \quad q_i = X_k \qquad (6)$$

$$\rho(q_i) = e_k \quad if \quad q_i = X_k \qquad (7)$$

and $\varphi(\mathbf{p}_i, q_i)$ is a two-valued function given by

$$\begin{aligned} \varphi(\mathbf{p}_i, q_i) &= 1 \quad if \quad q_i \notin \mathbf{p}_i \\ \varphi(\mathbf{p}_i, q_i) &= 0 \quad if \quad q_i \in \mathbf{p}_i \end{aligned} \qquad (8)$$

Using the elementary blocks just defined, the optimization problem can be described by the straight foreward chain shown in Fig. 3. The initial state $\mathbf{p}_m$ is the empty set, while the final state $\mathbf{p}_0$ is free.

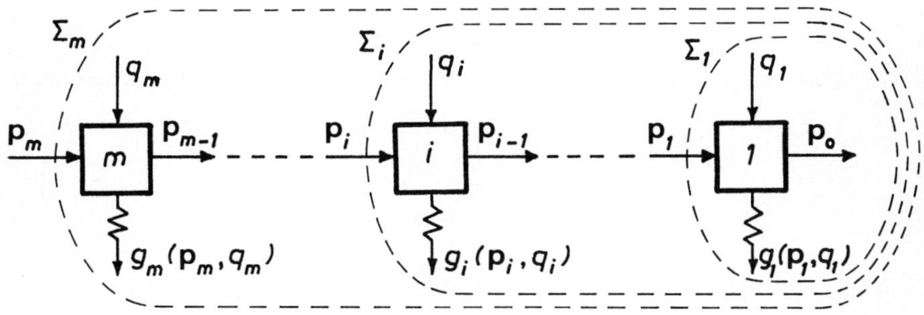

Fig. 3

The objective function, which should be minimized, is the sum of the costs of the single stages, that is

$$C(q_1,\ldots,q_m) = \sum_{i=1}^{m} g_i(\mathbf{p}_i, q_i) \tag{9}$$

Applying the section method (5) and proceeding from stage 1 back to stage m through sections

$\Sigma_1, \ldots, \Sigma_i, \ldots, \Sigma_m$, the Dynamic Programming algorithm gives the following functional equation

$$f_i(\mathbf{p}_i) = \min_{q_i} \left[g_i(\mathbf{p}_i, q_i) + f_{i-1}(\mathbf{p}_{i-1}) \right] \tag{10}$$

for i = 1,...,m starting with $f_o = 0$.

The optimal policy indicates which vertex of $\mathbf{X}$ should be joined to a vertex of $\mathbf{Y}$ in order to obtain on $G = (R_0, \mathbf{X}, \mathbf{Y}, \Gamma_0, \Gamma_1)$ the set of paths starting from R_o and reaching all vertices Y_i with minimal cost.

4. COMPUTING ALGORITHM

Before illustrating the computing algorithm, let us introduce some definitions. Let $\mathbf{T}_i'$, $\mathbf{T}_i''$ and $\mathbf{T}_i$ be the following sets

$$\mathbf{T}_i' = \bigcup_{k=1}^{i} \mathbf{Q}_k \tag{11}$$

$$\mathbf{T}_i'' = \bigcup_{k=i+1}^{m} \mathbf{Q}_k$$

$$\mathbf{T}_i = \mathbf{T}_i' \cap \mathbf{T}_i'' \tag{12}$$

We define essential set of a state $\mathbf{p}_i^j$ the set

$$\boldsymbol{\pi}_i^j = \mathbf{p}_i^j \cap \mathbf{T}_i \tag{13}$$

Two states $\mathbf{p}_i^j$ and $\mathbf{p}_i^k$, with $\mathbf{p}_i^j, \mathbf{p}_i^k \in \mathbf{P}_i$ and $j \neq k$, are said to be equivalent and we write

$$\mathbf{p}_i^j \equiv \mathbf{p}_i^k \tag{14}$$

if

$$\pi_i^j = \pi_i^k \tag{15}$$

This notion of equivalence is important since only the states of P_i which are not equivalent should be considered for the optimization of the section Σ_i . Therefore, we can define a new reduced set $P_i' = \{ p_i^j \}$ of input states for the i-th stage as follows:

$$\begin{aligned} &\Gamma_1\, p_i^j \supseteq \{ Y_m \,.\,.\,.\,.\,.\, Y_{i+1} \} \;;\; \forall\; p_i^j \in P_i' \\ &|p_i^j| \leq m - i \;;\; \forall\; p_i^j \in P_i' \\ &p_i^j \neq p_i^k \;;\; \forall\; p_i^j, p_i^k \in P_i',\; j \neq k \end{aligned} \tag{16}$$

It is, of course, $P_i' \subseteq P_i$.

The reduced set P_i' is not uniquely determined by Eqs.(16); what is unique, is the set Π_i of the essential sets of the elements of a set P_i' that is

$$\Pi_i = \{ \pi_i^j \} \,|\, \pi_i^j = p_i^j \cap T_i,\ \forall\ p_i^j \in P_i' \tag{17}$$

Note that $|\Pi_i| = |P_i'|$.

We can now illustrate the computing algorithm in a compact form.

There are five preliminary steps which start the procedure

Step a - Determine the sets $Q_i\{q_i^j\}$ for i=1,...,m using Eq.(3)

Step b - Determine the sets $T_i' = \bigcup_{k=1}^{i} Q_k$ (i=1,...,m) using the recurrent formula $T_i' = T_{i-1}' \cup Q_i$ and starting with $T_0' = \phi$

Step c - Determine the sets $T_i'' = \bigcup_{k=i+1}^{m} Q_k$ (i=m-1,...,1) using the recurrent formula $T_i' = T_{i+1}'' \cup Q_k$ and starting with $T_m'' = \phi$

Step d - Determine the sets $T_i = T_i' \cap T_i''$ for i=1,...,m

Step e - Determine the integers $K_i = \mathrm{Inf}(m-i, |T_i|)$ for i=1,...,m

The optimization of a section Σ_i (i=1,...,m) is then carried out through the following steps

Step 1 - Form all possible combinations $\overset{*}{\pi}{}_i^j$ of k elements of T_i with $0 \leq k \leq K_i$. Their number is, of course, $\sum_{k=0}^{K_i} \binom{|T_i|}{k}$. Any one of these combinations represents the essential set of a possible input state, that is of a state p_i^j such that $\Gamma_1 p_i^j \geq \{Y_m \ldots\ldots Y_{i+1}\}$, if and only if the set $(T_i - \overset{*}{\pi}{}_i^j)$ is equal to or contains none of the sets $Q_{i+1}, \ldots, Q_m$

Step 2 - For each $\overset{*}{\pi}{}_i^j$ test the feasibility condition $\overset{*}{\pi}{}_i^j$ is feasible $\Longleftrightarrow (T_i - \overset{*}{\pi}{}_i^j) \not\supseteq Q_t$ for t=i+1,...,m and form with the feasible $\overset{*}{\pi}{}_i^j$ the set $\Pi_i = \{\pi_i^j\}$

Step 3 - Solve the functional Eq.(10), for all p_i^j having essential sets $\pi_i^j \in \Pi_i$

The number of cases which should be examined for the optimization of a section Σ_i is

$$N_i = |Q_i| \cdot |\Pi_i| \tag{18}$$

and the overall process optimization is carried out examining

$$N = \sum_{i=}^{m} |Q_i| \cdot |\Pi_i| \tag{19}$$

cases (*).

5. NUMERICAL EXAMPLE

Consider the graph shown in Fig. 4 and find the set of paths starting from R_0 and reaching $Y_1, \ldots, Y_4$ with minimal cost.

The problem can be described by means of the straight foreward chain of Fig. 3 with m = 4.

(*) It is worth while noting that the number of cases which should be examined for the overall process optimization depends on the order in which the vertices Y_i are examined.

The results of the preliminary steps are given in Table 1.

Proceeding from stage 1 to stage 4 through sections $\Sigma_1,\dots,\Sigma_4$ we obtain:

Section Σ_1 - Step 1 : $\overset{*}{\Pi}_1=\{0,X_1,X_2,X_1X_2\}$

Step 2 : $\Pi_1=\{0,X_1,X_2,X_1X_2\}$

Step 3 : see Table 2

Section Σ_2 - Step 1 : $\overset{*}{\Pi}_2=\{0,X_1,X_2,X_3,X_1X_2,X_1X_3,X_2X_3\}$

Step 2 : $\Pi_2=\{X_2,X_3,X_1X_2,X_1X_3,X_2X_3\}$

Step 3 : see Table 3

Section Σ_3 - Step 1 : $\overset{*}{\Pi}_3=\{0,X_2,X_3\}$

Step 2 : $\Pi_3=\{X_2,X_3\}$

Step 3 : see Table 4

Section Σ_4 - Step 1 : $\overset{*}{\Pi}_4=\{0\}$

Step 2 : $\Pi_4=\{0\}$

Step 3 : the optimal policy is $\{X_1,X_3,X_1,X_3\}$ and the corresponding total cost is C = 13.

The optimal arborescence is shown in Fig. 5.

REFERENCES

(1) Biondi E. - Divieti L. - Roveda C. and Schmid R. "On the optimal implementation of multivariable discrete linear systems" for presentation at 1969 IFAC Congress.

(2) Ford L. and Fulkerson D. : "Flows in Networks" Princeton University Press, Princeton, N.Y., 1962.

(3) Aris R. : "Discrete Dynamic Programming" Blaisdell Publishing Company, New York, 1964.

(4) Brioschi F. and Locatelli A. : "Extremization of a constrained multivariable function: Structural Programming", IEEE Trans. on SSC, Nov. 1967, pp. 105-111.

(5) Biondi E. - Brioschi F. - Divieti L. and Rozzoni P. : "Structures of multistage decision processes" in "Identificazione e Ottimizzazione" , C.N.R., Roma, 1967, pp. 325-344.

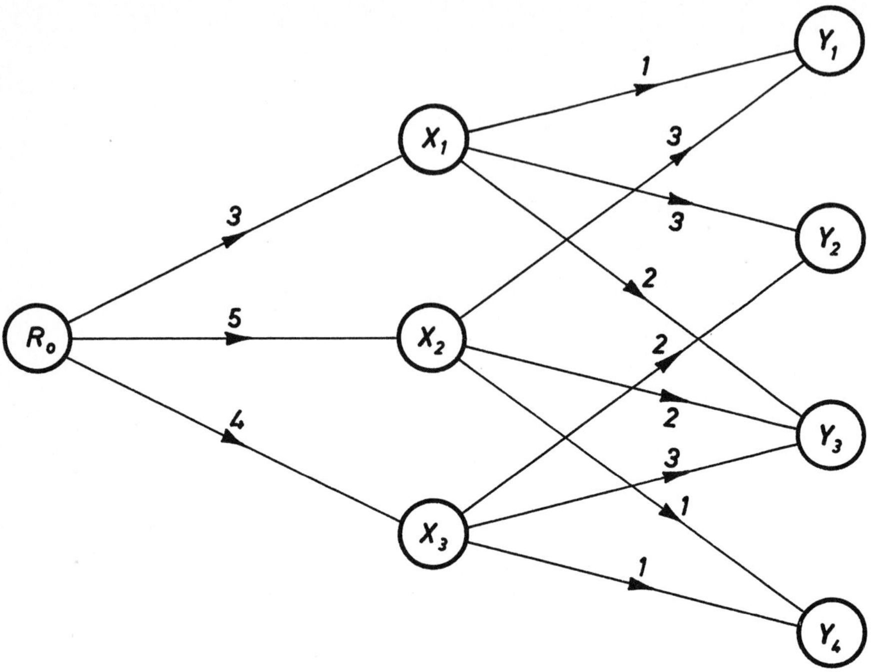

Fig. 4

Block	Y_i	Q_i	T_i'	T_i''	T_i	K_i
1	Y_1	$X_1 X_2$	$X_1 X_2$	$X_1 X_2 X_3$	$X_1 X_2$	2
2	Y_2	$X_1 X_3$	$X_1 X_2 X_3$	$X_1 X_2 X_3$	$X_1 X_2 X_3$	2
3	Y_3	$X_1 X_2 X_3$	$X_1 X_2 X_3$	$X_2 X_3$	$X_2 X_3$	1
4	Y_4	$X_2 X_3$	$X_1 X_2 X_3$	0	0	0

Table 1

π_i^j	Decision	Opt. Policy	Cost
0	X_1	X_1	4
X_1	X_1	X_1	1
X_2	X_2	X_2	3
$X_1 X_2$	X_1	X_1	1

Table 2

π_i^j	Decision	Opt. Policy	Cost
X_2	X_1	$X_1\ X_1$	7
X_3	X_3	$X_1\ X_3$	6
$X_1 X_2$	X_1	$X_1\ X_1$	4
$X_1 X_3$	X_3	$X_1\ X_3$	3
$X_2 X_3$	X_3	$X_2\ X_3$	5

Table 3

π_i^j	Decision	Opt. Policy	Cost
X_2	$\begin{cases} X_1 \\ X_2 \end{cases}$	$\begin{cases} X_1\ X_1\ X_1 \\ X_1\ X_1\ X_2 \end{cases}$	$\begin{cases} 9 \\ 9 \end{cases}$
X_3	X_1	$X_1\ X_3\ X_1$	8

Table 4

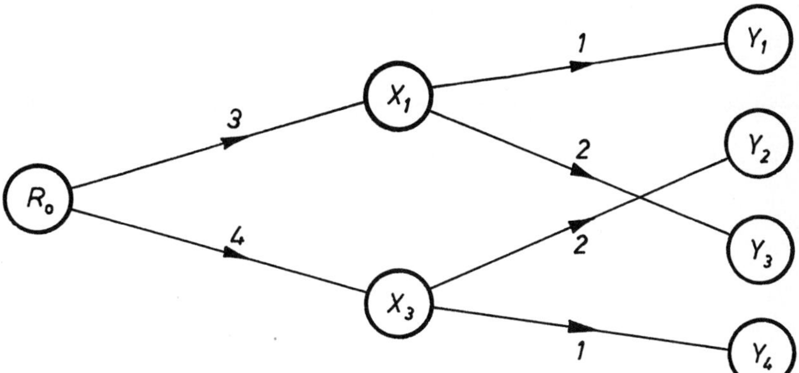

Fig. 5

A LINEAR CONTROL PROBLEM FOR A SYSTEM GOVERNED BY A PARTIAL DIFFERENTIAL EQUATION.

(Approximation and computational results)

A.BOSSAVIT

C.N.R.S. Institut Blaise Pascal. Paris. France.

1. A LINEAR CONTROL PROBLEM

1.1. The problem : Given a function y^w in $L^2(0,1)$ find a $u \in L^2(0,T)$ which minimizes the fonctional

$$I(u) = \int_0^1 |y^w(x) - y^u(T;x)|^2 \, dx \qquad (1)$$

subject to the constraints

$$|u(t)| \leqslant 1 \quad \text{a.e.} \quad \text{on } [0,T]. \qquad (2)$$

the function y^u is the solution of the boundary value problem

$$y_t - y_{xx} = 0 \quad \text{in } [0,T] \times [0,1] \qquad (3)$$

$$y(0,x) = 0 \qquad \forall\ x \in [0,1], \qquad (4)$$

$$y_x(t,0) = 0 \qquad \forall\ t \in [0,T], \qquad (5)$$

$$y_x(t,1) = \beta[u(t) - y(t,1)], \quad t \in [0,T]. \qquad (6)$$

(β is a positive constant).

We propose to associate with this control problem, which we shall call "problem P" a family $P_{\xi\varsigma}$ of optimization problems in a finite dimensional space, in such a way that the vector-valued solution $u_{\xi\varsigma}$ of $P_{\xi\varsigma}$ be consistent with the solution u of P, in the sense of the theorems established below.

We shall now follow (2), chap. 3 , to show how the existence and the uniqueness of a solution to the problem P are established.

1.2. Existence : Let Y (observation space) and $\mathcal{U}$ (control space) be two separable real Hilbert spaces and let $\mathcal{L}(\mathcal{U},Y)$ be the set of all linear continous mappings from $\mathcal{U}$ into Y . Let $G \in \mathcal{L}(\mathcal{U},Y)$, let $\mathcal{U}_{ad}$ (admissible controls) be a closed convex set in $\mathcal{U}$, and let Y^w be a given point of Y . We seek a $u \in \mathcal{U}_{ad}$ which minimizes the functional :

$$I(v) = |Gv - y^w|_Y^2 , \quad v \in \mathcal{U}_{ad} .$$

(The symbols $(\; , \;)_E$ and $| \; |_E$ denote the scalar product and the norm in E.)

Remark 1.1. – This is the problem P if we assume that $Y \equiv L^2(0,1)$, $\mathcal{U} \equiv L^2(0,T)$, with $\mathcal{U}_{ad}$ given by (2) and G by (3) ... (6). G is defined for each $u \in \mathcal{U}$ and is continuous as a consequence of general results to be found in (1).

Let us define :

$$a(u,v) \triangleq (Gu , Gv)_Y \tag{8}$$

$$L(v) \triangleq (Gv , y^w)_Y \tag{9}$$

The bilinear form $a(u,v)$ and the linear form $L(v)$ are continuous on $\mathcal{U}$. To minimize $I(u)$ on $\mathcal{U}_{ad}$ is equivalent to finding a solution to the inequation

$$a(u,u-v) \leq L(u-v) \qquad \text{for all} \qquad v \in \mathcal{U}_{ad} \tag{10}$$

It is shown in (2) that if there exists an $\alpha > 0$ such that

$$a(u,u) \geq \alpha |u|_{\mathcal{U}}^2 \qquad \forall u \in \mathcal{U} \tag{11}$$

(coercivity condition), then (10) has a unique solution in $\mathcal{U}_{ad}$

It is well knownthat G (defined by (3) ... (6)) does not map $\mathcal{U}$ onto Y and morever that Ker (G) is non void (see (6)), so the coercivity condition is not satisfied in the problem P. We make the following observation :

Remark 1.2. – The set $\mathcal{U}_{ad}$ defined by (2) is bounded.

It is shown in (3) that when $\mathcal{U}_{ad}$ is bounded, there exists a set of controls satisfying (10), so that P has (at least) one solution.

1.3. Uniqueness : Let us observe that in problem P the set $\mathcal{U}_{ad}$ has the special form :

$$\mathcal{U}_{ad} = \{u \in L^2(0,T;U) \mid u(t) \in K \quad \text{a.e.}\} \tag{12}$$

where U is a separable Himbert space and K a closed convex subset of U (Here $U \equiv \mathbb{R}$ and $K \equiv [0,1]$).

For each u we introduce the adjoint state

$$p(u) = G^*(Gu - y^w) \tag{13}$$

The inequality (1.10) now becomes :

$$(p(u), u-v)_{\mathcal{U}} \leq 0 \tag{14}$$

and problem P is equivalent to finding a $u \in \mathcal{U}_{ad}$ which satisfies (14) for every $v \in \mathcal{U}_{ad}$, i.e., taking (12) into account,

$$\int_0^T p(u,t) \, . \, [u(t) - v(t)] \, dt \leq 0 \, . \tag{15}$$

This shows that for a.e. t in $[0,T]$ the inequality

$$p(u,t) \, . \, [u(t) - v] \leq 0 \tag{16}$$

holds. The function $p(u,t)$ can be written (see (2)) as

$$p(u,t) = z(t,1) \, , \tag{17}$$

where z is the unique solution of the "adjoint" problem :

$$-z_t - z_{xx} = 0 \quad \text{in } [0,T] \times [0,1] \tag{18}$$

$$z(T,x) = y^u(T,x) - y^w \quad \forall \, x \in [0,1] \tag{19}$$

$$z_x(t,0) = 0 \quad \forall \, t \in [0,T] \tag{20}$$

$$z_x(t,1) + \beta z(t,1) = 0 \quad \forall \, t \in [0,T] \tag{21}$$

It is clear that $p(u,t)$ so defined is an analytic function of t . Hence, if $y^u(T,x) \not\equiv y^w$ when u is optimal, i.e. if y^w is not reachable by any control in $\mathcal{U}_{ad}$, then $p(u,t)$ can be zero only on a finite set of points, and

$$u(t) = - \operatorname{sgn} [p(u,t)] \tag{22}$$

holds a.e. in $0,T$. This is the "bang-bang" property, and it ensures uniqueness of u , the optimal control. We finally obtain the following result :

Proposition 1. If there exist no admissible control satisfying $y(x) = y(T,x)$ a.e., then the problem P has a unique solution and the bang-bang property holds.

2. DISCRETE OPTIMIZATION PROBLEMS DERIVED FROM P .

2.1. Notations. Let ξ [resp. ξ] be a set of indices, containing zero as an accumulation point. Let $\mathcal{U}_\xi$ [resp. Y_ξ] be a family of finite dimensional spaces and let q_ξ and s_ξ [resp. p_ξ and r_ξ] be two families of linear continuous operators with the following properties

$$q_\xi \in \mathcal{L}(\mathcal{U}_\xi \, , \mathcal{U}) \text{ is one-to-one,} \tag{23}$$

$\{ q_\xi r_\xi v \longrightarrow v$ in the strong topology of $\mathcal{U}$ when $\xi \longrightarrow 0$ (for every fixed $v \}$ (24)

The quantities Y_ξ , p_ξ , r_ξ have similar properties.

By (24) we can norm as follows :

$$|u_\xi|_{u_\xi} = |u_\xi|_\xi \triangleq |q_\xi u_\xi|_{\mathcal{U}} \, . \tag{26}$$

Let $G_\xi \in \mathcal{L}(\mathcal{U}, Y_\xi)$ be a linear continuous operator such that

$$\| G_\xi \|_{\mathcal{L}(\mathcal{U}, Y_\xi)} \leq C_1 \quad \forall \xi \tag{27}$$

where C_1 is a constant, and

$$\begin{cases} \text{If} \quad q_\zeta u_\zeta \longrightarrow u \text{ weakly [resp. strongly] in } \mathcal{U}, \text{ then} \\ p_\xi G_\xi q_\zeta u_\zeta \longrightarrow Gu \text{ weakly [resp. strongly] in } Y. \end{cases} \tag{28}$$

Let $\mathcal{U}_\zeta^{ad}$ be a closed convex set in $\mathcal{U}_\zeta$ such that

$$q_\zeta \mathcal{U}_\zeta^{ad} \subset \mathcal{U}_{ad} \quad \text{and} \quad s_\zeta \mathcal{U}_{ad} \subset \mathcal{U}_\zeta^{ad} . \tag{29}$$

2.2. Weak convergence. We now associate with each couple ξ, ζ the following discrete problem :

Problem $P_{\xi\zeta}$: Find $u_{\xi\zeta}$ in $\mathcal{U}_\zeta^{ad}$ such that

$$(p_\xi G_\xi q_\zeta u_\zeta , p_\xi G_\xi q_\zeta (u_\zeta - v_\zeta))_Y \leqslant (p_\xi G_\xi q_\zeta (u_\zeta - v_\zeta), y^W)_Y \tag{30}$$

for each v in $\mathcal{U}_\zeta^{ad}$.

The set $\mathcal{U}_\zeta^{ad}$ being bounded as a result of (29), $P_{\xi\zeta}$ has at least one solution. Let $u_{\zeta\xi}$ be such a solution. Comparing (IO) with $v = q_\zeta u_{\zeta\xi}$ and (30) with $v_\xi = s_\zeta u$ (where u is the unique solution of (10)), we reach the following conclusion :

Theorem 1 . - Under the assumptions (23) ... (29), the sequence $\{q_\zeta u_{\zeta\xi}\}$ where $u_{\zeta\xi}$ is a solution of $P_{\xi\zeta}$ converges in the weak topology of $\mathcal{U}$ to u, the unique solution of (10).

2.3. Strong convergence. We shall now use the bang-bang structure of the optimal control to improve the above result.

Let us suppose that $\mathcal{U}_{ad}$ is of the form (12) and that K is uniformly convex, in the following sense :

Definition : A set K is uniformly convex if there exists a positive monotone real function δ, with $\delta(0) = 0$, defined for positive arguments, such that if $x \in K$ and $y \in K$, then the open ball of radius $\delta(|x - y|)$ and center $(x + y)/2$ lies in K .

In a uniformly convex set, every sequence converging weakly to a boundary point converges also strongly. This leads to the following result :

Theorem 2 . - If $\mathcal{U}_{ad}$ has the form (1.12) with K uniformly convex, if (23) ... (29) are satisfied, and if the bang-bang property holds, then the sequence $q_\zeta u_{\zeta\xi}$ in theorem 1 converges strongly to u , the unique solution of (10).

It is clear that K is uniformly convex in the problem P. We have still to show that assumptions (23) ... (29) are satisfied.

2.4. Approximation . Let m be an integer and $\zeta = m^{-1} \times T$. As $\mathcal{U}_\zeta$ we take $\mathbb{R}^m$, i.e.,

$$u_\zeta = \{u_\zeta^1 , \ldots , u_\zeta^i , \ldots , u_\zeta^m\} \tag{31}$$

and let q_ζ be defined by

$$q_\zeta u_\zeta = \sum_{t=1}^{m} u_\zeta^i \varpi_i \tag{32}$$

where ϖ_i is the characteristic function of the interval $[(i-1)\zeta, i\zeta[$. The operator s_ζ will be known if we know the coordinates of vector $s_\zeta u$ for a given u :

$$(s_\zeta u)_i = m\int_{(i-1)\zeta}^{i\zeta} u(t)\,dt \tag{33}$$

In the same way, we define :

$$y_\xi = \{ y_\xi^1, \ldots, y_\xi^j, \ldots, y_\xi^n \} \tag{34}$$

with $\xi = n^{-1}$, n integer, and $Y_\xi = \mathbb{R}^n$,

$$p_\xi y_\xi = \sum_{j=1}^{n} y_\xi^j \pi_j \tag{35}$$

where π_j is the characteristic function of $[(j-1)\xi, j\xi[$.

The set $\mathcal{U}_\zeta^{ad}$ is then defined as follows :

$$\mathcal{U}_\zeta^{ad} = \{ u_\zeta | \, |u_\zeta^i| \leqslant 1, \; i = 1,\ldots, m \} \tag{36}$$

It is clear that (23) ...(26) and (29) are satisfied for the quantities defined above. We have still to construct G_ξ , which will be done in two steps. First we write the space discretization of (3) ... (6), following (4) :

$$\begin{aligned} \dot y^1 &= \xi^{-2}(y^2 - y) \\ \dot y^i &= \xi^{-2}(y^{i-1} - 2y^i + y^{i+1}) , \; i = 2,\ldots, n-1 \\ \dot y^n &= \xi^{-2}[y^{n-1} - (1+\gamma)\, y^n] + \gamma\xi^{-1} u(t) , \end{aligned} \tag{37}$$

where $\gamma = (1 + \xi\beta/2)^{-1}\xi\beta$. Then we solve (37) by a Runge-Kutta procedure, with a convenient step size (function of ξ). Other discretization shemes may be used, provided that hypothesis (2.6) is satisfied (see (4)).

The discrete problems $P_{\xi\zeta}$ are now described in such a way that theorems 1 and 2 apply.

3. SOLUTION OF THE DISCRETE PROBLEM

3.1. The functional. Let ϖ_i be the characteristic function defined in 2.4 and let

$$a_{ij} = (P_\xi G_\xi \varpi_i , P_\xi G_\xi \varpi_j)_Y \tag{38}$$

$$b_i = (P_\xi G_\xi \varpi_i , y^W)_Y \tag{39}$$

Then $P_{\xi\zeta}$ is equivalent (see (2.8)) to the minimization of the quadratic form :

$$J(u) = \sum_{ij=1}^{m} a_{ij}\, u^i u^j - 2\sum_{i=1}^{m} b_i u^i , \tag{40}$$

subject to the constraints (36) . This is a standard problem but difficulties arise, due to ill-conditioning of the matrix. This is a consequence of the remark made above that the coercivity property (11) is not present in the problem considered.

3.2. Optimization. The classical methods show very different performances for the optimization problem. Let us give three examples :

1°) Goldsteins' method (gradient projection, (5)),

2°) The gauss-Seidel algorithm in conjunction with a truncation procedure when constraints are encountered,

3°) A method using as direction of descent the projection of the gradient on the linear manifold determined by active constraints, and a conjugate direction at the next step if no other constraint becomes active.

Results are presented in the following table. The function y^W used was :

$$y^W(x) = -\,0.4\,x^2 - 0.014\,x + 0.012, \tag{41}$$

and the parameters $\beta = 1$, $T = 1$, $\xi = 1/40$, $\zeta = 1/30$. The computation time tabulated includes the preliminary computation of coefficients a_{ij} and b_i which is about 3 minutes. The computer was a C.D.C. 3600 with an ALGOL compiler.

Table 1 . Speed of convergence.

Method	Nb of iterations	Time m.	s.	ms.
1	15000	27	39	797
2	563	4	05	482
3	78	3	17	649

The resulting control function is :

$$u(t) = \sum_{i=1}^{30} u^i\, \bar{\omega}_i \tag{42}$$

where

$$\left.\begin{aligned} u^i &= 1 \quad \text{for } i = 1, \text{—}, 14 \\ u^{15} &= 0.76 \\ u^i &= -1 \quad \text{for } i = 16,\dots,30 . \end{aligned}\right\} \tag{43}$$

3.3. Accuracy . We shall describe to what amounts in pratice theoretical convergence. Tables 2 and 3 show the behavior of the minimum of the objective function I for different ξ

and ζ.

Table 2 . $\xi = 1/40$

ζ	1/27	1/28	1/29	1/30	1/31	1/32	1/33
computed minimum of I (multiplied by 10^4)	1.445	1.500	1.495	1.428	1.453	1.496	1.466

Table 3 . $\zeta = 1/30$

ξ	1/37	1/38	1/39	1/40	1/41	1/42	1/43
computed minimum of I (multiplied by 10^4)	1.472	1.448	1.433	1.428	1.430	1.432	

These results indicate that to obtain a good accuracy in computing the actual value of I requires small values for ξ and ζ. However, this makes the computation very time-consuming since the computation time grows as ζ^{-2} and ξ^{-3}. Various experiments seemed to indicate that the source of poor accuracy lies principally in the errors resulting from the replacement of G by G_ξ i.e. in the approximation of the boundary-value problem.

In conclusion, the main task in the numerical solution of a control problem of the kind exposed in this paper is to produce a good approximation scheme for the boundary value problem.

-=-§-=-

References cited.

1 J.L.LIONS, E.MAGENES " Problèmes aux limites non homogènes et applications. " DUNOD. Paris, 1968.

2 J.L.LIONS. " Contrôle optimal de systèmes gouvernés par des équations aux dérivées partielles." DUNOD. Paris, 1968.

3 J.L.LIONS, G.STAMPACCHIA "Inéquations variationnelles non coercives." C.R.A.S., 261, (1965) pp.25-27.

4 J.P.AUBIN Thèse. Paris, 1966.

5 A.A.GOLDSTEIN in " Computing Methods in Optimization Problems." Ed. by A.V. BALAKRISHNAN and L.NEUSTADT. A.P.

PENALTY FUNCTIONS AND NONCONVEX CONTINUOUS OPTIMAL CONTROL PROBLEMS

Jane Cullum

IBM Watson Research Center
Yorktown Heights, New York

1. Introduction. The use of penalty functions to replace a constrained optimization problem by a sequence of unconstrained or partially unconstrained optimization problems has been examined by many authors (1), (2), (3), (4). This paper concentrates on the applicability of this technique for the removal of state-space constraints in the computation of optimal solutions of "nonconvex" continuous optimal control problems.

For the purposes of this paper, a continuous optimal control problem consists of a system of ordinary differential equations $\dot{x} = f(x, u, t)$, relating control functions u to state trajectories x ; intermediate control and state constraints, initial and terminal state constraints, a fixed time interval of duration, and the objective of minimizing the first component of the state trajectory at the final time. A global assumption is that admissible trajectories exist, and the optimal cost is finite.

The use of penalty functions for the removal of both types of state constraints is very appealing. The usual method for solving any optimization problem is to determine a quantity that satisfies the associated necessary conditions for optimality. For continuous optimal control problems, these conditions consist of Pontryagin's maximum principle and its extensions (5). If intermediate state constraints are present, the adjoint variables appearing in these conditions may have discontinuities (6) at times that are not known a priori. If such constraints are not present, then the variables are continuous. However, it is still not easy to determine a quantity that satisfies the necessary conditions because it requires the solution of a two-point boundary-value problem that has an unstable system of equations. This instability can be circumvented if there are no terminal state constraints (7), (8).

Papers on penalty functions that contain results applicable to continuous optimal control problems include the papers by Butler and Martin (3) and Russell (4). However, it is not easy to identify the most general class of problems to which the results in (3) are applicable. This would require a reformulation in the terminology used in (3), and this is difficult (see (9)). Russell uses the usual formulation, and under the hypotheses that the system of differential equations is linear in the control variables, he obtains results for penalty functions that correspond to intermediate state constraints. Many of the problems arising from physical applications such as trajectory optimization do not satisfy the hypothesis of linearity. Since such problems are being attacked by the penalty-function technique (7), (8), which is used to remove both the terminal and the intermediate state constraints, it is desirable to inquire if the results in (4) can be extended to include problems with more general differential systems and to include penalty functions corresponding to terminal state constraints.

In Theorem 2 it is proved that if penalty functions are used to remove both types of state constraints of a problem P, then the sequence of unconstrained problems generated approximates the relaxation of P, P^R. That is, the corresponding sequence of optimal costs converges to the optimal cost of P^R, and any corresponding sequence of optimal trajectories, if such a sequence exists, "converges" to an optimal trajectory of P^R. Hence, the results in (4) extend to the use of penalty functions to remove both the terminal and the intermediate state constraints of a general problem if and only if the problem is the same as its relaxation.

In Theorem 3, it is proved that if penalty functions are used to remove the intermediate state constraints, and the sequence of optimal costs of the partially unconstrained problems generated converges, it converges to some value between the optimal cost of P and the optimal cost of its relaxation P^R. Examples demonstrate that convergence to either extreme may occur. Therefore, in this case, neither the conclusion of Theorem 2 nor the result in (4) is valid for general continuous optimal control problems.

Comments concerning the significance of the results obtained are made. No results are obtained or comments made about the computational difficulties inherent in the application of the penalty function technique.

2. Notation and Problem Statement. Let E^n denote n-dimensional Euclidean space. Throughout the paper, P will denote a fixed time, continuous optimal control problem of the following type.

System equations: $\dot{x} = f(\bar{x}, u, t)$ a. e. $t \in [0, T]$
$(x = (x_1, \bar{x}),\ f = (f_1, \bar{f}))$. (1)

System constraints: $u(t) \in U \subset E^r$, a. e. $t \in [0, T]$
$x(t) \in A \subset E^{n+1}$, $t \in [0, T]$
$t \in [0, T]$
$x(0) = x^0$, $b(\bar{x}(T)) = 0$. (2)

Objective: Minimize $x_1(T)$ over all pairs (x, u) of absolutely continuous functions x and measurable functions u that satisfy Eqs. (1) and (2). (3)

It is always assumed that admissible pairs exist, and that the optimal cost, C(P) , is finite. Moreover, it is assumed that f is not a function of x_1 , f is continuous on an open set O containing $\{A \times U \times [0, T]\}$, U is compact and A is closed.

Definition 1. A trajectory of P is an absolutely continuous curve x defined on $[0, T]$ such that $x(0) = x^0$ and x is a solution of the differential equations of P for some measurable function u that satisfies the control constraints. If a trajectory satisfies all of the state constraints of P , then it is an admissible trajectory of P .

Definition 2. A minimizing sequence for P is a sequence $x(k)$, $k = 1, 2, \ldots$ of trajectories admissible for P with $x_1(k, T)$, $k = 1, 2, \ldots$ convergent to the optimal cost of P .

Definition 3. P is convex if for each (x, t) the set of admissible velocities $F(x, t) = \{y \mid y = f(\bar{x}, u, t),\ u \in U\}$ is closed and convex. Otherwise, P is said to be nonconvex.

Corresponding to each P there exists an optimization problem P^R obtained from P by including in the minimization all absolutely continuous functions x defined on $[0, T]$

that satisfy the state constraints in P and the condition

$$\dot{x}(t) \in G(x(t), t), \text{ a. e. } t \in [0, T] \tag{4}$$

where $G(x, t)$ denotes the convex hull of the closure of the set $F(x, t)$. Warga (10) calls P^R the relaxed problem associated with P. It is clear that $C(P^R) \leq C(P)$, and that if f satisfies suitable growth conditions P^R has an optimal solution.

Let $p(k)$, $k = 1, 2, \ldots$ be a sequence of penalty functions corresponding to the terminal and/or the intermediate state constraints of a problem P. Generate problems $P(k)$, $k = 1, 2, \ldots$ from P as follows. Let $z = (z_1, z_2, \tilde{z})$, $\hat{z} = (z_1, \tilde{z})$ and $\bar{z} = (z_2, \tilde{z})$. Then $P(k)$ is the continuous optimal control problem with

System equations:
$$\dot{z} = h(z, u, t) \equiv \begin{pmatrix} f_1(\tilde{z}, u, t) + p(k, \bar{z}, \dot{\tilde{z}}) \\ f_1(\tilde{z}, u, t) \\ \bar{f}(\tilde{z}, u, t) \end{pmatrix} \tag{5}$$
a. e. $t \in [0, T]$

System constraints:
$u(t) \in U \subset E^r$ a. e. $t \in [0, T]$
$t \in [0, T]$
$z(0) = (0, x^o)$
$\bar{z}$ satisfies any state constraints of P not removed by $p(k)$ (6)

Objective: Minimize $z_1(T)$. (7)

Remarks. (1) Associated with any trajectory x admissible for P, for each k, is a trajectory $z(k)$ admissible for $P(k)$ with $\bar{z}(k, t) \equiv x(t)$ and $z_1(k, t) \equiv x_1(t) + \int_0^t p(k, x(s), \dot{x}(s))ds$. The cost of x considered as a trajectory of $P(k)$ is denoted by $C(k, x)$ and given by $z_1(k, T)$. (2) If x_1 is not constrained, then z can be replaced by $\hat{z}$ and h by $((f_1 + p(k)), \bar{f})$. (3) The notation in Eqs. (5) through (7) is used throughout the paper. In any discussion, the differential equation and the initial-value state constraints are always operative. A problem is unconstrained in the state if $b \equiv 0$ and $A = E^{n+1}$.

The inner product of two vectors a, b in E^m will be denoted by (a, b). The norm in E^m will be denoted by $|\cdot|$. $L_2(C)$ denotes the family of functions whose squares are

Lebesgue integrable on $[0, T]$ (that are continuous on $[0, T]$). Int(A) and c. h. (A) denote the interior and the convex hull of the set A, respectively. $\overline{\text{Lim}}\, a(n)$ and $\underline{\text{lim}}\, a(n)$ denote, respectively, the limit superior and limit inferior of the sequence $a(n)$, $n = 1, 2, \ldots$

<u>Definition 5</u>. (<u>4</u>) A sequence of functions $p(k)$, $k = 1, 2, \ldots$ is a sequence of penalty functions of the first kind for a closed set A if there is an open set $B \supseteq A$ such that (a) each $p(k)$ is defined, nonnegative, and continuous on B; (b) for any compact set $D \subseteq \text{Int}(A)$, the maximum value of $p(k)$ on D converges to zero as $k \to \infty$; (c) for any compact set $D \subset B - A$, the minimum value of $p(k)$ on D converges to $+\infty$ as $k \to \infty$.

<u>Definition 6</u>. (<u>4</u>) A sequence of pairs of functions $(x(k), u(k))$, $k = 1, 2, \ldots$ defined on intervals $I(k)$, $k = 1, 2, \ldots$ is an approximation of type 1 to a pair of functions (x^o, u^o) defined on an interval I^o if $I(k) \to I^o$ and $x(k)$ converges pointwise to x^o on the interior of I^o It is an approximation of type 2 (3) if it is of type 1 and there exist extensions or restrictions of the $u(k)$ to I_0 that converge in the weak L_2-topology (strong L_2-topology) to u^o.

3. <u>Extensions of Russell's Results</u>. Russell (<u>4</u>) considered problems P with (a) differential equations that are linear in the control, (b) U convex, (c) x_1 not constrained, and (d) an optimal trajectory that is approximable from the interior of A. He proved that the removal of the intermediate state constraint, $\bar{x}(t) \in A$, $t \in [0, T]$, by the introduction of a sequence of penalty functions of the first kind $p(k)$, $k = 1, 2, \ldots$ yields a sequence of problems $P(k)$, $k = 1, 2, \ldots$ that approximates P That is, the sequence of optimal costs of the $P(k)$, $C(P(k))$, $k = 1, 2, \ldots$ converges to $C(P)$, the optimal cost of P; and any sequence $(z(k), u(k))$, $k = 1, 2, \ldots$ of trajectories and controls admissible for the corresponding $P(k)$ and with costs less than $C(P(k)) + \epsilon(k)(\epsilon(k) \to \infty$ as $k \to \infty)$ contains a subsequence that "converges" to an optimal solution of P. The trajectories converge in the weak C-topology, and the controls converge in the weak L_2-topology.

The following theorem extends these results to problems that are relaxations of problems satisfying Eqs. (1), (2), and (3) in Section 2 and to certain penalty functions that correspond to terminal state constraints.

Remarks. (1) A typical sequence of penalties used for the terminal constraint $b(\bar{x}(T)) = 0$ is $kb^2(\bar{x}(T))$, $k = 1, 2, \ldots$ The integrand of the corresponding integral formulation of such a penalty is

$$q(k, w, v) = k\{2b(w)((\frac{\partial b}{\partial x})(w), v) + \frac{b^2(\bar{x}^0)}{T}\} . \tag{8}$$

(2) The definition given in Eqs. (5), (6), and (7) can be easily extended to any problem P^R that is the relaxation of a continuous optimal control problem P. Define z, $\bar{z}$ and $\hat{z}$ as before and let $G(x, t)$ denote the convex hull of the set $F(x, t)$. If $p(k)$, $k = 1, 2, \ldots$ denotes a sequence of penalty integrands corresponding to the intermediate and/or the terminal state constraints of P, then $P^R(k)$, $k = 1, 2, \ldots$ denotes the following problem. Minimize $z_1(T)$ over all trajectories z such that (a) $z(0) = (0, x^0)$, (b) $\bar{z}$ satisfies any state constraints in P not considered in $p(k)$ and (c) there exists a measurable function $g = (g_1, \bar{g})$ defined on $[0, T]$ such that $g(t) \in G(z(t), t)$ and

$$\dot{z} = \begin{pmatrix} g_1 + p(k, \bar{z}, \bar{g}) \\ g \end{pmatrix} \quad \text{a. e. on } [0, T] . \tag{9}$$

(3) Finally, let $h(k)$, $k = 1, 2, \ldots$ denote a sequence of penalty functions of the first kind for the set A. The sequence $P^R(k)$, $k = 1, 2, \ldots$ in Theorem 1 denotes the sequence of problems defined in Eq. (9) with $p(k) = h(k), q(k)$ or $(h(k) + q(k))$ where $q(k)$ is defined in Eq. (8).

Theorem 1. Let P^R be the relaxation of a continuous optimal control problem P satisfying Eqs. (1), (2), and (3) in Section 2 and the additional hypotheses. (a) There exists a compact sphere $B \subset E^{n+1}$ such that if x is any trajectory of P^R, $x(t) \in B$ for $t \in [0, T]$. (b) f is continuous on an open set $0 \supset \{B \times U \times T\}$. (c) f is continuously differentiable in x on $\{J \times U \times T\}$ where J is an open set containing B. (d) b is continuously differentiable. (e) There exists a minimizing sequence $x(k)$, $k = 1, 2, \ldots$ for P^R with

$$\lim_{k \to \infty} \int_0^T p(k, x(k), \dot{x}(k)) = 0 . \tag{10}$$

Then (1) $C(P^R(k)) \to C(P^R)$, as $k \to \infty$; (2) Any sequence of trajectories $z(k)$, $k = 1, 2, \ldots$ admissible for the corresponding problem $P^R(k)$, $k = 1, 2, \ldots$ with $z_1(k,T) = C(P^R(k)) + \epsilon_k$ ($\epsilon(k) \to 0$, $k \to \infty$) contains a subsequence (w. l. o. g. denoted by k) such that $\hat{z}(k)$, $k = 1, 2, \ldots$ is an approximation of type 1 to an optimal trajectory of P^R.

Proof. The method used in (12) can be used to construct a convergent subsequence. The remainder of the proof parallels the proof in (4) because for each k and t, $\int_0^t q(k)$ is nonnegative, and $\int_0^T q(k)$ is zero if and only if the trajectory being considered satisfies the terminal constraint.

4. Terminal and Intermediate State Constraints. The following theorem demonstrates that if penalty functions are used to remove both types of state constraints, the resulting unconstrained problems approximate the relaxation of P, P^R.

In Theorem 2, $P(k)$, $k = 1, 2, \ldots$ denotes the sequence of problems defined in Eqs. (5) through (7) with $p(k) = h(k) + q(k)$ where $h(k)$, $k = 1, 2, \ldots$ is any sequence of penalty functions of the first kind corresponding to A, and $q(k)$, $k = 1, 2, \ldots$ is the sequence of functions defined in Eq. (8).

Theorem 2. Let P be a continuous optimal control problem defined in Eqs. (1), (2), and (3) and satisfying hypotheses (a), (b), and (c) of Theorem 1 and the following hypotheses: (d') b is twice continuously differentiable; (e) There exists a minimizing sequence $x(k)$, $k = 1, 2, \ldots$ of P with

$$\lim_{k \to \infty} \int_0^T p(k, x(k), \dot{\bar{x}}(k)) = 0 . \tag{11}$$

Then, (1) $C(P(k)) \to C(P^R)$ as $k \to \infty$. (2) Any sequence $z(k)$, $k = 1, 2, \ldots$ of trajectories admissible for the corresponding $P(k)$, $k = 1, 2, \ldots$ with $z_1(k, T) \leq C(P(k)) + \epsilon(k)$ ($\epsilon(k) \to 0$, $k \to \infty$) contains a subsequence (w. l. o. g. denoted by k) such that $\hat{z}(k)$, $k = 1, 2, \ldots$ is an approximation of type 1 to an optimal trajectory x^o of the relaxation of P.

Lemma 1. Let P satisfy the hypotheses of Theorem 2. Then for each $k = 1, 2, \ldots$ $P^R(k)$ coincides with $(P(k))^R$.

Proof. By definition, $P^R(k) = (P(k))^R$ if and only if any trajectory admissible for $P^R(k)$ is also an admissible trajectory of $(P(k))^R$ and vice versa. If z is a trajectory of $P(k)$, $\dot{\tilde{z}} = \bar{f}(\tilde{z}, u, t)$ a. e. and $q(k, \tilde{z}, \dot{\tilde{z}}) = q(k, \tilde{z}, \bar{f}(\tilde{z}, u, t))$. Let $F(k, z, t)$ denote the set of velocities admissible at (z, t) for the problem $P(k)$. Since f is continuous and U is compact, for each k, z, t, $F(k, z, t)$ is a compact set. Therefore, the set of velocities admissible at (z, t) for the problem $(P(k))^R$ is the c. h. $\{F(k, x, t)\}$ which is denoted by $G(k, z, t)$. But Carathéodory's Theorem (13) states that if $A \subset E^{n+1}$ and $x \in$ c. h. $\{A\}$, then there exist points $x(i)$, $1 \leq i \leq s$, in A with $s \leq n + 2$ such that x is a point in the simplex whose vertices are $x(i)$. Hence,

$$G(k, z, t) = \left\{ \begin{pmatrix} \sum_{i=1}^{n+2} \lambda_i (f_1(\tilde{z}, u_i, t) + p(k, \bar{z}, \bar{f}(\tilde{z}, u_i, t))) \\ \sum_{i=1}^{n+2} \lambda_i f(\tilde{z}, u_i, t) \end{pmatrix} \middle| \begin{array}{l} \sum_{i=1}^{n+2} \lambda_i = 1 \\ \lambda_i \geq 0 \\ u_i \in U \end{array} \right\}$$

But, $\sum_{i=1}^{n+2} \lambda_i p(k, \bar{z}, \bar{f}(\tilde{z}, u_i, t)) = p(k, \bar{z}, \sum_{i=1}^{n+2} \lambda_i \bar{f}(\tilde{z}, u_i, t))$. So

$G(k, z, t) = \{(\begin{smallmatrix} g_1 + p(k, \bar{z}, \bar{g}) \\ g \end{smallmatrix}) \mid g = (g_1, \bar{g}) \in G(\bar{z}, t)\}$, where $G(x, t)$ denotes the set of velocities admissible for P^R at the point (x, t). Let $H(k, z, t)$ denote the set of velocities admissible at (z, t) for the problem $P^R(k)$. By Eqs. (8) and (9), $H(k, z, t) = G(k, z, t)$.

Lemma 2. (10) If P satisfies the hypotheses of Theorem 2, $A = E^{n+1}$, and $b \equiv 0$, then $C(P) = C(P^R)$.

Proof of Theorem 2. It is clear that for each k, $C(P(k))$ is finite. By Lemma 2, for each $k = 1, 2, \ldots$ $C(P(k)) = C((P(k))^R)$. By Lemma 1, for each $k = 1, 2, \ldots$ $(P(k))^R \equiv P^R(k)$. But by Theorem 1, $C(P^R(k)) \to C(P^R)$ as $k \to \infty$.

5. Intermediate State Constraints. In this section $P(k)$, $k = 1, 2, \ldots$ denotes a sequence of partially unconstrained problems obtained from P by introducing penalty functions of the first kind for A.

Theorem 3. Let P satisfy the hypotheses of Theorem 2. Then $C(P^R) \leq \underline{\lim}\, C(P(k)) \leq \overline{\lim}\, C(P(k)) \leq C(P)$.

Proof. Let $q(j)$, $j = 1, 2, \ldots$ be the sequence of penalty integrands given in Eq. (8) for the terminal constraint of P. Let $P(k, j)$ denote $P(k)(j)$. Then by Theorem 2, $C(P(k, j)) \to C(P^R)$ as $j, k \to \infty$. Clearly, for each j and k, $C(P(k, j)) \leq$

$C(P(k))$.

Let $x(k)$, $k = 1, 2, \ldots$ denote the sequence in hypothesis (e). Then given any $\varepsilon > 0$, for j and k large enough $C(P^R) - \varepsilon \leq C(P(k, j)) \leq C(P(k)) \leq C(k, x(k)) \leq x_1(k, T) + \varepsilon/2 \leq C(P) + \varepsilon$.

Corollary 1. If $C(P) = C(P^R)$, the $C(P(k)) \to C(P)$, as $k \to \infty$.

Examples. Example 1 demonstrates that the conclusion to Theorem 3.1 in (4) is not valid in general even if $\bar{f}$ is linear in the control. Example 2 demonstrates that the conclusion to Theorem 2 of this paper is not valid in general for sequences of problems generated by introducing penalty functions for only the intermediate state constraints. Each example is a modification of an example given in (10). In each case, x_1 is not constrained. Therefore, z can be replaced by $\hat{z}$, and h by $(f_1 + p(k), \bar{f})$.

Example 1. Let P be the continuous optimal control problem with $f(x, u, t) = ((x_2 - u^2), u, w(x_2))$ where $w(s)$ equals s^2 if $s \geq 0$, 0 if $-1 \leq s \leq 0$ and $(s+1)^2$ if $s \leq -1$; $A = \{x \in E^3 \mid x_2 \geq 0\}$, $U = \{u \in E^1 \mid |u| \leq 1\}$, $[0, T] = [0, 1]$, $x(0) = (0, 0, 0)$, and $x_3(1) = 0$.

Exactly one trajectory, $x \equiv (0, 0, 0)$ is admissible for P . Hence, $C(P) = 0$. For each (x, t), the set $G(x, t)$ is a two-dimensional parabolic cup. When $x_2 = 0$, this cup contains the point $(-1, 0, 0)$. Therefore, $x \equiv (-t, 0, 0)$ is a trajectory of P^R, and $C(P^R) = -1$.

For $k = 1, 2, \ldots$ set $p(k, z) = kz_2^2 h(-z_2)$ where $h(s) = 0$ if $s \leq 0$ and 1 if $s > 0$, and for $i = 0, 1, \ldots, (k-1)$ set $I(i, k) = [i \mid k, (i+1) \mid k]$. For $t \in I(i, k)$, define $u(k, t) = -1$ if i is even and 1 if i is odd. Then for $t \in [0, 1]$, $-1/k \leq z_2(k, t) \leq 0$, $z_3(k, t) \equiv 0$, and $z_1(k, 1) \leq -1 + 1/k$. Therefore, $C(P(k)) \leq -1 + 1/k$. Hence, from Theorem 3, $C(P(k)) \to C(P^R)$ as $k \to \infty$.

Example 2. Let P be the continuous optimal control problem obtained from the problem in Example 1 by replacing w by the function v where $v(x, t) = [(x_2-t)(x_2+t)(x_2-t^2/2)x_2]^2$. P has exactly three admissible trajectories: $x(1) = (0, 0, 0)$, $x(2) = ((t^2/2-t), t, 0)$, and $x(3) = (-t^3/6, t^2/2, 0)$. Therefore, $C(P) = -1/2$. Clearly, $x = (-t, 0, 0)$ is admissible for P^R and hence $C(P^R) = -1$. For $k = 1, 2, \ldots$ set $p(k, z) = kz_2^2 h(-z_2)$

where $h(s) = 0$ if $s \leq 0$ and 1 if $s > 0$. Then each problem, $P(k)$, has four admissible trajectories. Hence, for large k, $C(P(k)) = C(P) = -1/2$.

6. Convergence of Trajectories. Throughout this section, P is a continuous optimal control problem satisfying the hypotheses of Theorem 2. In some cases one is interested not only in obtaining $C(P)$, but also in obtaining a good approximation to an optimal trajectory and/or optimal control of P. Theorem 2 demonstrates that for the case considered there approximations to optimal trajectories of P^R are obtained by solving $P(k)$ for large k. This result extends to any general sequence $P(k)$, $k = 1, 2, \ldots$ (corresponding to the removal of the intermediate and/or the terminal state constraint of P) for which $C(P(k))$, $k = 1, 2, \ldots$ converges to $C(P^R)$.

Lemma 4. Let $C(P(k))$, $k = 1, 2, \ldots$ converge to $C(P^R)$. Let $z(k)$, $k = 1, 2, \ldots$ be any sequence of trajectories admissible for the corresponding problems $P(k)$ with $z_1(k, T) \leq C(P(k)) + \varepsilon(k)(\varepsilon(k) \to 0,\ k \to \infty)$. Then $\hat{z}(k)$, $k = 1, 2, \ldots$ contains a subsequence that is an approximation of type 1 to an optimal trajectory of P^R.

The following theorem demonstrates that under hypotheses slightly more general (the cost functional need not be a linear function of the control variable u) than those in (4), $C(P) = C(P^R)$ and limiting trajectories obtained in Lemma 4 will be trajectories of P.

Theorem 4. Let P be an optimal control problem satisfying the hypotheses of Theorem 2 and the following conditions. (a) $\bar{f}$ is linear in the control variables u. (b) f_1 is a convex function of u for each $\bar{x}$. (c) U is convex. (d) x_1 is not constrained. Then (1) $C(P) = C(P^R)$. (2) Given any sequence of trajectories $z(k)$, $k = 1, 2, \ldots$ satisfying the hypotheses of Lemma 4, there exists an optimal solution x^o of P and a subsequence (w. l. o. g. denoted by k) such that $\tilde{z}(k)$, $k = 1, 2, \ldots$ is an approximation of type 1 to $\bar{x}^o$.

Proof. The proof is straightforward and given in (15).

Corollary 4.1. If P satisfies the hypotheses of Theorem 4, and f_1 is jointly convex in x and u, then the approximation obtained in Theorem 4 is of type 2.

7. Summary and Conclusion. The purpose of this paper was to examine the applicability of the penalty function technique to the removal of state space constraints in a nonconvex continuous optimal control problem P. Theorem 2 states that if penalty functions are introduced for both the intermediate and the terminal state constraints in such a problem, the ability of optimal solutions of the sequence of unconstrained problems generated to approximate optimal solutions of P depends upon the relationship between P and its relaxation, P^R. In particular, if $C(P) \neq C(P^R)$, then not even the optimal cost of P can be approximated. However, the following remark must be made. In some physical situations the state constraints are not hard (the satisfaction of these constraints to within a specified tolerance is permissible). In such a case, Lemma 2 states that $P = P^R$; that is, the problem actually under consideration is the relaxation of P. Therefore, in this situation the penalty function technique, applied to the removal of both types of state constraints, yields the correct result.

The situation corresponding to the removal of only the intermediate state constraints is not so clear. A literature search, admittedly limited, uncovered few problems with intermediate state constraints that have been solved numerically, (16), (17), (18). The types of problems considered in these papers are, in fact, included in Theorems 2 and 4 of this paper. Examples 1 and 2 demonstrated that the conclusions to Theorem 2 in this paper or Theorem 3.1 in (4) do not hold in general for the removal of only the intermediate state constraints. This case needs further study, because the alternative procedures for solving continuous optimal control problems with intermediate state constraints (6) are not very attractive.

References

(1) Courant, R., "Variational methods for the solution of problems of equilibrium and vibrations," AMS Bull. 49 (1943) 1-23.
(2) Rubin, H., and Ungar, P., "Motion under a strong constraining force," Comm. Pure App. Math. 10 (1957) 65-87.
(3) Butler, T., and Martin, A. V., "On a method of Courant for minimizing functionals," J. Math. Physics, 41 (1962) 291-299.
(4) Russell, D. L., "Penalty functions and bounded phase co-

ordinate control," J. SIAM Control. 2 (1965) 409-422.

(5) Pontryagin, L. A., et al, The Mathematical Theory of Optimal Processes, Interscience Pub., New York, 1962.

(6) McIntyre, J., and Paiewonsky, B., "On optimal control with bounded state variables," Advances in Control Systems (ed. C. T. Leondes) 5 (1967) 389-419, Academic Press, New York.

(7) Kopp, R. E., and Moyer, H. G., "Trajectory optimization techniques," Advances in Control Systems (ed. C. T. Leondes), 4 (1966) 104-154, Academic Press, New York.

(8) Kelley, H. J., "Method of gradients," Optimization Techniques with Applications to Aerospace Systems (ed. G. Leitmann), Academic Press, New York (1962) 205-252.

(9) Neustadt, L. W., "An abstract variational theory, II. Applications," J. SIAM Control, 5 (1967) 90-137.

(10) Warga, J., Relaxed variational problems," J. Math. Anal. Appl., 4 (1962) 111-128.

(11) Lee, E. B., and Markus, L., "Optimal control for nonlinear processes," Arch. Ratl. Mech. Anal., 8 (1961) 36-58.

(12) Roxin, E., "The existence of optimal controls," Mich. Math. J., 9 (1962) 109-119.

(13) Eggleston, H. G., Convexity, Cambridge Univ. Press, Cambridge, 1958.

(14) Cullum, J., "Discrete approximations to continuous optimal control problems," to appear SIAM J. Control.

(15) Cullum, J., "Penalty functions and nonconvex continuous optimal control problems," IBM Research, RC 2154 (1968).

(16) Falco, M., "Supersonic transport climb path optimization," AIAA J. 1 (1963) 2859-2862.

(17) McGill, R., "Optimal control, inequality state constraints, and the generalized Newton-Raphson algorithm," J. SIAM Control, 3 (1965) 291-298.

(18) Denham, W. F., and Bryson, A. E. Jr., "Optimal programming problems with inequality constraints," II, AIAA J., 2 (1964) 25-34; "I" AIAA J., 1 (1963) 2544-2550.

AN ALGORITHM FOR THE SOLUTION OF CONCAVE-CONVEX GAMES

John M. Danskin
Clark University

ABSTRACT

This paper, which summarizes a portion of [1], presents without proof an algorithm which will solve any concave-convex game over two polyhedra provided a gradient-finding algorithm is available for each of the polyhedra. All the details, particularly those involving approximation and the boundary, were worked out in [1]. The algorithm is in flow-chart form, ready for the programmer. A gradient-finding algorithm is presented for a class of polyhedra of interest in applications.

1. Purpose

This paper presents without proofs or explanation an algorithm which will solve concave-convex games over polyhedra to arbitrary accuracy. It is based on the "derivative game" of [1], where full details and convergence proofs are given.

These are in fact four algorithms presented here. The basic one is the Max-Min algorithm $\mathfrak{A}$. The Min-Max algorithm $\mathfrak{A}^*$ is gotten from $\mathfrak{A}$ by a change of sign. A flow-chart for $\mathfrak{A}$ is given in section 4. It employs a y-minimization algorithm, which we give in section 3. The "doubled algorithm" $\mathfrak{D}$ of section 5 is the algorithm referred to in the title. It consists simply of running $\mathfrak{A}$ and $\mathfrak{A}^*$ simultaneously with some rule of alternation and making a test each time x^0 or y^{0*} moves. If that test is passed the problem is solved. Finally we give in section 6 a gradient-finding algorithm for a particular class of polyhedra.

We state here the objective of the algorithm. Suppose given a concave-convex function $F(x,y)$ defined on the product of two compact polyhedra $\mathfrak{X}$ and $\mathfrak{Y}$. Let $\rho > 0$. *Then under the hypotheses stated in section 2 the algorithm will in finitely many steps* produce an $\bar{x} \in \mathfrak{X}$ and a $\bar{y} \in \mathfrak{Y}$ such that

$$F(x,\bar{y}) < F(\bar{x},\bar{y}) + \rho \text{ for all } x \in \mathfrak{X}; \qquad (1)$$

$$F(\bar{x},y) > F(\bar{x},\bar{y}) - \rho \text{ for all } y \in \mathfrak{Y}. \qquad (2)$$

It should be possible to write machine programs directly from this paper, using [1] if desired as a reference.

2. Hypotheses, definitions, and notation

We suppose given two compact polyhedra $\mathfrak{X}$ and $\mathfrak{Y}$. The hypotheses, notation, and the description of the Max-Min algorithm $\mathfrak{A}$ are made relative to $\mathfrak{X}$. The corresponding hypotheses and notation hold for $\mathfrak{Y}$; a star will denote the corresponding quantities.

$\mathfrak{X}$ is defined by a set of linear inequalities

$$b_q \cdot x \le c_q, \; q = 1,\dots,Q. \qquad (3)$$

Among the inequalities (3) there is at least one which holds at some point of $\mathfrak{X}$ with strict inequality. Let S be the set of such inequalities and s their number. For each $q \in S$, let t_q be the thickness of $\mathfrak{X}$ in the direction normal to b_q. Put

$$t^* = \min_{q \in S} t_q. \qquad (4)$$

We choose a number d_0 satisfying

$$0 < d_0 < t^*/s. \qquad (5)$$

Other conditions will later be imposed on d_0, which is essentially a minimum step size for the algorithm $\mathfrak{A}$.

Let $x^0 \in \mathfrak{X}$. Let d_q be the distance of x^0 from the plane $b_q \cdot x = c_q$. A unit vector γ is admissible at x^0, i.e. $\gamma \in \Gamma(x^0)$, if

$$b_q \cdot x \le 0 \text{ for all } q \text{ with } d_q < d_0. \qquad (6)$$

We assume that there is available for $\mathfrak{X}$ a linear form algorithm which for every vector Ω in R^n either states that $\Omega \cdot \gamma \le 0$ for all $\gamma \in \Gamma(x^0)$ or else finds a unit γ maximizing the form $\Omega \cdot \gamma$. This and the requirement concerning $d_1(d_0)$ referred to below are the only conditions on $\mathfrak{X}$. We give such an algorithm for a particular class of spaces in section 6.

A point x^0 is said to be in the core of $\mathfrak{X}$ if $d_q(x^0) \ge d_0$ for all $q \in S$. We denote the core by C. Condition (3) assures that C is not empty. If $x \in \mathfrak{X}$, put

$$D(x,d_0) = \min_{x' \in C} |x - x'|. \qquad (7)$$

$D(x,d_0)$ is uniformly continuous in d_0 and x taken

together. Put

$$d_1(d_0) = \underset{x \in \mathfrak{X}}{\text{Max}}\ D(x,d_0). \tag{8}$$

$d_1(d_0)$ is continuous and monotone nondecreasing in d_0, and $d_1(d_0) \geq d_0$. The meaning of this function is the following: any point of $\mathfrak{X}$ is not more than $d_1(d_0)$ from a point of the core of $\mathfrak{X}$. The second requirement concerning $\mathfrak{X}$ is that there be available a method of estimating $d_1(d_0)$ as a function of d_0. Such an estimate for a particular class of spaces is given as (33) in section 6.

The function F(x,y) is supposed continuous along with the partial derivatives $F_{x_i}(x,y)$ and $F_{y_j}(x,y)$ on the space $\mathfrak{X} \times \mathcal{Y}$. We assume F concave in x and convex in y. No other assumptions are imposed on F.

We put

$$\omega=\omega(d_0) = \underset{\substack{|x'-x|\leq d_0 \\ y\in\mathcal{Y} \\ \gamma\in\Gamma}}{\text{Max}} |D_\gamma F(x',y)-D_\gamma F(x,y)|. \tag{9}$$

Here we are using the notation

$$D_\gamma F(x,y) = \sum \gamma_i F_{x_i}(x,y), \tag{10}$$

and Γ is the entire unit sphere. Also we put

$$\tau_0=\tau(d_0) = \underset{\substack{|x'-x|\leq d_0 \\ y\in\mathcal{Y}}}{\text{Max}} |F(x',y)-F(x,y)|, \tag{11}$$

and

$$\tau_1=\tau(d_1(d_0))= \underset{\substack{|x'-x|\leq d_1(d_0) \\ y\in\mathcal{Y}}}{\text{Max}} |F(x',y)-F(x,y)|. \tag{12}$$

A point $x^0 \in \mathfrak{X}$ is said to be <u>obstructed relative to a distance</u> $d > 0$ if $0 < d_q(x^0) < d$ for some $q \in S$.

Let δ be the diameter of $\mathfrak{X}$.

We shall use two different values of d_0 during the computation. We determine first the larger value d_0^0, by requiring it to satisfy besides the inequality (5) also the inequalities

$$\omega = \omega(d_0) < \rho/36 \tag{13}$$

and

$$\tau_0 = \tau(d_0) < \rho/36\delta. \tag{14}$$

At a given point $x^0 \in \mathfrak{X}$ we ask whether it is obstructed relative to the distance d_0^0. If it is and if x^0 meets the test at 4.9, 4.10 that Mas (N) $< 13\rho/36\delta$ (and so might be the solution), we replace d_0^0 by the smaller d_0^1 which satisfies the requirement, stronger than (14), that

$$\tau_1 = \tau(d_1(d_0)) < \rho/36\delta \ . \qquad (15)$$

If Max (N) is still less than $13\rho/36\delta$ the problem is solved; otherwise the algorithm proceeds with $d_0 = d_0^1$ until it is solved or x^0 becomes unobstructed relative to d_0^0.

During the course of algorithm $\mathfrak{A}$ we need a y-minimization, to accuracy

$$\varepsilon(d) = \rho d/36\delta \ , \qquad (16)$$

d being a quantity $\geq d_0$ in the machine. The minimum step distance will now be $D_0(d)$ chosen first to satisfy the analogue in $\mathcal{Y}$ to (5), and taking on two values $D_0^0(d)$ and $D_0^1(d)$ according as y is unobstructed or obstructed relative to $D_0^0(d)$. This last must be chosen so that the oscillation of $F(x^0,y)$ over a distance $\leq D_0^0(d)$ is less than $\varepsilon(d)/2$ and the oscillation of the directional derivative $D_gF(x^0,y)$ (g a direction in $\mathcal{Y}$) is less than $\varepsilon(d)/4\Delta$. Here Δ is the diameter of $\mathcal{Y}$. For the obstructed case we choose $D_0^1(d)$ so that the oscillation of $F(x^0,y)$ over a distance $D_1(D_0)$ is less than $\varepsilon(d)/2$; the condition on the directional derivative remain unaltered. $D_1(D_0)$ has the meaning analogous to $d_1(d_0)$.

3. <u>The y-algorithm</u>

This algorithm is subordinated to algorithm $\mathfrak{A}$ of section 4.

1. <u>A point</u> x <u>is given, and a</u> d > 0. <u>Put</u> $D_0 = D_0^0$ and $D = \Delta/2$.

2. <u>A point</u> y <u>is given</u>.

3. <u>If</u> y <u>is unobstructed relative to</u> D_0^0 <u>put</u> $D_0 = D_0^0$ <u>and replace</u> D <u>by</u> Max (D,D_0^0).

4. <u>Put</u>

$$Z_j = -F_{y_j}(x,y), \qquad (17)$$

R = S = 0.

5. <u>Apply the linear form algorithm to the form</u> $Z\cdot g = Z_jg_j$ <u>with the set of admissible directions</u> g <u>in the</u> y<u>-space corresponding to</u> y <u>and</u> D_0. <u>If that algorithm determines that this form has a nonpositive maximum, go to</u> 8. <u>Otherwise it finds a</u> g^0 <u>yielding a positive maximum, which we denote by</u> Max.

6. If

$$\text{Max} \leq \varepsilon(d)/\Delta \qquad (18)$$

go to 8.

7. Go to 12.

8. If y is unobstructed relative to D_0 go to 24.

9. If $D_0 = D_0^1$ and

$$\text{Max} \leq \varepsilon(d)/2\Delta \qquad (19)$$

go to 24.

10. If $D_0 = D_0^1$ go to 12.

11. Put $D_0 = D_0^1$ and go to 5.

12. If $y + Dg^0 \notin \mathcal{Y}$, put S = 1 and cut down D to the largest value for which $y + Dg^0 \in \mathcal{Y}$.

13. Put $y' = y + Dg^0$.

14. If

$$\frac{F(x,y') - F(x,y)}{D} < -\varepsilon(d)/4\Delta \qquad (20)$$

go to 15. Otherwise go to 18.

15. (This is a blank, for use in algorithm $\mathfrak{A}$.)

16. Replace y by y'.

17. If R = 0 go to 22. If R = 1 go to 20.

18. Put R = 1, S = 0, D = Max $(D/2, D_0)$.

19. Go to 13.

20. Put D = Max $(D/2, D_0)$.

21. Go to 2.

22. If S = 1 replace D by $\Delta/2$. 23. Go to 2.

24. The problem is solved; y minimizes F(x,y) to accuracy $\varepsilon(d)$ as required.

We refer to steps in the y-minimization algorithm by prefixing with a 3, as 3.15.

4. The algorithm $\mathfrak{A}$.

1. Put $d_0 = d_0^0$ and $d = \delta/2$. A y^0 is given.

2. A point x is given. N = 1.

3. If x^0 is unobstructed relative to d_0^0 put $d_0 = d_0^0$ and replace d by Max (d, d_0^0).

4. Go to 3.1 with $x = x^0$, $y = y^0$ and the given value of d.

5. When 3.24 is reached put $\bar{y} = y^0 = y$.

6. Put $\Omega = \gamma = 0$.

7. Put I = J = K = L = 0.

8. Replace $\bar{y}$ by $\dfrac{(N-1)\bar{y} + y^N}{N}$. Replace Ω by $\dfrac{(N-1)\Omega + F_{x_i}(x^0,y^0)}{N}$.

9. Apply the linear form algorithm to the form

$$\Omega \cdot \gamma = \sum \Omega_i \gamma_i \tag{21}$$

with the set $\Gamma(x^0)$ of admissible directions corresponding to d_0. If that algorithm determines that (21) has a non-positive maximum, go to 12. Otherwise it finds a maximizing γ, which we denote by γ^N. Denote the value of that maximum by

$$\text{Max }(N) = \Omega \cdot \gamma^N . \tag{22}$$

10. If

$$\text{Max }(N) \leq 13\rho/36\delta \tag{23}$$

go to 12.

11. Go to 16.

12. If x^0 is unobstructed relative to d_0 go to 39.

13. If $d_0 = d_0^1$ go to 39.

14. Put $d_0 = d_0^1$.

15. Go to 6.

16. Replace $\bar{\gamma}$ by $\dfrac{(N-1)\bar{\gamma} + \gamma^N}{N}$.

17. If $x^0 + d\bar{\gamma} \notin \mathcal{Y}$ put $J = 1$ and cut down d to the largest value for which $x^0 + d\bar{\gamma} \in \mathcal{Y}$.

18. Put $\bar{x} = x^0 + d\bar{\gamma}$.

19. If $d = d_0$ go to 32.

20. Go to 3.1 with $x = \bar{x}$ and $y = y^0$.

21. If 3.15 is reached, go to 23.

22. If 3.24 is reached, go to 24.

23. If

$$\frac{F(\bar{x},y') - F(x^0,y^0)}{d_0} \geq \rho/18\delta \tag{24}$$

go to 3.16. Otherwise go to 26.

24. Replace x^0 by $\bar{x}$.

25. If $I = 0$ go to 30. If $I = 1$ go to 28.

26. Put $I = 1$, $J = 0$, $d = \text{Max}(d/2, d_0)$.

27. Go to 18.

28. Replace d by Max $(d/2, d_0)$.

29. Go to 2.

30. If $J = 1$ or $K = 1$ replace d by $\delta/2$.

31. Go to 2.

32. If $K = 1$ go to 35. If $K = 0$ put $K = 1$ and go to 33.

33. Go to 3.1 with $x = x^0$ and $y = y^0$.

34. When 3.24 is reached replace y^0 by y.

35. Go to 3.1 with $x = \bar{x}$ and $y = y^0$.

36. When 3.24 is reached put $y^N = y$.

37. If
$$\frac{F(\bar{x},y^N) - F(x^0,y^0)}{d_0} \geq \rho/18\delta \qquad (25)$$
go to 24.

38. Replace N by N + 1 and go to 8.

39. The problem is solved, i.e. $\bar{x} = x^0$ and $\bar{y}$ satisfy (1) and (2) with ρ replaced by $17\rho/>6\delta$.

5. The doubled algorithm $\mathfrak{D}$

This is very simply described. We have a Max-Min algorithm $\mathfrak{A}$ and a Min-Max algorithm $\mathfrak{A}^*$
$\quad x \quad y \qquad\qquad\qquad\qquad y \quad x$
gotten from $\mathfrak{A}$ by a change of sign. We alternate steps of these in a manner appropriate to F. We do not give precise details, because these are superfluous. The essential idea is that, at least after a number of steps have been taken, one should, each time x^0 moves in algorithm $\mathfrak{A}$ or y^{*0} moves in algorithm $\mathfrak{A}^*$, check the inequality
$$F(x^{0*},y^{0*}) - F(x^0,y^0) < 17\rho/18. \qquad (26)$$
Here x^0 and y^0 are the quantities arrived at by the point 4.4 in $\mathfrak{A}$, and y^{0*} and x^{0*} the quantities arrived at by the point 4.4* in $\mathfrak{A}^*$. If (26) holds, then (1) and (2) hold, and we terminate. For a proof see [1].

The main point of $\mathfrak{D}$ is this. If $\mathfrak{A}$ is used alone, it will finally reach a terminal x^0 at which it comes eventually out through 39. Similarly $\mathfrak{A}^*$ will reach a terminal y^{0*}. If both algorithms are run simultaneously, and each has reached a terminal point, the test (117) will, according to Theorem VII of [1], pass, so that the problem is solved. This avoids the possibility of long terminal iteration within the individual algorithms.

6. The linear form algorithm in a special case

We are interested in the case when $\mathfrak{x}$ is the polyhedron defined by the conditions
$$\textstyle\sum_i x_{hi} = 1 \text{ for all } h \qquad (27)$$
and
$$\alpha_{hi} \leq x_{hi} \leq \beta_{hi} \text{ for all } h,i, \qquad (28)$$
where the sets $\{\alpha_{hi}\}$, $\{\beta_{hi}\}$ satisfy
$$\textstyle\sum_i \alpha_{hi} < 1 < \sum \beta_{hi} \text{ for all } h \qquad (29)$$
and
$$0 \leq \alpha_{hi} < \beta_{hi} \text{ for all } h,i. \qquad (30)$$

We assume here concerning d_0 only that

$$2d_0 < \min_{h,i} (\beta_{hi} - \alpha_{hi}). \tag{31}$$

An estimate of $d_1(d_0)$ in this case will be found at the end of this section. There further conditions, (32), are imposed on d_0.

We shall say that the pair $(h,i) \in L_h$ if $x_{hi} < \alpha_{hi} + d_0$; $(h,i) \in U_h$ if $x^0_{hi} > \beta_{hi} - d_0$. Because of (31) these sets do not intersect.

Fix on an h. We shall define a set D_h of distinguished elements by a step-by-step process. First we distinguish all those elements with $\alpha_{hi} + d_0 \leq x^0_{hi} \leq \beta_{hi} - d_0$. If there are $N_h > 0$ such elements we put provisionally

$$\mu_h = \frac{1}{N_h} \sum{}' \Omega_{hi}, \tag{32}$$

the prime always denoting summation over the distinguished elements. If $N_h = 0$ we put provisionally

$$\mu_h = \min_i \Omega_{hi} . \tag{33}$$

The remainder of the distinguishing follows an elementary algorithm.

1. Start with an index I_h, initially zero.
2. If all the undistinguished elements of L_h have $\Omega_{hi} \leq \mu_h$, put $I_h = 1$ and go to 5.
3. Find the undistinguished pair $(h,i) \in L_h$ with the largest value of Ω_{hi}, distinguish it, and replace μ_h by $(N_h\mu_h + \Omega_{hi})(N_h + 1)$.
4. Go to 2.
5. If all the undistinguished elements of U_h have $\Omega_{hi} \geq \mu_h$, go to 8.
6. Find the undistinguished pair $(h,i) \in U_h$ with the smallest value of Ω_{hi}, distinguish it, and replace μ_h by $(N_h\mu_h + \Omega_{hi})/(N_h + 1)$.
7. Go to 5.
8. If $I_h = 0$ go to 2.
9. The definition of the distinguished set D_h is complete.

Now form the sum

$$S = \sum_D (\Omega_{hi} - \mu_h)^2 \tag{34}$$

over the set $D = D_h$ of distinguished elements. If $S = 0$ the maximum of the linear form $\Omega \cdot \gamma$ is non-positive and the problem is solved. If $S > 0$ put $\lambda = \sqrt{S}$ and

$$\gamma^0_{hi} = \frac{\Omega_{hi} - \mu_h}{\lambda} \text{ if } (h,i) \in D; \qquad \gamma^0_{hi} = 0 \text{ otherwise.} \tag{35}$$

λ^0 then maximizes $\Omega \cdot \gamma$ as desired.

Estimate of $d_1(d_0)$.

Suppose d_0 satisfies in addition to (31) the conditions

$$d_0 < \frac{1}{I^2}(1 - \sum_i \alpha_{hi}), d_0 < \frac{1}{I^2}(\sum_i \beta_{hi} - 1) \tag{36}$$

for all h. Under these conditions one can prove ([2], section 14) that

$$d_1(d_0) \leq \sqrt{H}\,(I + 1)d_0 , \tag{37}$$

H and I being the number of indices h and i respectively.

7. A linear-exponential allocation game

This algorithm has found application to a problem in anti-submarine warfare. Suppose that the indices h,i,j,k,ℓ,m have the following meaning:

h: submarine type
i: submarine mission
j: anti-submarine weapons type
k: place
ℓ: kind of place
m: stage of mission.

A submarine mission is described by a matrix $\|e_{ijkm}\|$ gives the number of exposures he has to a weapon of type j at the place k before he can accomplish the mth stage of the mission. The effect of the weapons is characterized by a matrix $c_{hj\ell}$ with the following meaning: $\exp[-c_{hj\ell}y]$ is the probability a submarine of type h survives y units of weapons of type j at a place of kind ℓ. Thus the probability he accomplishes stage m of the mission is $\exp[-\theta_{him}]$, where

$$\theta_{him} = \sum_{jk} e_{ijkm} c_{hj\ell(k)} y_{jk} \tag{38}$$

$\ell(k)$ being a function denoting the kind of the place k and y_{jk} being the number of forces of type j assigned to the kth place. Let x_{hi} be the proportion of submarines of type h sent on the ith mission; we suppose x_{hi} satisfies conditions of the type $\sum_i x_{h_i} = 1$ for all h, with also upper and lower bounds on the individual x_{hi}. We suppose also that $\|y_{jk}\|$ satisfies similar conditions. Suppose V_{him} is the value of accomplishing stage m on mission i if the submarine is of type h. The total expected value of the submarine force with the allocation $\|x_{hi}\|$ is then the linear-exponential function

$$F(x,y) = \sum_{hi} x_{hi}\left(\sum_{m} V_{him}e^{-\theta_{him}}\right) , \quad (39)$$

which thus defines a game of the kind we have been studying. The algorithm is being applied to this problem in spaces of very high dimension, for instance with the number of indices h, i, j, k, m being 5, 25, 10, 200 and 5 respectively; of course in practice most of the e_{ijkm} and $c_{hj\ell}$ are zero. The details of this application will be found in [2].

BIBLIOGRAPHY

[1] J. Danskin, The derivative game in Max-Min and the solution of concave-convex games, submitted to the SIAM Journal of Applied Mathematics.

[2] J. Danskin, Programming aspects of a non-linear game problem, to appear.

ON THE OPTIMIZATION OF INFINITE DIMENSIONAL LINEAR SYSTEMS

S. DE JULIO

UNIVERSITA' DI ROMA
ISTITUTO ELETTROTECNICO
ROME, ITALY

1. Introduction

A new method for the computation of optimal controls has been recently proposed (1,2) which bypasses the difficulty of solving the differential equation governing the behavior of the system to be optimized. The main feature of this method is that it transforms a dynamical problem into a non-dynamical one and this is achieved by adding a sort of penalty function to the cost functional defining the optimization problem which accounts for the dynamics of the system.

The solution of the non-dynamical problem (the ε-problem, in the sequel) is approximate but can be made arbitrarily close to the solution of the optimization problem.

The ε-problem approach is also useful for proving existence of optimal controls, which we shall do in this paper referring to two broad categories of infinite dimensional linear systems, namely systems with distributed control and systems with boundary control.

In the case of infinite-dimensional linear systems the state of the system $x(t)$ is for each t an element of an (infinite-dimensional) abstract linear vector space H_1. We shall confine ourselves to the case where H_1 is a Hilbert space and shall denote by $||\cdot||_{H_1}$ its norm.

In section 2 we shall deal with systems governed by equations of the type

$$\dot{x}(t) = A\, x(t) + B\, u(t) \qquad x(0) = 0 \tag{1}$$

where the dot denotes differentiation with respect to the time variable t, A is an (unbounded) linear operator mapping a domain D(A) dense in H_1 into H_1, u is the control and for almost every $t \varepsilon [0,T]$ u(t) is an element of an abstract linear vector space H_2, B is a linear bounded operator mapping H_2 into H_1.

Also H_2 will be a Hilbert space whose norm we shall denote by $||\cdot||_{H_2}$.

The solution of (1) will be taken in the space $L^2(T;H_1)$ of all functions f(t) measurable with respect to t, with values (a.e.) in H_1, and such that

$$\int_0^T ||f(t)||^2_{H_1}\, dt < \infty.$$

$L^2(T;H_1)$ will be normed by

$$||f||_1 = \left(\int_0^T ||f(t)||^2_{H_1}\, dt\right)^{\frac{1}{2}}$$

and will therefore be a Hilbert space.

Let $L^2(T;H_2)$ be analogously defined, and denote by $||\cdot||_2$ its norm. Let $U \subset L^2(T;H_2)$ be a closed convex set containing the origin. We say that a control u is admissible if $u \varepsilon U$.

In section 3 we shall consider systems whose mathematical model is

$$\begin{aligned} \dot{x}(t) &= A\, x(t) \qquad x(0) = 0 \\ c\, x(t) &= u(t) \end{aligned} \tag{2}$$

where A is again an (unbounded) linear operator mapping a domain D(A) dense in H_1 into H_1, c is a linear operator mapping $D(c) \supset D(A)$ into H_2.

Also in this case the solution of (2)will be contaken in $L^2(T;H_1)$ and the set U of admissible controls will be a closed convex subset of $L^2(T;H_2)$.

2. The Abstract Distributed Control Problem.

In this section we deal with the optimization problem for infinite-dimensional linear systems whose mathematical model is given by (1). This is an abstract formulation which coincides with what is usually colled a distributed control problem when A is a partial differential operator.

We shall define the optimization problem along with what we have called the ε-problem, following Balakrishnan (1). The solution of the latter will be proved to give an approximate solution to the former.

The main result of this section is an existence theorem which applies to a broad class of optimization problems. The proof of the theorem is constructive in nature, in the sense that it suggests an algorithm for the computation of optimal controls.

2.1. Problem Statement

Let (1) be the system equation. Namely,

$$\dot{x}(t) = A\,x(t) + B\,u(t) \quad x(0) = 0 \tag{3}$$

and let the hypotheses set forth in the previous section hold.

Define the operator S

$$S = \frac{\partial}{\partial t} - A \tag{4}$$

by

$$(Sf)(t) = Sf(t)$$

over the domain D:

$$D = \{f \varepsilon L^2(T;H_1) : f \text{ is continuously differentiable in } t,\ f(0) = 0,\ f(t) \varepsilon D(A)\ \ \forall t \varepsilon [0,T],\ Sf \varepsilon L^2(T;H_1)\} \tag{5}$$

which is obviously dense in $L^2(T;H_1)$. We assume that A is such that the operator S is closable. Let $\overline{S}$ be the minimal closed extension of S with domain $D(\overline{S})$.

The solution of (3) will be taken in the weak sense. Namely, we say that $x \varepsilon D(\overline{S})$ is solution of (3) corresponding to u if

$$[x, S^*\phi] = [Bu, \phi] \tag{6}$$

for all $\phi \varepsilon D(S^*)$, [,] denoting the inner product of $L^2(T;H_1)$, S^* the adjoint of S.

Incidentally we note that D(S) being dense in $L^2(T;H_1)$, S^* always exists. Moreover, since S is closable and we are dealing with Hilbert spaces, $D(S^*)$ is dense in $L^2(T;H_1)$ and we have (3)

$$S^{**} = \overline{S} \tag{7}$$

Therefore, (6) is equivalent to

$$\overline{S}\, x = B\, u \tag{8}$$

Let a real functional J(u;x) defined over $L^2(T;H_2) x L^2(T;H_1)$ be given with the following properties

(p_1) $J(u;x) \geq 0$ for all u,x

(p_2) J is weakly lower semi-continuous

(p_3) J is radially unbounded.

Property (p_3) means that if $\{u_n, x_n\}$ is a sequence such that

$$\lim_{n\to\infty} (||u_n||_2 + ||x_n||_1) = \infty$$

then

$$\lim_{n\to\infty} J(u_n;x_n) = \infty.$$

The optimization problem that we intend to solve is the following:

The Optimization Problem. Given the system governed by the Eq. (3) and a cost functional $J(u;x)$ enjoying the properties (p_1), (p_2), (p_3), find $u^o \varepsilon U$, $x^o \varepsilon D(\overline{S})$ such that

$$J(u^o;x^o) = j_o = \operatorname*{Inf}_{\substack{u\varepsilon U\\ x\varepsilon D}} J(u;x) \quad \text{subject to } \overline{S}\,x = B\,u.$$

In theorem 2 we shall prove that under the above assumptions such optimal control and trajectory, u^o and x^o respectively, indeed exist. The proof is based on the formulation of a new problem, which we call the ε-problem, closely related to the optimization problem, in which we get rid of the constraint (8) by adding a sort of penalty function to the functional J, approximately accounting for the dynamics of the system.

The ε-Problem. Let a new functional J_ε be defined by

$$J_\varepsilon(u;x) = J(u;x) + \frac{1}{\varepsilon}||\overline{S}x - Bu||_1^2 \tag{9}$$

where $\varepsilon>0$. Determine $u_\varepsilon \varepsilon U$, $x_\varepsilon \varepsilon D(\overline{S})$, such that

$$J_\varepsilon(u_\varepsilon;x_\varepsilon) = j_\varepsilon = \operatorname*{Inf}_{\substack{u\varepsilon U\\ x\varepsilon D}} J_\varepsilon(u;x).$$

2.2. Existence of Optimal Controls

We now pass to prove that under the above assumptions both the optimization problem and the ε-problem have solution.

We begin with the ε-problem.

Theorem 1.

Given the system (3) and a cost functional $J(u;x)$ satisfying conditions (p_1), (p_2), (p_3), there exist $u_\varepsilon \varepsilon U$, $x_\varepsilon \varepsilon D(\overline{S})$ which solve the ε-problem. Namely,

$$J_\varepsilon(u_\varepsilon;x_\varepsilon) = j_\varepsilon = \underset{\substack{u\varepsilon U \\ x\varepsilon D}}{\mathrm{Inf}} \; J_\varepsilon(u;x)$$

where J_ε is given by (9).

Proof.

Let $\{u_n, x_n\}$, $u_n \varepsilon U$, $x_n \varepsilon D$, be a sequence realizing the infimum of J_ε:

$$J_\varepsilon(u_n;x_n) \downarrow j\varepsilon.$$

Being a decreasing sequence, $\{J_\varepsilon(u_n;x_n)\}$ is obviously bounded. Recalling the definition (9) of J_ε, we see that, due to the property (p_1) of J, J_ε is the sum of two non-negative quantities. Therefore, also $\{J(u_n;x_n)\}$ is bounded. Hence, due to property (p_3), there will exist constants C_1 and C_2 such that

$$||u_n||_2 \leq C_1$$

$$||x_n||_1 \leq C_2$$

for all n. u_n being bounded in norm and B being a bounded operator, there will also exist a constant C_3 such that

$$||Sx_n||_1 \leq C_3$$

Now, in a Hilbert space every bounded set is weakly compact. Therefore, there exist subsequences (relabel them $\{u_n\}$, $\{x_n\}$) and functions $u_\varepsilon \varepsilon L^2(T;H_2)$, x_ε,

$y_\varepsilon \varepsilon L^2(T;H_1)$ such that

$$\text{w-}\lim_{n\to\infty} u_n = u_\varepsilon$$

$$\text{w-}\lim_{n\to\infty} x_n = x_\varepsilon$$

$$\text{w-}\lim_{n\to\infty} Sx_n = y_\varepsilon \ .$$

Since U is closed and convex, it is also weakly closed. Hence,

$$u_\varepsilon \ \varepsilon U \ .$$

Let ϕ be any function in the domain of S^*. Then, using the definition of weak convergence, we have

$$[y_\varepsilon,\phi] = \lim_{n\to\infty} [Sx_n,\phi] = \lim_{n\to\infty} [x_n,S^*\phi] = [x_\varepsilon,S^*\phi].$$

Since $D(S^*)$ is dense in $L^2(T;H_1)$ and, as we have pointed out in (7) $S^{**} = \overline{S}$, the equality

$$[y_\varepsilon,\phi] = [x_\varepsilon,S^*\phi]$$

for all $\phi\varepsilon D(S^*)$ implies

$$x_\varepsilon \ \varepsilon D(\overline{S}) \qquad \text{and} \qquad \overline{S}\, x_\varepsilon = y_\varepsilon \ .$$

Finally, exploiting the weak lower semi-continuity of J (property (p_2)) and of the norm, we have

$$j_\varepsilon = \lim_{n\to\infty} J_\varepsilon(u_n;x_n) = \lim_{n\to\infty} J(u_n;x_n) +$$

$$\lim_{n\to\infty} \frac{1}{\varepsilon} ||Sx_n - Bu_n||_1^2$$

$$\geq J(u_\varepsilon;x_\varepsilon) + \frac{1}{\varepsilon}||\overline{S}x_\varepsilon - Bu_\varepsilon||_1^2 = J_\varepsilon(u_\varepsilon;x_\varepsilon)$$

for which only equality can hold. This ends the proof of the theorem.

We now pass to prove that the optimization problem has a solution to which the solution of the ε-problem can be made arbitrarily close, by choosing ε sufficiently small.

It is important to point out that in the following existence theorem no assumption whatsoever is made, regarding the existence of solutions of Eq.(8), but that, as a result, it will be shown that at least for the optimal control a solution indeed exists.

Theorem 2

Let $\{\varepsilon_n\}$ be a sequence of positive real numbers such that

$$\lim_{n\to\infty} \varepsilon_n = 0 .$$

Then there exists a subsequence (relable it $\{\varepsilon_n\}$) such that

$$\text{w-}\lim_{n\to\infty} u_{\varepsilon_n} = u^o \qquad \text{w-}\lim_{n\to\infty} x_{\varepsilon_n} = x^o \tag{10}$$

$$\lim_{n\to\infty} J_{\varepsilon_n}(u_{\varepsilon_n};x_{\varepsilon_n}) = J(u^o;x^o) \tag{11}$$

where $u^o \varepsilon U$, $x^o \varepsilon D(\overline{S})$ satisfy

$$J(u^o;x^o) = j_o = \operatorname*{Inf}_{\substack{u\varepsilon U\\ x\varepsilon D}} J(u;x) \text{ subject to } \overline{S}x=Bu \tag{12}$$

Proof.

Let us first of all notice that under the condition (8) $J_\varepsilon = J$. Therefore, j_o can be considered the infimum of J_ε subject to the additional condition (8). Hence,

$$j_o \geq j_{\varepsilon_n} = J_{\varepsilon_n}(u_{\varepsilon_n};x_{\varepsilon_n})$$

and j_o is well defined since the set $\{(u,x): u \varepsilon U, \bar{S}x = Bu\}$ is nonvoid because at least the (0,0) element is in it.

As in theorem 1 we then infer that u_{ε_n}, x_{ε_n}, Sx_{ε_n} are bounded in norm, that there exist subsequences (relable them $\{u_{\varepsilon_n}\}, \{x_{\varepsilon_n}\}$) and functions $u^o \varepsilon L^2(T;H_2)$, $x^o, y^o \varepsilon L^2(T;H_1)$ such that

$$\underset{n\to\infty}{\text{w-lim}}\ u_{\varepsilon_n} = u^o$$

$$\underset{n\to\infty}{\text{w-lim}}\ x_{\varepsilon_n} = x^o$$

$$\underset{n\to\infty}{\text{w-lim}}\ Sx_{\varepsilon_n} = y^o$$

and that

$$u^o \ \varepsilon\ U,\ x^o \ \varepsilon\ D(\bar{S}),\ \bar{S}\, x^o = y^o \ .$$

Moreover there also exists a positive constant K such that

$$\frac{1}{\varepsilon_n} ||\bar{S}x_{\varepsilon_n} - Bu_{\varepsilon_n}||_1^2 \leq K^2 \tag{13}$$

for all n, or

$$||\bar{S}x_{\varepsilon_n} - Bu_{\varepsilon_n}||_1 \leq K\sqrt{\varepsilon_n}$$

for all n, whence

$$\lim_{n\to\infty} ||\bar{S}x_{\varepsilon_n} - Bu_{\varepsilon_n}||_1 = 0. \tag{14}$$

We now show that u^o and x^o satisfy Eq. (8). Consider indeed the following inequality

$$0 \leq ||(\bar{S}x_{\varepsilon_n} - Bu_{\varepsilon_n}) - (\bar{S}x^o - Bu^o)||_1^2 =$$

$$= ||\bar{S}x_{\varepsilon_n} - Bu_{\varepsilon_n}||_1^2 + ||\bar{S}x^o - Bu^o||_1^2 -$$

$$- 2[\bar{S}x_{\varepsilon_n} - Bu_{\varepsilon_n}, \bar{S}x^o - Bu^o].$$

Passing to the limit as n goes to infinity and taking (14) and the definition of weak convergence into account, we get

$$0 \leq -||\bar{S}x^o - Bu^o||_1^2$$

which implies

$$\bar{S}\, x^o = B\, u^o \qquad (15)$$

Finally, to prove (11) and (12), we use the weak lower semi-continuity of J and the fact that $\frac{1}{\varepsilon_n}||\bar{S}x_{\varepsilon_n} - Bu_{\varepsilon_n}||_1^2$ is non-negative:

$$j_0 \geq \overline{\lim_{n\to\infty}}\, J_{\varepsilon_n}(u_{\varepsilon_n};x_{\varepsilon_n}) \geq \underline{\lim}_{n\to\infty}\, J_{\varepsilon_n}(u_{\varepsilon_n};x_{\varepsilon_n})$$

$$\geq \underline{\lim}_{n\to\infty}\, J(u_{\varepsilon_n};x_{\varepsilon_n}) + \underline{\lim}_{n\to\infty}\, \frac{1}{\varepsilon_n}||\bar{S}x_{\varepsilon_n} - Bu_{\varepsilon_n}||_1^2 \geq J(u^o;x^o)$$

which would contradict the definition of the infimum unless equality holds throughout. The equality between the limit superior and the limit inferior implies the existence of the limit, thus showing (11), while the equality

$$j_0 = J(u^o;x^o)$$

together with (15) proves (12).

3. The Abstract Boundary Control Problem

In this section we shall tackle the optimization problem for systems governed by an equation of the type (2). Again, as in section 2, the formulation of the problem is abstract, but we keep in mind the application of the results to systems governed by partial differential equations with control on the boundary.

Also for this case we have been able to achieve quite general results concerning the existence of optimal controls. Some additional hypotheses on the operator A have seemed to be necessary and are formulated in section 3.1, where the optimization problem is also stated. Section 3.2 is devoted to proving the existence of solution for both the ε-problem and the optimization problem.

3.1. Problem Statement

Let (2) be the system equation. Namely,

$$\dot{x}(t) = A\, x(t) \qquad x(0) = 0$$
$$c\, x(t) = u(t) \tag{16}$$

A is a linear operator mapping a domain D(A) dense in H_1 into H_1, c is a linear operator mapping a domain $D(c) \supset D(A)$ into H_2.

We again define the linear operator S

$$S = \frac{\partial}{\partial t} - A \tag{17}$$

with domain D dense in $L^2(T;H_1)$

$$D = \{f\varepsilon L^2(T;H_1) : f \text{ is continuosly differentiable in } t,\ f(0)=0,\ f(t)\varepsilon D(A)\ \forall t\varepsilon[0,T],\ Sf\varepsilon L^2(T;H_1)\} \tag{18}$$

We assume that the operator A is such that S is closable.

Let us endow D, which is obviously a linear space, with the norm

$$||f||_V = \left(\int_0^T ||f(t)||^2_{H_1} dt + \int_0^T ||Sf(t)||^2_{H_1} dt\right)^{\frac{1}{2}} \tag{19}$$

The completion V of D in the norm topology (19) is a Hilbert space (4). It is clear that V is algebraically equal to the domain of $\bar{S}$.

Let us define the operator C by

$$(Cg)(t) = cg(t)$$

with domain

$$D(C)=\{g\varepsilon L^2(T;H_1):g(t)\varepsilon D(c) \text{ a.e.} t\varepsilon[0,T], \; Cg\varepsilon L^2(T;H_2)\}$$

We assume that $D(C) \supset D(\overline{S})$ and that the restriction of C to $D(\overline{S})$ is continuous as a mapping from V into $L^2(T;H_2)$.

Given $u\varepsilon U$, we say that $x\varepsilon D(\overline{S})$ is the solution of (16) corresponding to it if

$$\overline{S}\,x = 0 \qquad C\,x = u \tag{20}$$

Let a functional $J(u;x)$ defined over $L^2(T;H_2) \times L^2(T;H_1)$ be given, with the following properties

(b_1) $J(u;x) \geq 0$ for all u,x

(b_2) J is weakly lower semi-continuous

(b_3) J is radially unbounded with respect to x, namely

$$\lim_{n\to\infty} ||x_n||_1 = \infty$$

implies

$$\lim_{n\to\infty} J(u_n;x_n) = \infty \;\forall\; \{u_n\}.$$

The optimization problem that we are going tacklε is the following.

<u>The Optimization Problem.</u> Given the system governed by the equation (16), a cost functional J enjoying

the properties (b_1), (b_2), (b_3) and a closed convex set $U \subset L^2(T;H_2)$, find $u^0 \varepsilon U$, $x^0 \varepsilon D(\overline{S})$ such that

$$J(u^0;x^0) = j_0 = \inf_{\substack{u\varepsilon U \\ x\varepsilon D}} J(u;x) \text{ subject to } \begin{array}{l} \overline{S}x = 0 \\ Cx = u \end{array}$$

The ε-problem associated with the optimization problem will be the following.

The ε-Problem. Let a functional J_ε be so defined

$$J_\varepsilon(u;x) = J(u;x) + \frac{1}{\varepsilon}||\overline{S}x||_1^2 \qquad (21)$$

where $\varepsilon>0$. Determine $u_\varepsilon \varepsilon U$, $x_\varepsilon \varepsilon D(\overline{S})$ such that

$$J_\varepsilon(u_\varepsilon;x_\varepsilon) = j_\varepsilon = \inf_{\substack{u\varepsilon U \\ x\varepsilon D}} J_\varepsilon(u;x) \text{ subject to } Cx = u$$

3.2. Existence of Optimal Controls

The main result of this section is a theorem concerning the existence of optimal controls for the class of systems and cost functionals described in section 3.1.

We begin by proving the existence of solution to the ε-problem and then pass to prove the existence of optimal controls. The proofs of these theorems are somewhat similar to the proofs of theorems 1 and 2. Therefore, we shall not dwell on the details.

Theorem 3.

Given the system (16) and a cost functional $J(u;x)$ satisfying (b_1), (b_2), (b_3), there exist $u_\varepsilon \varepsilon U$, $x_\varepsilon \varepsilon D(\overline{S})$ which solve the ε-problem. Namely,

$$J_\varepsilon(u_\varepsilon;x_\varepsilon) = j_\varepsilon = \inf_{\substack{u\varepsilon U \\ x\varepsilon D}} J_\varepsilon(u;x) \text{ subject to } Cx = u \qquad (22)$$

where J_ε is given by (21).

Proof.

Let $\{u_n, x_n\}$, $u_n \varepsilon U$, $x_n \varepsilon D$, with $Cx_n = u_n$, be a minimizing sequence, i.e.

$$J_\varepsilon(u_n; x_n) \downarrow j_\varepsilon$$

Due to properties (b_1) and (b_3), there exist constants C_1, C_2 such that

$$||x_n||_1 \leq C_1$$

$$||Sx_n||_1 \leq C_2$$

for all n . Therefore, there exist a subsequence which we relable $\{x_n\}$ and functions $x_\varepsilon, y_\varepsilon \varepsilon L^2(T; H_1)$ such that

$$\text{w-}\lim_{n\to\infty} x_n = x_\varepsilon$$

$$\text{w-}\lim_{n\to\infty} Sx_n = y_\varepsilon .$$

As in theorem 1, it can be shown that

$$x_\varepsilon \; \varepsilon \; D(\overline{S}) \qquad \text{and} \qquad \overline{S}\, x_\varepsilon = y_\varepsilon .$$

Since $\{x_n\}$ obviously converges weakly to x_ε in the topology of V as well, and since by assumption C is continuous as a mapping from V into $L^2(T; H_2)$, we also have

$$\text{w-}\lim_{n\to\infty} u_n = u_\varepsilon \; \varepsilon \; U$$

where

$$u_\varepsilon = C\, x_\varepsilon \tag{23}$$

Finally, exploiting property (b_2) and the weak lower

semi-continuity of the norm, we have

$$j_\varepsilon = \lim_{n\to\infty} J_\varepsilon(u_n;x_n) = \lim_{n\to\infty} J(u_n;x_n) + \lim_{n\to\infty} \frac{1}{\varepsilon}||Sx_n||_1^2$$

$$\geq J(u_\varepsilon;x_\varepsilon) + \frac{1}{\varepsilon}||\overline{S}x_\varepsilon||_1^2 = J_\varepsilon(u_\varepsilon;x_\varepsilon)$$

which proves the theorem since, due to (23), only equality can hold.

Theorem 4.

Let $\{\varepsilon_n\}$ be a sequence of real positive numbers tending to zero. Then there exists a subsequence (relable it $\{\varepsilon_n\}$) such that

$$\text{w-}\lim_{n\to\infty} u_{\varepsilon_n} = u^o \qquad \text{w-}\lim_{n\to\infty} x_{\varepsilon_n} = x^o \tag{24}$$

$$\lim_{n\to\infty} J_{\varepsilon_n}(u_{\varepsilon_n};x_{\varepsilon_n}) = J(u^o;x^o) \tag{25}$$

where $u^o\varepsilon U$, $x^o\varepsilon D(\overline{S})$ are optimal, i.e.

$$J(u^o;x^o) = j_0 = \operatorname*{Inf}_{\substack{u\varepsilon U\\ x\varepsilon D}} J(u;x) \quad \text{subject to} \quad \begin{array}{l}\overline{S}x = 0\\ Cx = u\end{array} \tag{26}$$

Proof.

As in theorem 2 we can prove that the sequence $\{J_{\varepsilon_n}(u_{\varepsilon_n};x_{\varepsilon_n})\}$ is bounded and therefore, due to properties (b_1) and (b_3) the sequences $\{x_{\varepsilon_n}\}$, $\{\overline{S}x_{\varepsilon_n}\}$ are bounded in norm. Hence, there exist a subsequence, which we relable $\{\varepsilon_n\}$, and functions $x^o, y^o \varepsilon L^2(T;H_1)$ such that

$$\text{w-}\lim_{n\to\infty} x_{\varepsilon_n} = x^o$$

$$\text{w-}\lim_{n\to\infty} \overline{S}x_{\varepsilon_n} = y^o$$

where

$$x^o \varepsilon D(\overline{S}) \qquad \text{and} \qquad \overline{S}\, x^o = y^o$$

Again for the continuity of the mapping C we have

$$\text{w-}\lim_{n\to\infty} u_{\varepsilon_n} = u^o$$

where

$$u^o = C\, x^o \tag{27}$$

Moreover, as in theorem 2, it can be shown that

$$\overline{S}\, x^o = 0 \tag{28}$$

Finally, consider the chain of inequalities

$$j_o \geq \overline{\lim_{n\to\infty}}\, J_{\varepsilon_n}(u_{\varepsilon_n};x_{\varepsilon_n}) \geq \underline{\lim_{n\to\infty}}\, J_{\varepsilon_n}(u_{\varepsilon_n};x_{\varepsilon_n})$$

$$\geq \underline{\lim_{n\to\infty}}\, J(u_{\varepsilon_n};x_{\varepsilon_n}) + \underline{\lim_{n\to\infty}}\, \frac{1}{\varepsilon_n} ||\overline{S}x_{\varepsilon_n}||_1^2 \geq J(u^o;x^o)$$

Due to (27) and (28) and the definition of the infimum, we get

$$j_o = \lim_{n\to\infty} J_{\varepsilon_n}(u_{\varepsilon_n};x_{\varepsilon_n}) = J(u^o;x^o)$$

which completes the proof of the theorem.

4. Conclusions

Although the formulation of the optimization problem of the previous sections is abstract, the application to systems governed by partial differential equations is straightforward and has been treated by the author. (5).

The technique that we have presented appears to be powerful both from a practical and a theoretical point of view.

From the practical point of view the advantage of having to solve a minimization problem without differential constraints is obvious. Of course, there is no point in resorting to the ε-problem in cases where the explicit form of the solution of the system equation is available or solving the differential equation on the computer is an easy matter. The technique has been successfully tested on some examples and the computational results will be shortly reported in another paper.

From a theoretical standpoint we have shown how the ε-problem approach can be used to prove existence of optimal controls. We hope that the power of this method will be exploited furhter especially in the field of non-linear systems both of finite and infinite dimensions.

This research was partially supported by the U.S. Air Force Office of Scientific Research, Applied Mathematics Division under Grants 68-1408 and 700-69 and by the Consiglio Nazionale delle Ricerche.

The author is indebted to Prof.A.V.Balakrishnan for the many fruitful discussions.

References

1. BALAKRISHNAN, A.V., "On a New Compunting Technique in Optimal Control." J.SIAM Control, Ser. A, 6:149-73, May, 1968.

2. DE JULIO, S., "Computation of Optimal Controls for Infinite Dimensional Systems". Proceedings of the Second Annual Princeton Conference on Information Sciences and Systems. Princeton University, March 25-26, 1968, Princeton, New Jersey.

3. RIESZ, F. and B.Sz.-NAGY, Functional Analysis. New York, Frederick Ungar, 1955.

4. LIONS, J.L., Equations Differentielles Operationnelles. Berlin-Gottingen-Heidelberg, Springer-Verlag, 1961.

5. DE JULIO, S., "Study of a New Computing Technique for Distributed Parameter Systems". Ph.D. In Engineering. University of California, Los Angeles, 1968.

A VALUE ITERATION ALGORITHM FOR MARKOV RENEWAL PROGRAMMING

B. Finkbeiner

W. Runggaldier

Institute for Operations Research and
Electronic Data Processing
University of Zurich

1. Theoretical outline. We consider a sequential decision process over a homogeneous Markov chain with finitely many states over an infinite planning horizon, where future rewards are discounted. To each element s_i of the finite space of states $S = \{s_i\}$ $(i=1,...,N)$ belongs a finite decision set $D(i)$, whose elements $z \in D(i)$ are the possible actions in state s_i. As a strategy f we denote a rule assigning to each state s_i an action $z_f \in D(i)$. The set of all possible strategies f is a set D, the cartesian product of all $D(i)$ $(i=1,...,N)$. For each $f \in D$ a matrix of transition probabilities $P(f) = (p_{ij}^{z_f})$ and rewards $R(f) = (r_{ij}^{z_f})$ is given. ($p_{ij}^{z_f}$ and $r_{ij}^{z_f}$ denote probability and return for a transition from state i to state j, if in state i an action z_f corresponding to strategy f has been chosen). The expected immediate returns for strategy f are given by the vector $q(f) = (q_i^{z_f}) = (\sum_j p_{ij}^{z_f} \cdot r_{ij}^{z_f})$. As a policy we intend a rule fixing a strategy for each transition. Denoting by $v_i(n)$ the present value, discounted by a discounting factor $\beta (0 < \beta < 1)$, of the total expec-

ted return for a system in state i with n transitions remaining to the end, we define as optimal a policy maximizing the total expected return of the whole process. The discounting factor β may also be interpreted as probability that the process continues to earn rewards.

The principle of optimality (1) leads to the following recurrence relation for the optimal values $v_i(n)$:

$$v_i(n+1) = \max_z \{q_i^z + \beta \sum_{j=1}^{N} p_{ij}^z \cdot v_j(n)\} \qquad (1)$$

which also determines at each step n and for each state i the optimal action and consequently the optimal strategy and optimal policy. The algorithm based on this formula is called value iteration algorithm. Being interested only in processes with an infinite planning horizon, we investigate the mapping of the recurrence relation (1):

$$M(\cdot) = \max_{f \in D} \{q(f) + \beta P(f) \cdot\}$$

It is a contraction mapping with the unique fixed point v*,

$$v^* = \max_{f \in D} \{q(f) + \beta P(f)\, v^*\} \qquad (2)$$

which is to be interpreted as the total expected maximum reward of the process.
Since the set D is supposed to be finite, the maximum in Eq.(2) is certainly achieved for some $f^* \in D$. So we have:

$$v^* = \max_{f \in D} \{q(f) + \beta P(f)\, v^*\} = q(f^*) + \beta P(f^*)\, v^* \quad (3)$$

The mapping

$$T(f^*)(\cdot) = q(f^*) + \beta P(f^*)\ .$$

is also contracting with the same fixed point v*. This fact shows a result already obtained by Blackwell (2) and stating that among the optimal policies there is always a stationary optimal one. Stationary means that at each transition we have to apply the same strategy.

Based on this result we may limit ourselves to the search of only stationary optimal policies determining that strategy which will be iterated for the whole duration of the process. For this purpose Howard (3) has developed an elegant method. In his application however we may encounter some numerical inconveniences especially for systems with large number of states.

A) At every iteration step we have to solve a system of linear equations of order equal to the number of states.

B) The method gives us theoretically exact values, their numerical accuracy however depends on accuracy in data and numerical calculations.

C) The algorithm breaks up at the exact moment the optimal policy has been reached. It may however happen that the optimal policy has not yet been reached, but the corresponding values are already sufficiently near to the optimal ones. So we are performing iterations without sensible improvement.

Trying to overcome these difficulties we went back to the value iteration algorithm limiting ourselves to only suboptimal policies, yielding values differing from the optimal ones by an arbitrarily small amount possibly within accuracy of data and numerical calculations.

Before stating the algorithm we need some results with the following notations:

$v(f)$: fixed point of the contraction mapping

$$T(f)\,(\cdot) = q(f) + \beta P(f)\cdot \qquad (f \in D)$$

$v(f)$ is the present value of the total expected return for an infinite step process corresponding to a stationary policy obtained by iterating strategy f.

f_n : The strategy determined at the n-th step by value iteration.

Theorem: For $\varepsilon > 0$ there exists an N such that for all $n \geq N$ we have:

$$\|v^* - v(f_n)\| < \varepsilon$$

Proof: For a contraction mapping S(·) with contraction factor β we have (4):

$$\|v_n - v_{n+p}\| \leq \frac{\beta^n - \beta^{n+p}}{1 - \beta} \|S(v_0) - v_0\| \quad (4)$$

where v_n is the iterated vector at the n-th step. Considering v^* and $v(f_n)$ as $\lim_{p\to\infty} v_{n+p}$ obtained by application of the mappings M(·) and $T(f_n)$ (·) respectively, using inequality (4) we get:

$$\|v^* - v(f_n)\| \leq \|v^* - v_n\| + \|v(f_n) - v_n\| \leq$$

$$\leq \frac{\beta^n}{1-\beta}\| M(v_0) - v_0\| + \frac{1}{1-\beta}\| T(f_n)(v_n) - v_n\| \quad (5a)$$

where in the second term of the rightmost part, v_n is to be interpreted as starting vector v_0 for the mapping $S(\cdot) = T(f_n)(\cdot)$.

Since f_n is the strategy obtained at the n-th step by value iteration, we have $T(f_n)\ (v_n) = M(v_n)$ and we continue inequality (5a):

$$\frac{\beta^n}{1-\beta}\| M(v_0) - v_0\| + \frac{1}{1-\beta} \| T(f_n)(v_n) - v_n\| \leq$$

$$\leq \frac{\beta^n}{1-\beta}\| M(v_0) - v_0\| + \frac{\beta^n - \beta^{n+1}}{1-\beta} \cdot \frac{1}{1-\beta} \|M(v_0) - v_0\| =$$

$$= 2 \frac{\beta^n}{1-\beta} \|M(v_0) - v_0\| \quad (5b)$$

We now get the conclusion by requiring:

$$N = \frac{\log (\varepsilon \quad (1-\beta)/(2\| M(v_0) - v_0\|))}{\log \beta}$$

Corollary: There exists an N such that for all $n \geq N$ we have

$$f_n = f^* \qquad (f^* \text{ is such that } v(f^*) = v^*)$$

Proof: We need only to choose the above

$$\varepsilon < \min_{f \in D, f \neq f^*} \| v^* - v(f) \|$$

(In case the are more different f*, we mean by f* their whole class, so that the above minimum is certainly positive).

The theorem gives us a means for estimating already after the first iteration an upper bound for the still necessary number of iterations in order to obtain a strategy which, when iterated, leads to values differing by not more than ε from the optimal ones. If the norm used is the maximum norm, the estimated and actual number of iterations practically coincide.

The corollary shows that from a certain N on the policy generated by value iteration coincides with the stationary optimal one so that, if ε is chosen not too rough, the corresponding suboptimal policy is already the optimal one.

The suboptimal value iteration algorithm is shown in Figure 1.

2. Computational outline. In what follows some results from the numerical calculations are reported. The computations were done on an IBM 360/40 computer using Fortran programming.

In Table 1 a comparison is made between the number of iterations and computing times needed by the stated algorithm and that of Howard for the car replacement problem (3).

Figure 1. The algorithm.

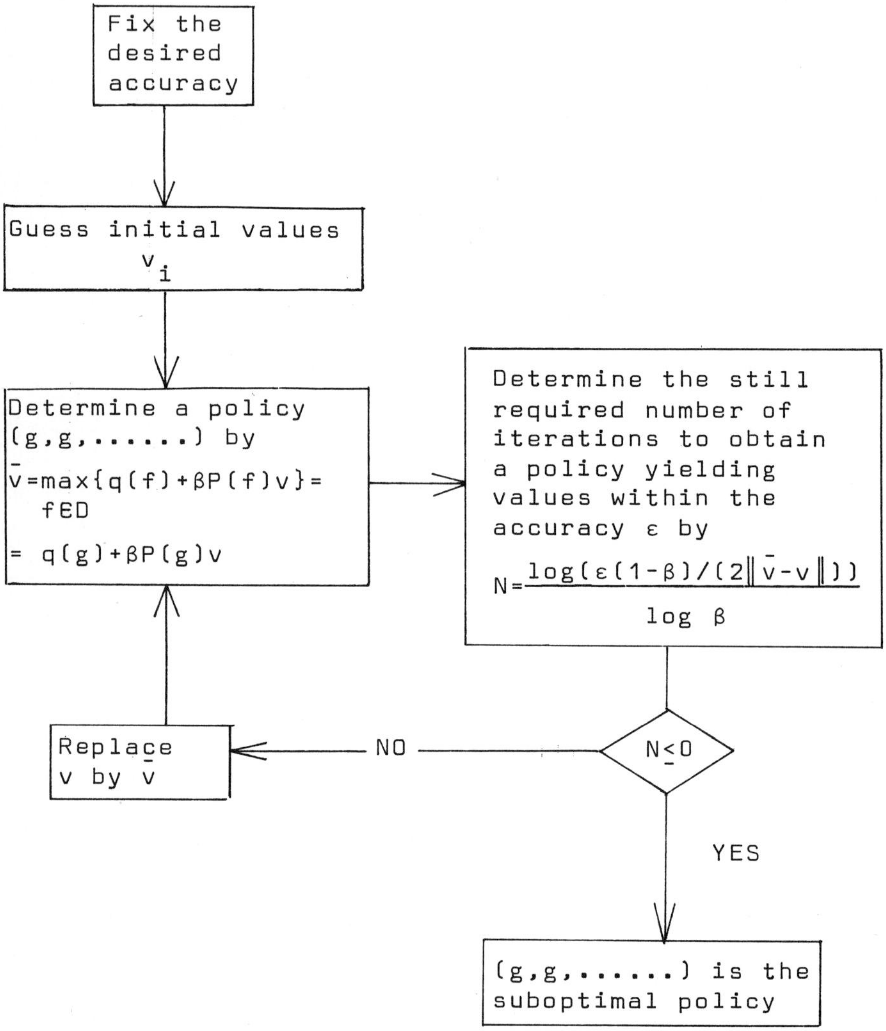

It must be remarked that for Beta going to one, the values tend to infinity. Therefore, since we have checked an absolute accuracy, the relative accuracy becomes stronger and stronger for Beta closer to one. This fact, together with the diminuished contraction, causes the very rapidly growing number of iterations with increasing Beta.

The car replacement problem is a special case: For each action we have only two probabilities different from zero.

In order to investigate the numerical behaviour of the stated algorithm in general, we generated transition probabilities and expected immediate rewards randomly, varying also randomly the number of action/state. In all such problems we found for the number of iterations the values reported in Table 2.

The number of states and actions/state had no influence on the number of iterations. They influence the time/iteration for which we found the values reported in Table 3.

Tables 2 and 3 show that in general the stated algorithm is advantageous for Beta not too close to one and for a number of actions/state not too large. However if the number of states is large, there is an advantage with respect to algorithms requiring on each step the solution of a system of equations, for which the computing time rises very quickly with the order as can be seen from Table 4.

If Beta is interpreted as probability that the process continues to earn rewards, we may go on by value iteration until either the required accuracy has been reached or the total probability that the process continues is less than a prefixed quantity whichever happens first.

At this point some considerations could be made about the opportunity of combining the two methods: The stated algorithm and Howard's method. This however depends to a certain extent on the special structure of the given problem.

A further observation could be made on a problem arising in connection with the structure of the computer. With growing number of states not all of the data can be kept in the central memory of the computer. This causes a time consuming input operation at every step. Since in general for value iteration we need more steps than for Howard's method, there is a range in the number of states where value iteration becomes again unfavorable until the moment when also for the solution of the system of linear equations input-output is needed. Table 5 illustrates the first part of this observation.

Acknowledgements

We wish to thank Professor P. Kall for introducing us to the subject and the Istituto di Elettrotecnica ed Elettronica of the University of Trieste for the encouragement.

References

(1) R.Bellman: "Dynamic Programming" 1957, Princeton University Press, Princeton,N.J.

(2) D.Blackwell: "Discrete Dynamic Programming" Annals of Mathematical Statistics, vol. 33, March 1962, pp. 719-726

(3) R.A.Howard: "Dynamic Programming and Markov Processes" M.I.T.Press, Cambridge 1960

(4) L.A. Ljusternik, W.I.Sobolew: "Elemente der Funktionalanalysis" Akademie-Verlag, Berlin 1965

(5) E.V.Denardo: "Contraction Mappings in the Theory Underlying Dynamic Programming" RM-4755-PR, March 1966, The RAND Corporation, Santa Monica.

Table 1. Car replacement problem.
(40 states, 41 actions/state)

	VALUE ITERATION ACCURACY (Units) 10		1		0.1		HOWARD'S Method	
Beta	Iter.	Time	Iter.	Time	Iter.	Time	Iter.	Time
0.55	7	4.65	11	7.75	15	10.84	4	83.06
0.65	10	6.69	16	11.14	21	14.90	4	83.11
0.75	16	10.76	24	16.75	32	22.38	4	83.10
0.85	30	20.19	44	30.01	59	40.50	5	103.75
0.95	113	75.67	158	106.24	205	138.13	6	124.36

Table 2. The general problem.

Beta	Number of iterations for accuracy (Units) 10	1	0.1
0.55	6	10	14
0.65	8	13	19
0.75	13	21	29
0.85	25	39	54
0.95	99	144	191

Table 3. Computing Times/Iteration.

		Max.Number Actions/State	
Number of States		8	15
	40	2.2 sec.	3.4 sec.
	60	4.8 sec.	7.4 sec.

Table 4. Computing Times for the solution of a system of linear equations of order N (Method Gauss-Jordan).

N	40	60
sec.	19.2	69

Table 5. Input of all the Data from Disk at every step. (60 States, Max.7 Actions/State)

VALUE ITERATION ACCURACY (Units)						
	10		1		0.1	
Beta	Input T.	Tot.T.	Input T.	Tot.T.	Input T.	Tot.T.
0.55	121.14	158.36	201.83	264.33	282.56	370.28
0.65	161.41	211.21	282.46	369.99	383.42	502.56

HOWARD'S METHOD		
Beta	Input Time	Total Time
0.55	80.81	310.05
0.65	80.74	309.64

COMPUTATION OF OPTIMAL PATHS IN FINITE GRAPHS

A. Gill and I. L. Traiger
Department of Electrical Engineering
and Computer Sciences
Electronics Research Laboratory
University of California
Berkeley, California

1. Introduction and Summary

This paper is concerned with finite, directed, branch-weighted graphs whose weights are real numbers having the general connotation of "cost" -- such as distance, transit time, expense, etc. The problem we wish to consider is the computation and characterization of the sets of "optimal" paths of given length $k \geq 1$ which begin at the "initial" vertex of the graph and exhibit the minimum average cost per branch. Thus, the optimality of a path of any length k emanating from the initial vertex is determined by a cost-comparison with other paths of the same length which also emanate from that vertex.

As we will use the term, a graph is a system $G = \langle V, B, W \rangle$ where $V = \{v_1, v_2, \ldots, v_n\}$ is a finite set of vertices; B is a finite set of ordered pairs from $V \times V$, called branches; and W is a set of weights which label the branches. The vertex v_1 will be taken as the initial vertex of a graph. A path is a string of $k \geq 1$ branches of this form

$$\pi = (v_{i_0}, v_{i_1})(v_{i_1}, v_{i_2}) \ldots (v_{i_{k-1}}, v_{i_k}) .$$

Research sponsored by the Air Force Office of Scientific Research, Office of Aerospace Research, United States Air Force under AFOSR Grant No. AF-AFOSR-639-67, and the United States Department of the Navy, Office of Naval Research under Contract Nonr-222(53).

A v_i-path has $v_{i_0} = v_i$, and a $v_i - v_j$ path has $v_{i_0} = v_i$, $v_{i_k} = v_j$. A cycle is a path such that $v_{i_0} = v_{i_k}$, and a proper cycle is a cycle such that only v_{i_0} and v_{i_k} are equal. For any $k \geq 1$, a vertex v_j is said to be k-connected to a vertex v_i if there exists a $v_i - v_j$ path of length k through the graph. A vertex v_j is connected to a vertex v_i if there exists a path of any length $k \geq 1$ from v_i to v_j. A graph is v_i-connected if all vertices $v_j \neq v_i$ are connected to v_i, and a graph is strongly-connected if it is v_i-connected for all $v_i \in V$.

We will restrict our attention to graphs having at least two vertices, where every vertex $v_j \neq v_1$ is connected to v_1. We will also require that every vertex have at least one branch leaving it, and that no more than one branch may go between a pair of vertices in the same direction. (If such "parallel" branches were allowed, we could obtain the same minimum-cost results by removing any branch having no smaller cost than a parallel one, and thus transforming the graph into one meeting our restriction.) Figure 1 illustrates such a graph. An arrowhead is used to mark the initial vertex v_1, and an arrow is drawn from v_i to v_j for every branch (v_i, v_j). Each branch is then labeled with the corresponding branch weight w_{ij}.

As stated above, we are interested in those v_1-paths of arbitrary length $k \geq 1$ which have the minimum average cost per branch. Such paths are the optimal paths of length k. As long as k is finite, one can give an equivalent definition of optimality in terms of total cost, rather than average cost, and not bother dividing by path length. When k is infinite, however, the total cost of a k-length path is indeterminate, and the concept of "average cost" must be handled in a special way. We will delegate the discussion of infinite-length paths to another paper (4), and assume for now that path-length k is finite.

2. Finite-Length Optimality

Let us denote by $r(k)$ the set of all optimal paths of finite length k, and by $R(G)$ the set of all optimal paths $\{\pi \in r(k), 1 \leq k < \infty\}$. The cost of any finite-length path π, denoted by $c(\pi)$, is just the sum of the weights of the individual branches making up the path. The cost associated with an optimal path of length k will be denoted by $w(k)$, so that $\pi \in r(k) \leftrightarrow c(\pi)=w(k)$. An optimal path of length k may not, in general, be an initial segment of all longer optimal paths, and may not be an initial segment of any longer one. Moreover, the quantities $\{w(k)\}$ need not be a monotonic function of k. In Figure 1, for example, $w(1)=1$, $w(2)=0$, $w(3)=-2$, $w(4)=-1$, $w(5)=-3$, etc.

One could use exhaustive methods to determine optimal paths and their associated costs. However, such methods are not efficient when either graph size or path length is large. By using a form of dynamic programming, we will be able to find these minimum costs iteratively, and then generate the required optimal paths from these and other quantities. We will also be able to develop some sufficient conditions under which arbitrary values $w(k)$ and path sets $r(k)$ may be determined directly from a fixed block of stored data. Under these same conditions, we will be able to construct a "finite-state acceptor" with which any v_1-path of any finite length k may be checked for optimality.

In order to calculate the minimum costs $w(k)$, we first define a "minicost algebra" having two operations, "$\oplus$" and "$\otimes$", which are generalizations of the usual operations of addition and multiplication. The set of elements over which the algebra will operate consists of the real numbers and the special character "$\#$." In the defining equations below, we will let a, b, c refer to any of these elements. We first establish the conventions

$$a + \# = \# + a = \#$$

$$\min\{a, \#\} = a ,$$

where "+" and "min" are the ordinary operations of addition and minimization. Then we define

$$a \oplus b = \min\{a, b\}$$

$$a \otimes b = a + b .$$

2.1. Propositions. $a \oplus b = b \oplus a$; $(a \oplus b) \oplus c = a \oplus (b \oplus c)$; $a \otimes b = b \otimes a$; $(a \otimes b) \otimes c = a \otimes (b \otimes c)$; $a \otimes (b \oplus c) = (a \otimes b)$

$\oplus$ (a $\otimes$ c). All of these facts follow from simple properties of addition and minimization.

Operations between vectors and matrices in this algebra work as one might expect. Thus, if c is a "scalar" and $\underset{\sim}{x}$ and $\underset{\sim}{y}$ are n-component "vectors," we define c $\otimes$ $\underset{\sim}{x}$ as that vector having components c $\otimes$ x_i; $\underset{\sim}{x} \oplus \underset{\sim}{y}$ as that vector having components $x_i \oplus y_i$, and the scalar product $\underset{\sim}{x}^t \otimes \underset{\sim}{y}$ as the quantity

$$(x_1 \otimes y_1) \oplus (x_2 \otimes y_2) \oplus \ldots \oplus (x_n \otimes y_n) .$$

If $\underset{\sim}{A}$ and $\underset{\sim}{B}$ are both n $\times$ n matrices, then the i,j-th term of the matrix product $\underset{\sim}{A} \otimes \underset{\sim}{B}$ is just

$$(a_{i1} \otimes b_{1j}) \oplus (a_{i2} \otimes b_{2j}) \oplus \ldots \oplus (a_{in} \otimes b_{nj}) .$$

Using the propositions above, one can prove the following:

<u>2.2. Propositions.</u> $\underset{\sim}{x}^t \otimes (\underset{\sim}{A} \otimes \underset{\sim}{B}) = (\underset{\sim}{x}^t \otimes \underset{\sim}{A}) \otimes \underset{\sim}{B}$; $\underset{\sim}{A} \otimes (\underset{\sim}{B} \otimes \underset{\sim}{C}) = (\underset{\sim}{A} \otimes \underset{\sim}{B}) \otimes \underset{\sim}{C}$. The last fact enables us to define the matrix product $\underset{\sim}{A} \otimes \underset{\sim}{B} \otimes \underset{\sim}{C}$ in an unambiguous way; and to define for any integer $k \geq 1$ the k-th "power" of $\underset{\sim}{A}$ as $\underset{\sim}{A}^k = \underset{\sim}{A} \otimes \underset{\sim}{A} \otimes \ldots \otimes \underset{\sim}{A}$ (k terms). Then $\underset{\sim}{A}^{k+1} = \underset{\sim}{A}^k \otimes \underset{\sim}{A} = \underset{\sim}{A} \otimes \underset{\sim}{A}^k$.

<u>Example.</u>

$$\begin{pmatrix} 1 & 2 & 1 \\ 3 & \# & 0 \\ 1 & -1 & 1 \end{pmatrix} \otimes \begin{pmatrix} 3 & -1 & 1 \\ \# & 0 & 2 \\ -1 & -2 & \# \end{pmatrix} = \begin{pmatrix} 0 & -1 & 2 \\ -1 & -2 & 4 \\ 0 & -1 & 1 \end{pmatrix}$$

For any $k \geq 1$ and vertex v_i, we define $P_i(k)$ as the set of all v_i-paths of length k. For every pair of vertices v_i, v_j we define $P_{ij}(k)$ as the set of all $v_i - v_j$ paths of length k. Then

$$w_{ij}(k) \triangleq \begin{cases} \min\{c(\pi), \pi \in P_{ij}(k)\} & \text{if } P_{ij}(k) \neq \emptyset \\ \# & \text{otherwise} \end{cases} .$$

$$r_{ij}(k) \triangleq \{\pi \in P_{ij}(k) \,|\, c(\pi) = w_{ij}(k)\} .$$

We refer to $r_{ij}(k)$ as the <u>optimal $v_i - v_j$ path set.</u> The terms w(k) and r(k) can now be determined by the equations

$$w(k) = \min_{1 \leq j \leq n} \{w_{1j}(k)\}$$

$$r(k) = \bigcup_j [r_{1j}(k) \mid w_{1j}(k) = w(k)] .$$

We will use the minicost algebra to find the quantities $\{w_{ij}(k)\}$ as a function of k, and then trace through the steps of the algebra to pick up elements of the sets $\{r_{ij}(k)\}$. First, for any graph G having any number of vertices n, we define $\underset{\sim}{W}(G)$, the <u>cost matrix</u> of G, as the $n \times n$ matrix having the typical element

$$w_{ij}(G) = \begin{cases} w_{ij} & \text{if } (v_i, v_j) \in B \\ \# & \text{otherwise} \end{cases} .$$

The k-th "power" of this cost matrix -- as calculated in the minicost algebra -- will be denoted by $\underset{\sim}{W}^k(G)$, with typical elements $\{w_{ij}^{(k)}(G)\}$.

<u>2.3. Lemma.</u> For any graph G, any $k \geq 1$, and any pair of vertices v_i, v_j, $w_{ij}^{(k)}(G) = w_{ij}(k)$, where $w_{ij}(k)$ is defined as above.

<u>Proof.</u> The proof hinges on the Principle of Optimality (<u>1</u>), and is explained in detail in (<u>2</u>).

The implication of this result is that one can perform iterative calculations with cost matrices to obtain any power $\underset{\sim}{W}^{k+1}$ as a function of $\underset{\sim}{W} = \underset{\sim}{W}(G)$ and the previously determined matrix $\underset{\sim}{W}^k$. Given the matrix $\underset{\sim}{W}^{k+1}$, we can then evaluate $w(k+1)$, the total cost of optimal paths of length $k+1$. Actually, the only quantities needed to find $\underset{\sim}{w}(k+1)$ are the n terms $w_{11}(k), w_{12}(k), \ldots, w_{1n}(k)$, and these in turn can be determined from $\underset{\sim}{W}$ and only the top row of the matrix $\underset{\sim}{W}^k$. Thus, we shall define for any $k \geq 1$ the <u>k-branch cost vector</u> $\underset{\sim}{w}(k)$, where

$$\underset{\sim}{w}(k) = (w_{11}(k)\ w_{12}(k)\ \dots\ w_{1n}(k))\,.$$

(Note that $\underset{\sim}{w}(k)$ is written as a row vector.) Then $\underset{\sim}{w}(k+1)$ is determined by the iterative relation $\underset{\sim}{w}(k+1) = \underset{\sim}{w}(k) \otimes \underset{\sim}{W}$, and all one needs to retain at any step of a calculation involving n vertices are the $n^2 + n$ quantities corresponding to $\underset{\sim}{W}$ and the last calculated cost vector.

Finding the optimal path sets $\{r_{ij}(k)\}$ as a function of k will not be quite as simple as finding their respective costs. For any $k \geq 1$ and any pair of vertices v_i, v_j, we define the <u>H-set</u>

$$H_{ij}(k) = \begin{cases} \{v_h \in V \mid w_{ih}(k-1) + w_{hj} = w_{ij}(k)\} \\ \qquad\qquad\qquad \text{if} \quad w_{ij}(k) \neq \# \\ \emptyset \qquad\qquad\quad \text{otherwise} \end{cases}$$

Then we obtain the following:

<u>2.4. Lemma.</u> For any $k \geq 1$ and any pair of vertices v_i, v_j, suppose $P_{ij}(k)$ is a non-empty set. Then

$$r_{ij}(k) = \begin{cases} \{(v_i, v_j)\} \quad \text{if} \quad k=1 \\ \bigcup_h \left[[r_{ih}(k-1)](v_h, v_j) \mid \ v_h \in H_{ij}(k) \right] \quad \text{otherwise} \end{cases}$$

<u>Proof.</u> See (<u>2</u>).

In order to determine an arbitrary optimal path set r(k), a straightforward application of these results would require that for every step t, $1 \leq t \leq k$, one must know w(t), $\underset{\sim}{W}$, and the n sets $\{r_{11}(t), r_{12}(t), \dots, r_{1n}(t)\}$. These terms would all be retained while one calculated $\underset{\sim}{w}(t+1)$, found the H-sets $\{H_{11}(t+1), H_{12}(t+1), \dots, H_{1n}(t+1)\}$, and then used Lemma 2.4 to determine the new sets $\{r_{11}(t+1), r_{12}(t+1), \dots, r_{1n}(t+1)\}$. Finally, at step k, one would evaluate w(k) and set $r(k) = \bigcup_j [r_{1j}(k) \mid w_{1j}(k) = w(k)]$. The difficulty with this technique is that for large k, it would be very uneconomical to have to store the lower order sets $\{r_{11}(t), r_{12}(t), \ldots, r_{1n}(t)\}$, since these sets would eventually have an arbitrarily large number of elements, each t branches long. A simple method for avoiding this difficulty is to store and retain only the cost vectors $\underset{\sim}{w}(1), \underset{\sim}{w}(2), \ldots, \underset{\sim}{w}(k)$, along with the cost matrix $\underset{\sim}{W}$, and then generate each $r_{1j}(k) \subseteq r(k)$ by applying Lemma 2.4 recursively. Then one could put the results into an output stream, branch-by-branch and path-by-path, and avoid tying up storage space with representations of entire sets.

2.5. Lemma. For any graph G, suppose that there exists a triple (τ, p, G) such that $\underset{\sim}{w}(\tau + p) = \theta \otimes \underset{\sim}{\omega}(\tau)$. Then for all $\Delta \geq 0$ and $h \geq 0$

$$\underset{\sim}{w}(\tau + \Delta + hp) = \theta^h \otimes \underset{\sim}{w}(\tau + \Delta),$$

where all operations are performed over the minicost algebra. (Thus θ^h is really $\theta \cdot h$ over the ordinary algebra.)

Proof. See (2).

One can verify that for graph G_1, $\underset{\sim}{w}(8) = -1 \otimes \underset{\sim}{w}(6)$, so that (τ, p, θ) is $(6, 2, -1)$. A graph for which there exists a triple (τ, p, θ) such that $\underset{\sim}{w}(\tau + p)\ \theta \otimes \underset{\sim}{w}(\tau)$ will be called vector-periodic. The least parameters τ and p will be called the vector transience and vector period, respectively. For any integer $k \geq 1$, we define

$$\tilde{k} = \begin{cases} k & \text{for } 1 \leq k \leq \tau + p - 1 \\ k+\delta & \text{for } k = \tau + hp + \delta,\ 0 \leq \delta \leq p-1,\ h \geq 0 . \end{cases}$$

2.6. Lemma. Let G be vector-periodic, with parameters (τ, p, θ). Then for any $k = \tau + hp + \delta$, $0 \leq \delta \leq p - 1$ and $h \geq 0$, $\underset{\sim}{w}(k) = \theta^h \otimes \underset{\sim}{w}(\tilde{k})$. Also, for any $k = \tau + hp + \delta$, $p \geq 2$, $h \geq 0$, $0 \leq \delta \leq p - 1$ and $1 \leq j \leq n$, $H_{1j}(k) = H_{1j}(\tilde{k})$. For any $k = \tau + hp$, $h \geq 1$ and $1 \leq j \leq n$, $H_{1j}(k) = H_{1j}(\tau + p)$.

Proof. See (2).

The significance of these results is that when G is a vector-periodic graph, any optimal path set r(k) may be generated from the fixed set of cost vectors $\underset{\sim}{w}(1), \underset{\sim}{w}(2), \ldots, \underset{\sim}{w}(\tau+p)$.

Lemma 2.6 gives us an expression for $\underset{\sim}{w}(k)$ and also tells us how to evaluate the required H-sets in terms of $\{H_{1j}(t), 1 \leq t \leq \tau + p\}$. These H-sets in turn may be evaluated from the first $\tau + p$ cost vectors.

In general, the work involved in generating an arbitrary optimal path set r(k) will still be complicated by the possibly large number of paths in the set, and the bookkeeping necessary to pick up all of these paths whenever an H-set has more than one element. However, vector-periodicity is a very useful property when we wish to find only a single element of any set r(k). In this case, one chooses only one element from every path set and keeps working on the same path from right to left.

We have seen that when a graph is vector-periodic, one may generate any optimal set r(k) from a fixed and finite amount of information -- namely the first $\tau + p$ cost vectors. A more interesting feature of vector-periodicity is that for any vector-periodic graph G, one can construct a "finite-state acceptor" $\mathcal{O}\!\mathcal{C}$(G) which scans any path π from left to right, and then signals whether or not the path is optimal. In other words, one can prove that if G is a vector-periodic graph, then $R(G) = \{\pi \in r(k), 1 \leq k < \infty\}$ is a "regular set." The exact construction of $\mathcal{O}\!\mathcal{C}$(G), as well as the proof that $\mathcal{O}\!\mathcal{C}$(G) recognizes the set R(G), are too lengthy to include in this paper. We will outline the procedure, and refer the reader to (2) for all details.

The first step is to construct a "recursive table" for the graph, where the entries of the table relate the members of any optimal path set r(k) to all shorter optimal paths. Such a table is illustrated in Table 1. The columns of the table are numbered from left to right as C_1, C_2, etc., and the path segments having their rightmost branch in any column C_t are called "C_t-elements." A recursive table having k columns and representing a graph G is denoted by $\Gamma(G, k)$, and a block of entries going from $k \leq t \leq k + q - 1$ is denoted by B(k, q).

Without describing the construction of $\Gamma(G, k)$ exactly, we can say that column elements are built up by column, starting at C_1, and contain the end segments of optimal paths whose initial segments or earlier segments have been listed earlier. For example, column C_9 in Table 1 contains only one entry,

TABLE 1. RECURSIVE TABLE $\Gamma(G_1, 12)$

C_1	C_2	C_3	C_4	C_5	C_6	C_7	C_8	C_9	C_{10}	C_{11}	C_{12}
(v_1, v_2)											
(v_1, v_3)											
	(v_3, v_4)										
		(v_4, v_5)									
		(v_4, v_2)	(v_2, v_2)								
		(v_4, v_3)	(v_3, v_4)								
		(v_4, v_5)	(v_5, v_5)								
				(v_4, v_5)							
				(v_4, v_2)	(v_2, v_2)						
				(v_4, v_3)	(v_3, v_4)						
				(v_2, v_4)	(v_4, v_5)						
					(v_5, v_5)						
						(v_4, v_5)					
						(v_4, v_2)	(v_2, v_2)				
						(v_4, v_3)	(v_3, v_4)				
						(v_2, v_4)	(v_4, v_5)				
					(v_4, v_3)	(v_3, v_4)	(v_4, v_5)				
							(v_5, v_5)				
								(v_4, v_5)			
								(v_4, v_2)	(v_2, v_2)		
								(v_4, v_3)	(v_3, v_4)		
								(v_2, v_4)	(v_4, v_5)		
							(v_4, v_3)	(v_3, v_4)	(v_4, v_5)		
									(v_5, v_5)		
										(v_4, v_5)	
										(v_4, v_2)	(v_2, v_2)
										(v_4, v_3)	(v_3, v_4)
										(v_2, v_4)	(v_4, v_5)
									(v_4, v_3)	(v_3, v_4)	(v_4, v_5)
											(v_5, v_5)

Fig. 1. Graph G_1

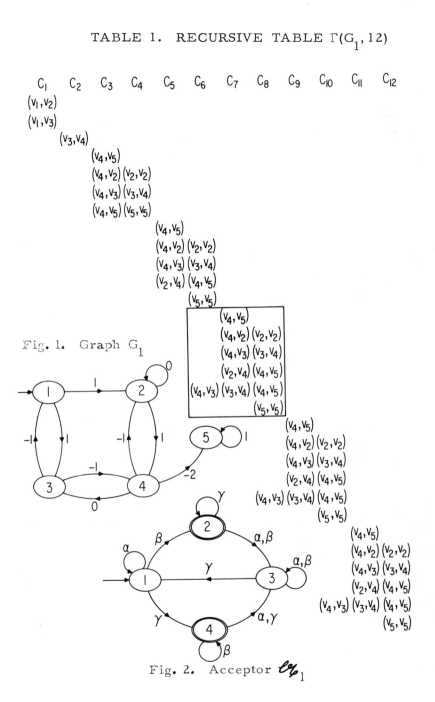

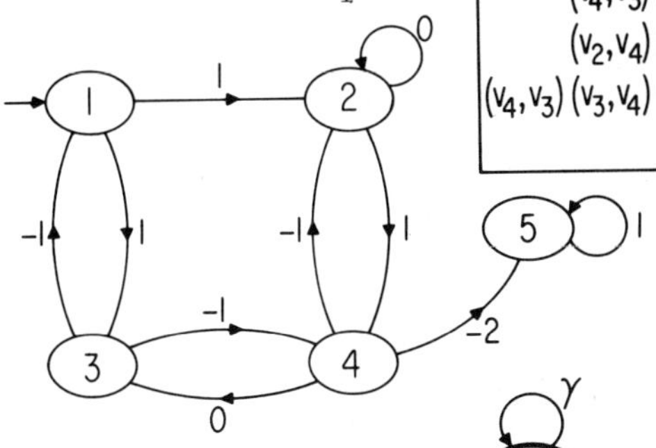

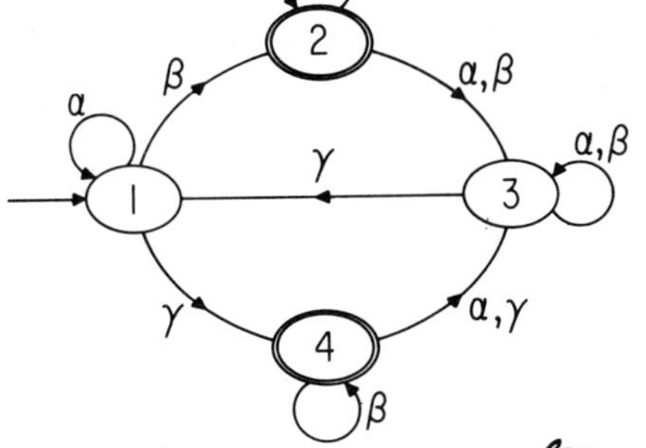

Fig. 2. Acceptor $\mathscr{A}_1$

"(v_4, v_5)." One can verify that for graph G_1, $r(9) = r_{15}(9) = [r_{14}(8)](v_4, v_5)$, and that $r_{14}(8)$ is a subset of $r(8)$. Thus, we can "depend" on the entry or entries in column C_8 which end at vertex v_{14}, and eventually work our way back to generate all of $r(9)$. (The rigorous definition of $\Gamma(G, k)$ contains a self-calling "recursive subroutine," hence the name "recursive table.")

The reader should note in Table 1 that the block of entries $B(7, 2)$ is identical to both $B(9, 2)$ and $B(11, 2)$. In general, a graph will be called block-periodic if there exist integers μ, α such that for all $h \geq 0$, $B(\mu + h\alpha, \alpha) = B(\mu, \alpha)$. The least such integers will be called the block transience and block period, respectively.

2.7. Lemma. If a graph G is vector-periodic, with parameters (τ, p, θ), then G is block-periodic with some parameters (μ, α). Furthermore, $\alpha \leq p$ and $\mu \leq \tau + np$, where n is the number of vertices of G.

Proof. The proof of this result is rather complex, and depends on the exact construction of $\Gamma(G, k)$. See (2).

The above result indicates that the class of vector-periodic graphs is a subclass of the class of block-periodic graphs. One can show, in fact, that there exist graphs which are block-periodic and not vector-periodic, so that vector-periodic graphs form a proper subclass.

We will now work with block-periodic graphs and their recursive tables, and show by construction that if G is block-periodic, then R(G) is a regular set. Before doing so, however, we will give definitions of finite-state acceptors and regular sets.

As we use the term, a finite-state acceptor is a deterministic, sequential system of the form

$$\mathcal{A} = \langle \Sigma, Q, q(0), \eta, F \rangle$$

where Σ is the finite input alphabet; Q is the finite state set; $q(0) \in Q$ is the initial state of the system at time $t = 0$; η is the state-transition function $Q \times \Sigma \rightarrow Q$; and $F \subseteq Q$ is the (non-empty) set of accept-states. (This definition will be equivalent to "finite state automaton" in (3).) The acceptor reads strings or "tapes" of input symbols, character-by-character, from left-to-right, and changes state according to its state-transition function. All tapes are read in at time $t = 0$, so that the final state induced by a typical input tape x is $\eta(q(0), x)$. The behavior of $\mathcal{O}\!\mathcal{L}$, denoted by $T(\mathcal{O}\!\mathcal{L})$, is defined as the set of input tapes which drive $\mathcal{O}\!\mathcal{L}$ into any of the accept-states. These are the tapes which are recognized by the acceptor. A set of tapes Z over a finite alphabet is called a regular set if there exists a finite-state acceptor which recognizes it -- that is, if there exists an acceptor $\mathcal{O}\!\mathcal{L}$ such that $T(\mathcal{O}\!\mathcal{L}) = Z$.

Example. Figure 2 is a graphical illustration of a four-state acceptor $\mathcal{O}\!\mathcal{L}_1$. The accept-states are indicated by double circles, and the initial state by an arrowhead. The acceptor reads character strings over the alphabet $\Sigma = \{\alpha, \beta, \gamma\}$, and recognizes an infinite set of such strings. Some of the strings recognized by $\mathcal{O}\!\mathcal{L}_1$ are $\gamma, \gamma\beta, \gamma\beta\beta, \beta, \beta\gamma, \beta\gamma\gamma, \beta\alpha\gamma\gamma$, etc.

The construction of $\mathcal{O}\!\mathcal{L}(G)$ from a recursive table $\Gamma(G, k)$ is essentially a matter of identifying states of an acceptor with every branch appearing in the table, setting up transitions from state to state according to table linkages, and then marking as accept-states those which correspond to the rightmost branches of entries in the table. Figure 3(a) contains an incompletely specified acceptor $\mathcal{O}\!\mathcal{L}_1(G_1)$ which was generated from Table 1. The states are coded so that (k, v_i) appears whenever v_i is the right-hand vertex of any branch in column C_k, for $1 \leq k \leq \mu + \alpha$. (It is generally necessary to use a higher order recursive table than $\Gamma(G, \mu + \alpha)$ to detect all of the branches that might occur in the first $\mu + \alpha$ columns -- since later entries may "reach back" to these columns. One can show that $\Gamma(G, 2(\mu + \alpha - 1))$ is sufficiently large.) The transitions from state to state are dictated by the structure of the table, and all undefined transitions are directed to the sink state denoted by (*). The accept-states are those which correspond to the right-most vertices of path segments in the table. Thus, if $1 \leq k \leq \mu + \alpha$ and $r_{1j}(k)$ is a subset of $r(k)$, then (k, v_j) is an accept-state of $\mathcal{O}\!\mathcal{L}_1(G)$, and any branch sequence that drives $\mathcal{O}\!\mathcal{L}_1(G)$ into state (k, v_j) is a member of $r_{1j}(k)$. One can verify that $\mathcal{O}\!\mathcal{L}_1(G_1)$ in Figure 3(a) recognizes exactly the set $R_1(G_1) = \{\pi \epsilon r(k), 1 \leq k \leq \mu + \alpha\}$.

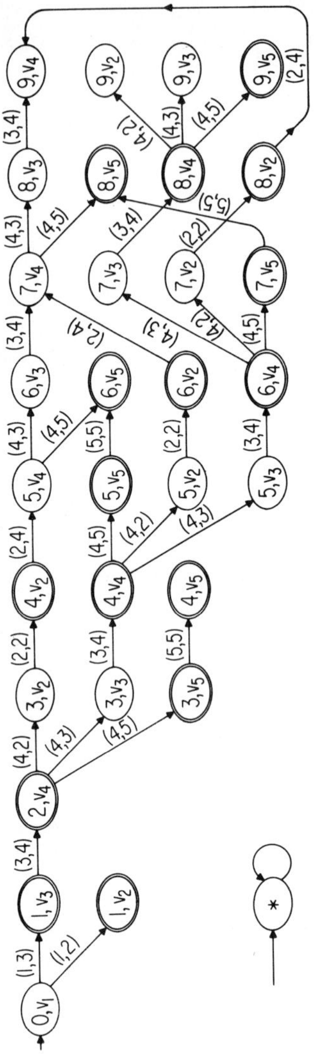

Fig. 3(a). Acceptor $\mathscr{C}_1(G_1)$

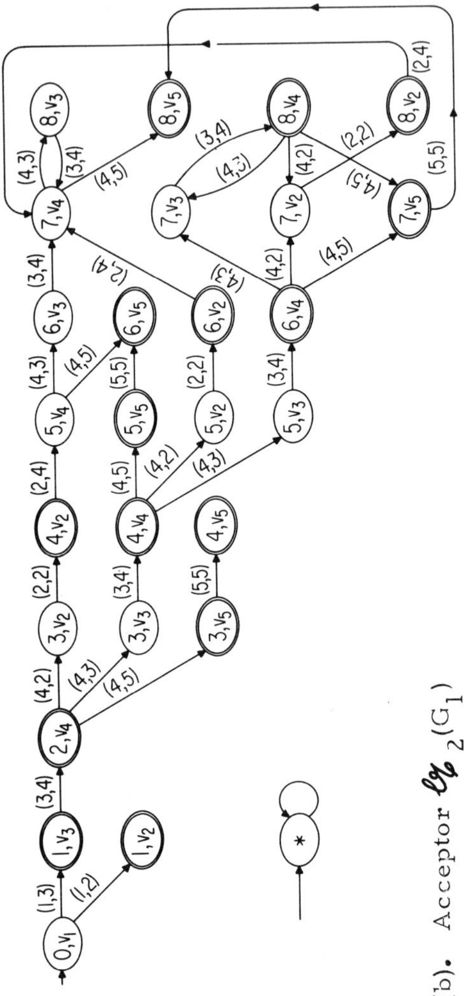

Fig. 3(b). Acceptor $\mathscr{C}_2(G_1)$

In going from $\mathcal{A}_1(G_1)$ to $\mathcal{A}_2(G_1)$ in Figure 3(b), one "merges" every state of the form $(\mu + \alpha, v_i)$ to a corresponding state (μ, v_i). We now claim that $\mathcal{A}_2(G_1)$ recognizes exactly the set $R(G_1) = \{\pi \epsilon r(k), 1 \leq k < \infty\}$, so that $R(G_1)$ is a regular set. Reference 2 contains a rigorous proof of this claim, which we will not be covering here.

<u>2.8. Theorem.</u> Let G be a block-periodic graph. Then $R(G) = \{\pi \epsilon r(k), 1 \leq k < \infty\}$ is a regular set.

<u>Corollary.</u> Let G be a vector-periodic graph. Then R(G) is a regular set.

Generally, one can employ "minimization" techniques to reduce the number of states in $\mathcal{A}_2(G)$. These techniques are similar to the merging process described above, and are explained in (3). The resulting <u>minimal acceptor</u> has the same behavior, and has the minimum number of states necessary to recognize R(G). We will call this acceptor $\mathcal{A}(G)$. Figure 4 contains the minimal acceptor $\mathcal{A}(G_1)$, while Figure 5 contains a more complex graph G_2 with its corresponding acceptor $\mathcal{A}(G_2)$.

<u>References</u>

1. Bellman, R., <u>Dynamic Programming</u>, Princeton Univ. Press, Princeton, N. J., 1957.
2. Traiger, I., "Output Optimization Problems in Sequential Machines," Ph. D. Thesis, Electrical Engineering Dept., Univ. of California, Berkeley, 1968.
3. Harrison, M., <u>Introduction to Switching and Automata Theory</u>, McGraw-Hill Book Co., Inc., New York, 1965.
4. Traiger, I. L. and A. Gill, "On an asymptotic optimization problem in finite, directed, weighted graphs," Information and control (in press).

<u>Acknowledgement</u>

The authors should like to thank Mr. F. J. Oertly of the Swiss Federal Institute of Technology for coining the term "minicost algebra."

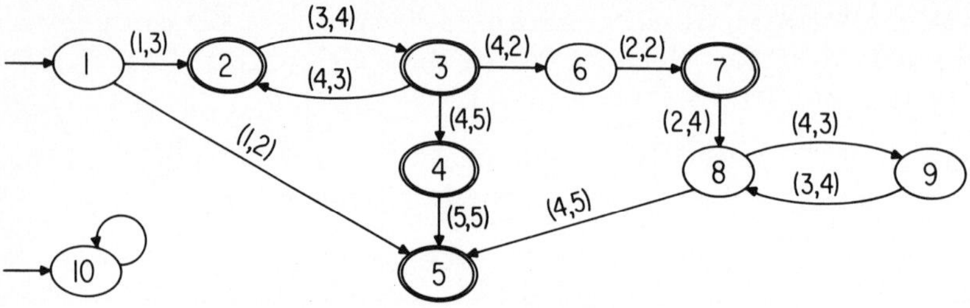

Fig. 4. Acceptor $\mathscr{A}(G_1)$

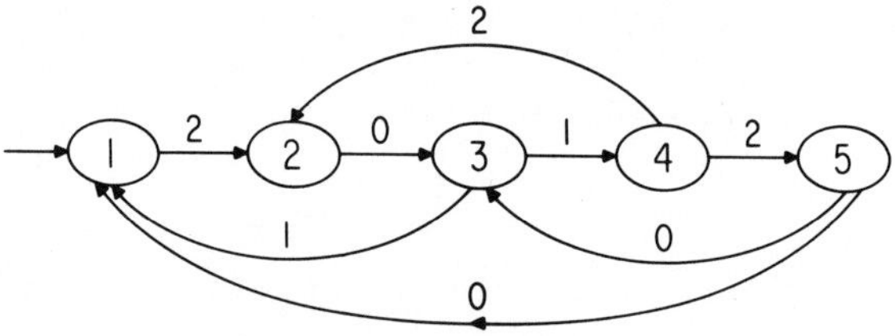

Fig. 5(a). Graph G_2

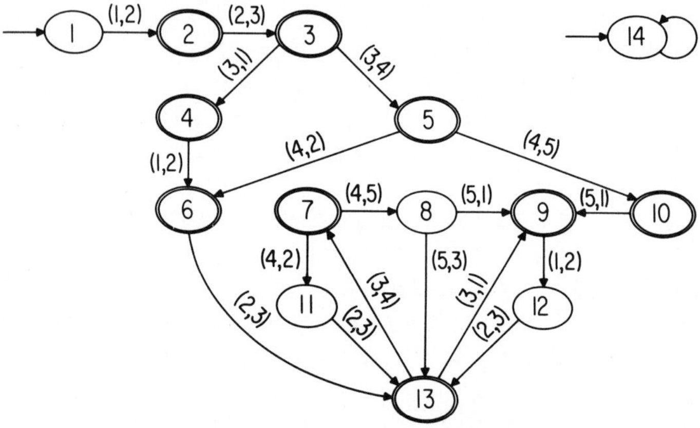

Fig. 5(b). Acceptor $\mathscr{A}(G_2)$

PICTURE PROCESSING: SOME APPLICATIONS

A. Grasselli
Istituto di Elaborazione dell'Informazione
Consiglio Nazionale delle Ricerche
Pisa, Italy

I - INTRODUCTION

In the last few years, digital computers have been employed for several picture processing tasks, which span over many disparate fields, from physics to medecine to geography to police work (for a fairly comprehensive coverage of different applications see (1) and (2)). The problems that have been approached and solved, or those currently under development, are intrinsically more complex than "classical" pattern recognition problems: in fact, the goal is often not that of merely assigning the input image to one of a set of classes, but that of extracting from it a wealth of highly structured information. While in "classical" pattern recognition there exists nowadays a reasonably satisfactory unifying methodology, picture processing can so far exhibit only the first steps toward methodological results, not all which have yet been field-proven (we will not attempt to give here a comprehensive list of published contributions: see (3), (4), (5); these references contain excellent bibliographies).

The purpose of this paper is to outline three applications of picture processing: their choice as illustrative examples does not descend from the desire of exhibiting an exhaustive bag of tricks, but merely from the fact that this author and coworkers are presently engaged in their solution.

II - CLASSIFICATION OF FINGERPRINTS

Galton, at the turn of the 19th century, had observed

on fingerprints the three fundamental figures (arch, loop and whorl) shown in Fig. 1 (a)-(c): these figures, and their transitional figures (one of which, called central pocket, is shown in Fig. 1(d)) still constitute the core of fingerprint classification systems (such as the Henry system employed by the FBI, the Gasti system employed by the italian police, and the system proposed by De Lestrange for anthropological correlations). Note that the figures in Fig. 1 can be described in terms of "quasi-parallel" systems of dermal ridges and their relative positions: the arch consists of one such system, while the other three figures are composed of three systems. As an example, Fig. 2 shows a loop.

It is well known that fingerprints are not only employed for the purpose of personal identification, but have also considerable interest in genetical, medical and anthropological correlation studies: for example, there is evidence that fingerprint and palm-print patterns are correlated with some congenital diseases.

While the above-mentioned classification schemes are more or less satisfactory for personal identification files, their adoption in correlation studies is an historical accident only. Schemes which are more complex than the basic ones can certainly be proposed: the one by De Lestrange (which has 6 varieties of the arch, 6 of the loop, and 6 of the whorl) is an example. Furthermore, these schemes can be refined, by taking various quantitative measurements, such as, for example, the counts of the number of dermal ridges between various characteristics points in the figures. However, these schemes have clearly a conventional nature: it seems more desirable to develop a "global" pattern description, treating the patterns as mathematical objects. For example, a pattern can be seen as a surface in 3 dimensions, where dermal ridges (discounting their interruptions and branchings, which, for the sake of a global description must anyway be considered local accidents) can be interpreted as contour lines; if a unique closed form is chosen to describe all fingerprint patterns, a set of values of the parameters in this form will then correspond to a specific fingerprint instance.

We are presently implementing a computer procedure

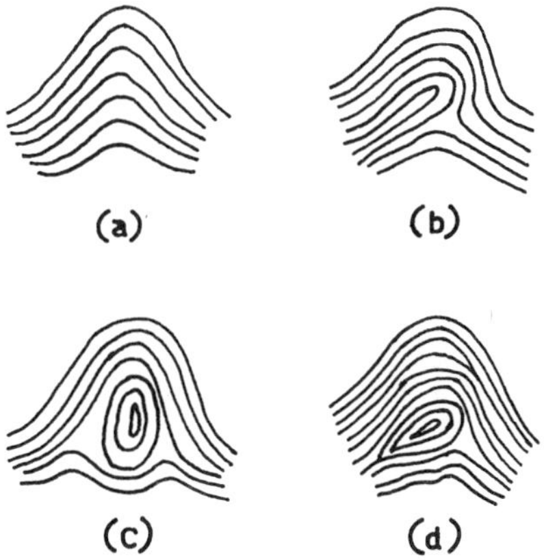

Fig. 1. Fingerprint classification: a) arch, b) loop, c) whorl, d) central pocket.

Fig. 2. A loop.

whose ultimate goal is to fit fingerprint patterns into a closed form: it will lead to a classification scheme in which the set of parameter values which fits an input fingerprint will be taken as the measure vector of the pattern. Only the first portion of the program will be described here: this portion is presently operational. The program will be very sketchily illustrated for the sake of brevity: a preliminary version of the procedure has been presented in (6); more details can be found in (7) and in a forthcoming paper (8).

The input image is in the form of a photograph (negative), which is digitized by a flying-spot scanner. The first step of the procedure is to obtain from the digitized picture a sampling matrix, shown in Fig. 3 for the fingerprint in Fig. 2. This matrix is derived by subdividing the digitized image into square windows (windows are of size 24 x 24 on the digitized image), and by determining for every window the predominant direction of ridges which pass through the window: this direction is digitized into one of 8 possible values. A special label is assigned to all windows in which the predominant slope cannot be reliably determined: these windows are blank in Fig. 3.

Note that there is a very substantial information reduction from the digitized image to the sampling matrix; however, the examination of the matrix in Fig. 3 will show that the gross pattern structure is still present, and the information in the matrix still allows to classify by eye this pattern as a loop.

The second phase of the procedure derives from the sampling matrix all systems of quasi-parallel ridges. This phase is linguistically-oriented, i.e. the matrix is subjected to transformations which can be seen as the application of bidimensional syntactic rules (see (3), (4)). It has been pointed out in (6) that although the entire procedure (from the digitized fingerprint to ridge systems) could have been framed into linguistic processing, this would have lead to very basic inefficiencies.

Ridge systems are individuated in a stepwise construction, in which paths are first obtained (see Fig. 4 which shows all the paths obtained from the sampling matrix in Fig. 3): paths can be seen as representing summarizing in-

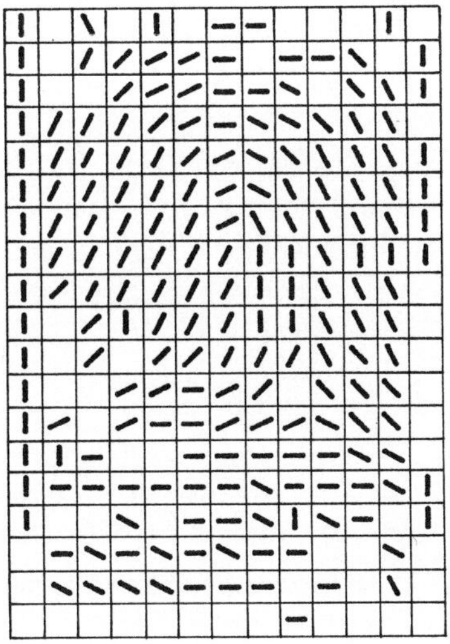

Fig. 3. Sampling matrix.

Fig. 4. Paths.

formation about a number of individual ridges in the original image. Paths are constructed in a number of steps: at every step, the "most likely" continuations of previously constructed path segments is sought.

Once paths have been obtained, systems of quasi-parallel paths are determined by orderly comparing paths with one another: system boundaries are shown with thick lines in Fig. 3. The determination of path systems concludes the first phase of the procedure.

The information gathered in the first phase constitutes the input to the second phase, which so far has not yet been implemented. Note that in the second phase we intend to "look back" at the original image, employing the information about path systems as a guideline: in this second look, additional information about ridges will be obtained.

III - CLASSIFICATION OF WHEAT CHROMOSOMES

Efforts toward systems for the automatic classification of chromosomes have been illustrated by several authors (see for example (9), (10) and (11)). We will not be able to review here the problem, nor to describe in any detail the algorithms which have been proposed: the motivation of this Section is rather that of giving a glimpse of some of the problems encountered, and of the techniques offered for their solution.

We are presently implementing a system for the classification of wheat chromosomes; a chromosome spread of the species "Aegilops squarrosa" is shown in Fig. 5. Note that all chromosomes have a central constriction, called centromere; an arm is the portion of chromosome on one side or the other of the centromere. Some chromosomes also have a secondary constriction, and the smaller portion on one side of this constriction is called satellite (see chromosome 1' in Fig. 5); sometimes, the satellite is detached, as for chromosome 1 in Fig. 5.

Classification parameters used by the cytologist in "manual" analysis are the overall length of the chromosome, and the ratio of the length of the arms: the cytologist paires those chromosomes for which the values of the parameters are "nearest". In Fig. 5, the chromosomes with the same digit in their labels constitute a pair. Machine analysis permits to measure the optical density over the chromosome: this strongly favors the adoption of integrated optical densities, which are linked to DNA content, as classification parameters (9), (10).

To avoid a lengthy discussion, we will not illustrate here the classification proper; rather, the phase in which classification parameters are obtained will be briefly described. The classification parameters are the integrated optical density of the entire chromosome, D, and the ratio of integrated optical densities of the arms (centromeric index C_D); also, some use is made in the classification phase of the length, L, and of the ratio of arm lengths (centromeric index C_L). Our system, like most of the ones that are being developed, operates on negatives (notable exception: Mendelsohn and coworkers scan directly the microscope slide (9)): the computer reads the negative by a flying-spot scanner.

The first operation is the segmentation of the input image into connected objects: as an object is isolated, it is characterized by computing several parameters, such as its perimeter, area, density, center of gravity, principal axis of inertia, rectangularity coefficient, etc. . As all the objects in the image have been found, some of these parameters (perimeter, area, density,....) are normalized against the values for the entire object set.

The parameter values allow the discrimination of chromosomes from extraneous objects, such as undivided cells and noise spots. It is important to note that, at this stage, any "dubious" object is retained in the list of possible chromosomes, as it is better to eliminate it later on when more information will be gathered about it.

The program, in its present status, is unable to deal with aggregates of chromosomes (touching or overlapping chromosomes): hence, the chromosome spread in Fig. 5, where chromosomes 4 and 7' overlap, is a "forbidden" picture. Also, we are currently implementing the handling of detached satellites. The program presently handles two types of chromosomes: straight and bent chromosomes. The subdivision in these two classes originates at the determination of the

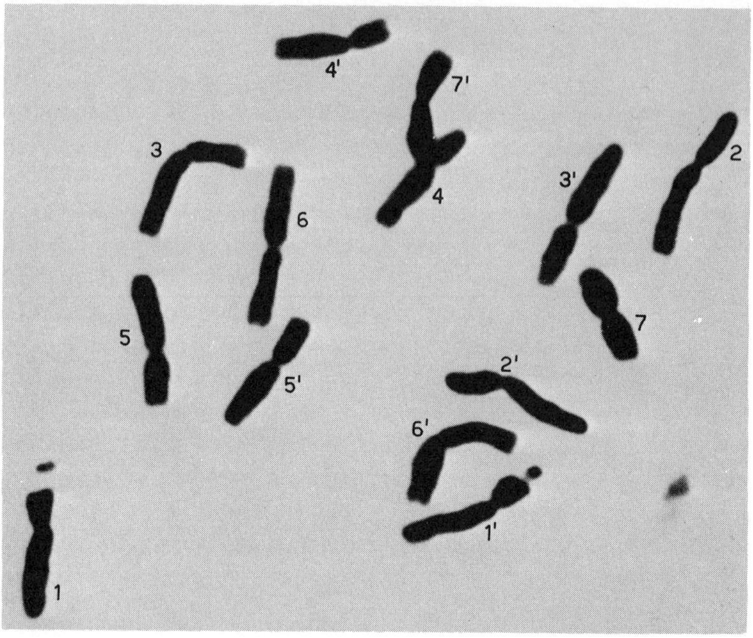

Fig. 5. A chromosome spread of "Aegilops squarrosa".

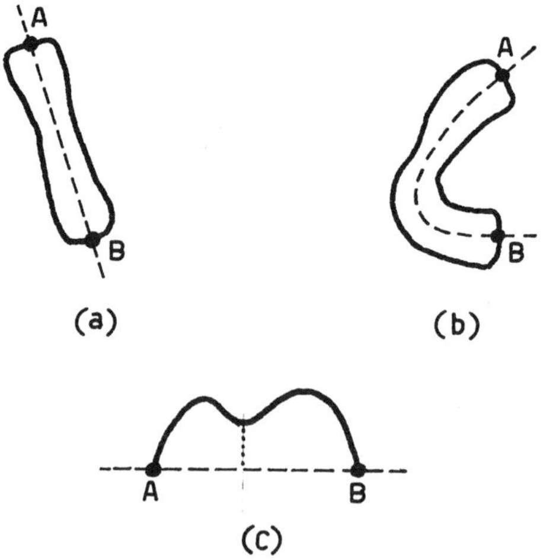

Fig. 6. Straight and bent chromosomes.

centromere: all chromosomes are treated first as straight ones, and a density profile is obtained by projecting orthogonally the optical densities onto the points of the principal axis of inertia (see Fig. 6 (a) and (c)). To be more precise, the two partial density profiles on the two sides of the principal axis are first obtained: if the "dip" in the profiles is approximately in the same position, then there are good guarantees that the chromosome is straight. If this condition is not satisfied, the chromosome is considered to be bent, and its simmetry axis (the dotted line labeled A-B in Fig. 6(b)) is obtained: the simmetry axis is determined by a variation of the esfoliation skeleton algorithm proposed by Rutovitz and Hilditch (12). The density profile is then referred to this axis.

In both cases, the profile has the aspect of Fig.6(c): the dip individuates the centromere. Note that the profile contains all the classification parameters D, C_D, L, C_L. Details about the program will be found in (13).

We will conclude this Section by considering briefly the problems of resolving chromosome aggregates. Although efforts have been produced toward the solution of this problem, there is no evidence so far that it will indeed be possible to resolve every case by an automatic procedure without human intervention. The problem looks formidable, and it is probably more reasonable to compromise. In our own system, we will try to approach the problem interactively, by having an operator which instructs the computer via a light-pen and a monitor screen.

IV - IDENTIFICATION OF FINGERPRINTS

There are two problems in the use of fingerprints for criminal identification. The first arises when ten fingerprints are available, and the search is then directed to the ten-fingerprint file. In this case, the ten fingerprints are first classified in one of various systems (for example, the FBI employs the Henry system), and this produces a descriptor which is used to access the file: all the records in the file having that descriptor are then compared with the fingerprints to be identified. The desirability of automating the ten-fingerprint problem depends from the size of the file and the rate of identification requests: for example, the FBI is taking steps toward a completely automated system, while the Italian Police can still get by with the present manual system.

A second problem is that of scene-of-crime fingerprints (latent fingerprints). Here, there is much less information to start with: in fact, very seldom prints of the ten fingers are found in such a case; often, only one finger print is available, and it is usually an incomplete one (see the impression in Fig. 7). Furthermore, various sources of noise (dirt, perspiration, etc.) obliterate completely one or several portions of the print.

It is clearly out of the question to search in this case the main file (ten-fingerprint file), which comprises from tens of millions (the italian police) to hundred of millions fingerprints (FBI). Partial files are created by type of crime, and even so, unless other clues are used which permit to narrow down the search to the records of a few suspects, latent fingerprints are not very useful, since search time becomes impossibly large.

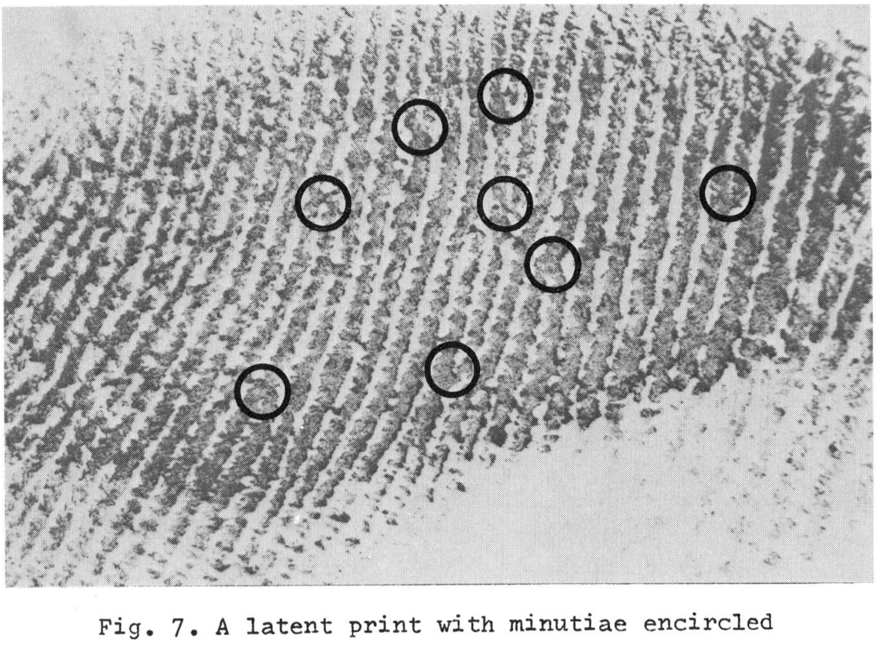

Fig. 7. A latent print with minutiae encircled

We have began a preliminary exploration on the possibility of a semi-automatic system for identifying latent prints. An excellent method of matching two fingerprints, to determine whether they coincide, has been developed by Wegstein (14): this system makes use of minutiae, i.e. ridge bifurcations or ridge endings. Minutiae are shown encircled in the print of Fig. 7. An open problem is that of finding a reliable descriptor which allows an efficient file search: we propose to use minutiae information for building up a descriptor: the basic descriptor constituents will be triplets of neighbooring minutiae. We are operating with a semi-automatic system, since the position of minutiae is coded by an operator on a scanning projector; it is however certainly feasible to envision a completely automatic system, in which minutiae are found by a flying-spot device, eventually a special-purpose one.

ACKNOWLEDGMENT

The work described in this paper is carried out by the author and his associates R. Clerici, G. Levi, A. Martelli, U. Montanari, F. Sirovich. The project on the classification of fingerprints is a collaboration between the above group and M. Ceccarelli, P. Giorgi and A. Paci of the Paediatric Clinic of the University of Pisa. The project on the classification of chromosomes is a collaboration with the Institute of Genetics of the University of Pisa. We are glad to acknowledge the substantial influence on the chromosome program of the work done by the Clinical and Population Cytogenetics Research Unit, London, headed by D. Rutovitz; special thanks are due to the members of this group for having so far digitized our negatives on their scanner.

REFERENCES

(1) G.C. Cheng, R.S. Ledley, D. Pollock and A. Rosenfeld, Eds., Pictorial Pattern Recognition (Thompson Book Co., Washington, 1968).

(2) A. Grasselli, Ed., Automatic image processing (Academic Press, New York, in press).

(3) R. Narasimhan, Optimality considerations in picture processing, presented at this Conference.

(4) T.G. Evans, ibid.

(5) A. Rosenfeld, Picture processing by computer (Academic Press, New York, in press).

(6) A. Grasselli, On the automatic classification of fingerprints, Int. Rept. II-64, Istituto di Elaborazione dell'Informazione, Pisa, January 1968, to appear in: Proc. Int. Conf. on Methodologies of Pattern Recognition, Honolulu, Hawaii, January 24-26, 1968 (Academic Press, New York, in press).

(7) F. Sirovich, Un algoritmo per la classificazione di impronte digitali, Nota Interna B68/7, Istituto di Elaborazione dell'Informazione, Pisa, July 1968, to appear in: Atti Secondo Congresso Nazionale Ass. Italiana Calcolo Automatico, Napoli, September 26-29, 1968.

(8) A. Grasselli, G.Levi and F. Sirovich, A method for the automatic classification of fingerprints, to be published.

(9) M.L. Mendelsohn, et al., Computer-oriented analysis of human chromosomes I. Photometric estimation of DNA content, Cytogenetics, 5, 223-242 (1966).

(10) M.L. Mendelsohn, et al., Computer-oriented analysis of human chromosomes II. Integrated optical density as a single parameter for kariotype analysis, Annals New York Acad. Sci., Conf. on Data Extraction and Processing of Optical Images in the Medical and Biological Sciences (1967).

(11) D. Rutovitz, Machines to classify chromosomes?, in: Human Radiation Cytogenetics (North Holland, Amsterdam, 1967).

(12) D. Rutovitz and J. Hilditch, Algorithms for chromosome recognition, Int. Report, Clinical and Population Cytogenetics Research Unit, Medical Research Council, London, 1967.

(13) G. Levi and N. Lijtmaer, Un metodo per la classificazione automatica dei cromosomi, Nota Interna B68/2, Istituto di Elaborazione dell'Informazione, Pisa, July 1968, to appear in: Atti Secondo Congresso Nazionale Ass. Italiana Calcolo Automatico, Napoli, September 26-29, 1968.

(14) J. Wegstein, Matching fingerprints by computer, Tech. Note 466, National Bureau of Standards, Washington, D.C., July 1968.

MARKER LAYOUT PROBLEM VIA GRAPH THEORY

Okan Gurel
IBM Corporation
New York Scientific Center
New York, New York

INTRODUCTION. Marker making can be defined as planning the layout of irregular patterns such that the cloth is used in the most efficient manner. Although several attempts to formulate the marker making problem and to solve it have been made [*1*], [*2*], presently the marker is laid out manually by the *marker maker.*

In a mathematical context the problem can be formulated by considering a number of quantities Ω_i's, $i=1,2,\ldots,n$ where n is a finite number, and defining the marker layout as fitting (clustering) Ω_i optimally in a given total quantity Ω. In one dimensional problems the given quantities are lengths, in two dimensional problems they are areas, and in three and higher dimensional geometries these quantities are volumes and hypervolumes. For the present case the Ω_i's are areas with irregular boundaries and Ω is in general a rectangle.

In the present study the main difficulties in connection with the marker making problem are pointed out, and an attempt is made to analyze the problem as an application of graph theory. There are a number of difficulties arising due to the fact that the patterns are completely irregular. The definition of optimality itself, i.e., what constitutes a good solution, becomes rather a problem. Some of these problems are discussed in detail in [*3*] and [*4*].

MATHEMATICAL MODEL. Let a point *set* $\Omega = \{\Omega_1,\ldots,\Omega_n,\Omega'_1,\ldots,\Omega'_m\}$ be defined. The set Ω will be composed of its *subsets* Ω_i and Ω'_j, $i \in I = \{1,2,\ldots,n\}$ and $j \in J = \{1,2,\ldots,m\}$ such that $\Omega_i \subset \Omega$, $\Omega'_j \subset \Omega$. Moreover, the union of these subsets form the set Ω, i.e., $\bigcup_{i\in I} \Omega_i \bigcup_{j\in J} \Omega'_j = \Omega$ and also ϕ denoting the *null set*, and $\cap$ the intersection $\Omega_i \cap \Omega_k = \phi$, $\Omega_i \cap \Omega'_k = \phi$, $\Omega'_j \cap \Omega'_k = \phi$, implying that the subsets have no common boundary. Here $\partial\Omega_i$ will denote the boundary of the set Ω_i.

The problem of clustering pattern pieces is essentially placing all *closed sets* Ω_i as given demands (orders), and all *open sets* Ω'_j as waste material to find a minimum set Ω. Here, we consider the topology induced by the *metric* ρ on Ω, which is a function, distance function, or mapping, written usually as $\rho\colon \Omega \times \Omega \to R$ where $\Omega \times \Omega$ is the Cartesian product on the set of ordered pairs (π_μ, π_ν) of points of Ω, and R is the set of real numbers.

In the case of the *metric space* (Ω,ρ) the set B of all spherical neighborhoods of points of the set Ω with a metric ρ is the *base* for the topology τ on Ω. In this metric space the distance metric ρ is given as $\rho(\Omega_i,\Omega_k)$ in the usual sense. Notice that a set can be determined by the n-th coordinate of each $\pi_\mu \in \Omega_i$.

This coordinate will be denoted by $\pi_{\mu n}$. Then the set $\lambda_n \subset \Omega_i$ is the set of all real numbers corresponding to n-th coordinate of π_μ's..

Here, we will be giving a definition which is one of the main concepts in the formulation of the marker layout problem. Considering the fact that the shapes under consideration are irregular a definition such as the following one will be quite general and may be applied to any shape.

Definition. The *extent* in the n-th direction is the metric $e_n = max\ \rho(\pi_{\mu n}, \pi_{\nu n})$ where $\pi_{\mu n}, \pi_{\nu n} \in \lambda_n$.

Therefore, in connection with a space (euclidean N-space, $E=E^N$) there are N extends defined for N where N is the *dimension* of this space. Using this definition we can state a theorem of a general nature. Here, we assume that closed sets Ω_i, $i \in I$, are given, and will be *clustered* in an optimal fashion according to the definition of optimality implied in the following theorem.

THEOREM. *For the given closed sets Ω_i, if a mapping $f: \bigcup_{i \in I} \Omega_i \to \Omega$ with an extent of the space Ω as $e_n = sup\,[\rho(\pi_{\mu n}, \pi_{\nu n})]$ is obtained, then the clustering is optimal.*

Proof. Let us assume that the sets Ω_i have extents given as e_{ni}. Then the mapping f of Ω_i onto Ω gives that $e_n = e_{ni}$. Taking the next mapping such that $\Omega_i \cap \Omega_{i+1} = \phi$, or a set of dimension N-1, then the extent for Ω is given by the inequality $e_n \leqslant e_{ni} + e_{n\,(i+1)}$. Then, for further additional mappings $e_n \leqslant \sum_i e_{ni}$. Since $e_{ni} = max\ [\rho(\pi_{\mu n}, \pi_{\nu n})]$, $\pi_\mu \in \Omega_i$, $\pi_\nu \in \Omega_i$, then $e_n \leqslant \Sigma\ max[\rho(\pi_{\mu n}, \pi_{\nu n})]$. Since $\Omega = \bigcup_i \Omega_i$ the points $\pi_\mu \in \Omega_i$ and also $\pi_\mu \in \Omega$. Then the last inequality holds true even for $\pi_\mu \in \Omega$. The maximum value, giving the upper bounds $e_n \leqslant \Sigma\ u.b.\ [\rho(\pi_{\mu n}, \pi_{\nu n})]$. To choose the least upper bound will then mean choosing a mapping which has the most overlapping, the greatest intersection, thus, smallest addition to Ω_i in n direction. Thus, the whole mapping (cutting stock) is minimized (optimized).

An important aspect is that there are a number of additional properties (constraints) in the definition of the sets Ω_i and also the set Ω. These constraints can be given in terms of extents. i) Some of the extents e_n defined for the set Ω may be restricted as $e_n < K_n$ is a given number. ii) The sets Ω_i are not invariant under rotation. Therefore, the mapping f can be done in a restricted fashion, however, for some cases a definite rotation angle θ_n is permitted.

The ordering in all directions is done by not violating the given theorem. Since the theorem and the restrictions are given in terms of the extent, one may refer to the extent for ordering.

In summary, we can add that for the two dimensional patterns $n = 1,2$, there are two extents orthogonal to each other. Assuming that for the given irregular shapes two orthogonal directions, x and y, parallel to the edges of the material from which the irregular pieces will be cut out, are determined the extents in the x- and y-directions can be computed.

DEFINITIONS OF OPTIMALITIES AND MEASURES OF OPTIMALITY.

Sets Ω_i are essentially points forming two dimensional figures (convex or concave). According to the style and the material they are *oriented* such that the individual coordinates x_i, y_i which are parallel relative to x and y of the cloth designate the sides of the rectangles encompassing these figures. We will refer to these rectangles as R_i. Convex area enclosing the given set is referred to as the *convex hull*, C_i. The rectangle R_i with the sides x_i and y_i, is, of course, a convex body, however, in general not equal to the convex hull. Therefore, in terms of areas there is an ordering such that $\Omega_i \subset C_i \subset R_i$. The following are true: a) If Ω_i is convex $\Omega_i = C_i$, b) If Ω_i is a rectangle $\Omega_i = C_i = R_i$. An obvious assertion is that if $\Omega_i = R_i$ holds true then the equalities hold. This case is simply the conventional two-dimensional cutting stock problem for which various mathematical programming algorithms have been developed, and appeared in the literature.

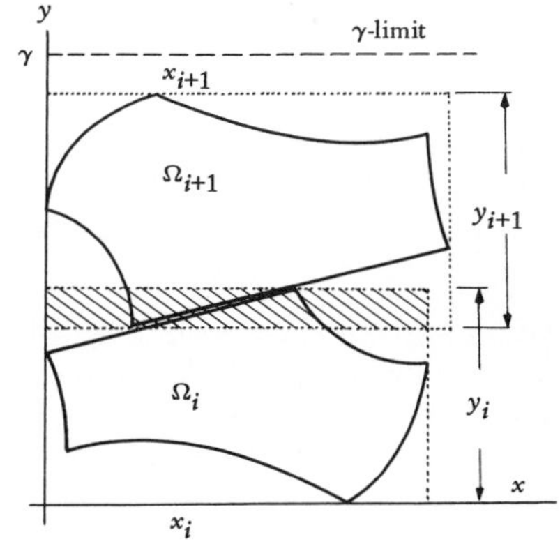

Figure 1

Let us now assume that the above ordering holds and give the following definition which will be an essential concept in the remaining discussions.

Definition. *Interlocking* is forming $\Omega^* = \bigcup_{i \in I^*} \Omega_i \bigcup_{j \in J^*} \Omega_j'$, $I^* \subset I$, $J^* \subset J$.

As was mentioned in the introduction, the measures in connection with various forms of optimality will be necessary. The most important optimal interlocking will be defined first.

Definition 1. [Densest Interlocking]. An optimal interlocking of two sets Ω_ℓ and Ω_k is obtained for $M^1(\Omega_\ell, \Omega_k) = max\ (R_\ell \cap R_k)$, $\ell, k \in I$.

This definition exactly indicates that first Ω_ℓ is placed and then Ω_k is added either in y-direction or x-direction with the side condition $\Omega_\ell \cap \Omega_k = \phi$. However, for certain cases we will see that the first measure M^1 is misleading, then another measure based on the boundaries $\partial\Omega_i$ will be more meaningful.

Definition 2. [Longest Matching]. An optimal interlocking of two sets Ω_ℓ and Ω_k is obtained for $M^2(\Omega_\ell, \Omega_k) = max\ (\partial\Omega_\ell \cap \partial\Omega_k)$, $\ell, k \in I$.

The laying out is bounded in the direction, thus Y_m being the combined y-coordinates of interlocked pieces Ω_i, $Y_m \leqslant \sum_{i \in I^*} y_i \leqslant \gamma$ where γ is the bound on y-direction. Therefore, this is a side condition which should be kept in mind while the algorithm for computational purposes will be developed.

On the other hand, while satisfying the bound in y-direction we might try to minimize the extent in the x-direction. Taking e^* as the extent of the interlocked pieces in the x-direction another definition can be given.

Definition 3. [Least Extent]. An optimal interlocking of two sets Ω_ℓ and Ω_k is obtained for $M^{3i}(\Omega_\ell, \Omega_k) = [M^i(\Omega_e, \Omega_k)\,|\,min\ e^*]$ $\ell, k \in I$, $i = 1,2$.

In the following mathematical developments of the clustering problem the two measures M^1 and M^{31} will be frequently used. Although, at certain places reference to the second measure M^2 will prove useful, even necessary.

Geometric Constraints due to Design. We will first classify the various constraints. The design on a material can be classified as one of the following three forms: 1) Plain design, 2) Stripes, 3) Plaids, see [*4*]. These three forms of design represent the geometry constraints which can be encountered in the marker

layout problem. In addition to these main classifications we should also note the following subcategories related to stripes. These are i) Even stripes, ii) Uneven stripes. It is also possible to give another subclassification i) Lengthwise stripes, ii) Crosswise stripes,and iii) Diagonal stripes.
Definition: *Repeat* (*Periodicity*) of a stripe is the width ζ of a group of stripes adjacent to each other such that in a width equal to $n\zeta$ there are exactly n such groups of stripes. For the lengthwise stripes ζ will be measured in the y-direction, thus ζ_y.

Definition: Suppose that a line λ in the running direction of the stripes can be drawn such that the stripes lying on one side of this line form a mirror image (symmetric) of those lying on the other side, then the stripes are called *even.*

Therefore we can classify the lengthwise (crosswise) stripes as a design with a periodicity $\zeta_y(\zeta_x)$ and the *line of evenness* $\lambda_y(\lambda_x)$. Diagonal stripes can also be determined by the quantities ζ_x and ζ_y defined above. For this let us consider the following line equation $\zeta_y = a + \beta\,\zeta_x$. In this equation a, and β are constants, and ζ_x and ζ_y are as defined before. It is obvious that for various cases discussed above the constants can be considered as parameters. A summary of all these various cases is given on the following Table I; here $\eta(\lambda_x)$ denotes the number of λ_x lines. For the lengthwise stripes $\zeta_y = a$ will be given. In addition to this

Table 1 Various Design Constraints and Corresponding Parameters

		a	β	ζ_x	ζ_y	$\eta(\lambda_x)$	$\eta(\lambda_y)$
1	Plain Design	0	0	0	0	0	0
2	Lengthwise Even Stripes	>0	0	Undet.	a	∞	$\geqslant 1$
3	Lengthwise Uneven Stripes					∞	0
4	Crosswise Even Stripes	<0	1	a	0	$\geqslant 1$	∞
5	Crosswise Uneven Stripes					0	∞
6	Diagonal Even Stripes	0	$[-\infty, +\infty]$	any	$\beta\zeta_x$		
	a. In x-direction					$\geqslant 1$	0
	b. In y-direction					0	$\geqslant 1$
7	Diagonal Uneven Stripes					0	0
8	Even Plaids	-	-	any	any		
	a. In x-direction					$\geqslant 1$	0
	b. In y-direction					0	$\geqslant 1$
	c. In both directions					$\geqslant 1$	$\geqslant 1$
9	Uneven Plaids					0	0

information for each pattern Ω_i there will be a number ψ_i given. This quantity refers to the y-coordinate of a point on the boundary $\partial\Omega_i$,which is planned to lie on a certain section of the design of the stock material. If the two pieces are compared to determine the measures, say $M^1(L)$: $\tilde{\psi}_j - \psi_i\,\theta\,\zeta_y$, $\theta \in Z$, where $\tilde{\psi}_j = \psi_j + \delta y_{i\,max}$, must be valid, Z is the set of all integers, $\delta \in [0,1]$ $y_{i\,max}$ is the y-coordinate of R_i. Difference between the lengthwise and crosswise stripes is simply the direction of the stripes. Therefore we can write the side condition as (C): $\tilde{\omega}_j - \omega_i = \theta\zeta_x$, $\theta \in Z$ where ω_i refers to the x-coordinate of a predetermined point on the boundary of the piece, $\partial\Omega_i$, $\tilde{\omega}_j = \omega_j + \delta x_{i\,max}$.

The constraints for the diagonal stripes are three in number. These are formulated as follows.

$$\tilde{\psi}_i - \psi_j = \theta_1 \zeta_y, \quad \theta_1 \in Z \qquad (D_1)$$

$$\tilde{\omega}_i - \omega_j = \theta_2 \zeta_x, \quad \theta_2 \in Z \qquad (D_2)$$

$$\zeta_y = \beta \zeta_x, \qquad \beta \in [-\infty, +\infty] \qquad (D_3)$$

A summary of all the measures is given below in a schematic diagram, Figure 2. In this diagram various functions f_{ij}, i and j as indicated, are summarized as follows, here E is the extent constraint, L, C, and D are constraints for lengthwise, crosswise and diagonal stripes, respectively. For the plaids D_3 is not necessary.

M^1	
M^2	
$M^3 = f_{i_3}(M^i) = \{M^i \mid E\}$	$i = 1,2$
$M^j = f_{ij}(M^i) = \{M^i \mid L\}$	$i = 1,2,3; j = 4,5,6,$
$M^j = f_{ij}(M^i) = \{M^i \mid C\}$	$i = 1,2,3; j = 7,8,9$
$M^j = f_{ij}(M^i) = \{M^i \mid D_k, k = 1,2,3\}$	$i = 1,2,3; j = 10,11,12$
$M^j = f_{lj}(M^i) = \{M^i \mid D_k, k = 1,2\}$	$i = 1,2,3; j = 13,14,15;$ $l = 10,11,12$

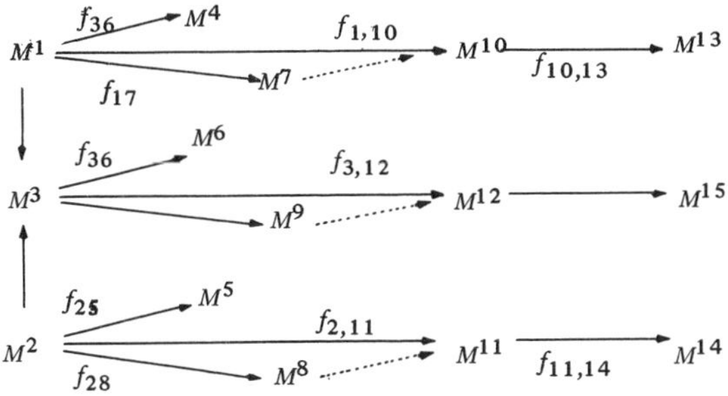

Figure 2

MODEL OF CLUSTERING. Here the pattern, an entire set of pieces Ω_i, $i \in I$, under consideration is designated by the set σ, i.e., $\sigma = \{\Omega_1, ..., \Omega_n\}$. Elements of this set can be related to each other by a function Γ over the sets σ such that Γ maps σ into σ, or $\Omega_j \in \Gamma\, \Omega_i$ for all $i, j \in I$. This function is the interlocking (*matching*) mentioned above by considering pieces in pairs. The element Ω_i of the set σ is called a *point* or *vertex*, and the pair (Ω_i, Ω_j) with $\Omega_j \in \Gamma\, \Omega_i$ an *arc*, or *edge* of the *graph* $G = (\sigma, \Gamma)$. As known from the graph theory for the set σ, in addition to defining a function Γ, thus having the graph $G(\sigma, \Gamma)$, we can also attach to it a value, thus make it a *valued graph*. Interlocking the pieces in pairs we determine this value namely the *measures* as $M^i (i = 1,2,3)$. The values for the arcs ij and ji defined by the measures may or may not be equal, i.e. $M^i(\Omega_\ell, \Omega_k) \neq M^i(\Omega_k, \Omega_\ell), i = 1,2,3$. Therefore, the graph is a *nonsymmetric graph*. It is in fact a valued one except not in the simple sense, instead all the values are maximum values. In the process of matching we will obtain values either below or equal to these values but never above them. Then the graph is called a *maximum valued graph.*

Taking $M_{\ell k}$ as the measure between Ω_ℓ and Ω_k the *incidence matrix* $[G]$ can be formed as shown below. This matrix is an $n \times n$ matrix with the main diagonal having all zero elements.

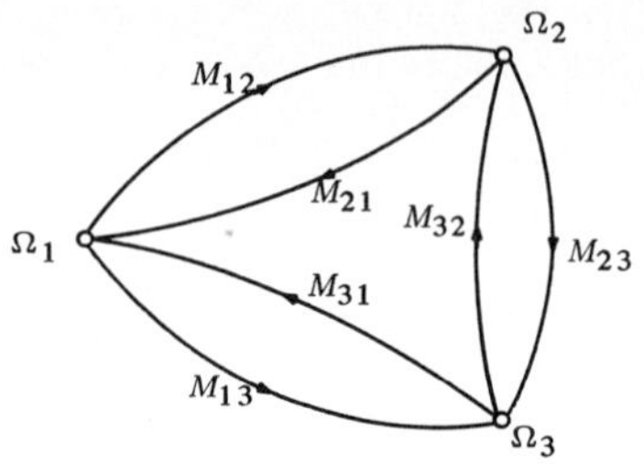

Figure 3

Maximum Valued Incidence Matrix

	Ω_1	Ω_2		Ω_ℓ	Ω_k		Ω_{n-1}	Ω_n
Ω_1	0	M_{12}		$M_{1\ell}$	M_{1k}			M_{1n}
Ω_2	M_{21}	0						
Ω_ℓ	$M_{\ell 1}$			0	$M_{\ell k}$			
Ω_{n-1}							0	$M_{n-1,n}$
Ω_n	M_{n1}						$M_{n,n-1}$	

For the above graph not only maximum M^1 measure but also another measure say M^2 or M^3 can be added. It is desired that the pieces are interlocked in the densest possible way, also in the x-direction the extent is minimized. Therefore, we can take our graph as a *multi-graph* which represents in a set σ many types of relations (measures $M^1, M^2, \ldots$ thus $\Gamma_1, \Gamma_2, \ldots$ such that the graph is $G(\sigma, \Gamma_1, \Gamma_2, \ldots)$).

AN ALGORITHM OF CLUSTERING. For conceptual reasons a graph is very illustrative, for computational purposes an associated matrix and thus matrix methods are more advantageous. The problem in this form can be programmed for a computer. The *maximum valued incidence matrix* (MVIM) given as $[G]$ will be used for the computational algorithm.

In the algorithm a *chain* of adjacent pieces is considered in the increasing y-direction, i.e. the piece Ω_j is placed next to Ω_i in the increasing y-direction. All the measures M^i, $i = 1,2,3$ are based on this consideration. Each break is formed independently, and then along the x-axis the breaks are placed next to each other. Each break will consist of a chain of adjacent pieces placed according to the proposition below, [3].

PROPOSITION 1. *Suppose that Ω_i is placed. The next piece to be added, Ω_j is the one with the greatest M^1_{ij} providing that $R_j - R_k \leqslant M_{ij} - M_{ik}$ for all k.*

The following two points should be kept in mind.

1. In all breaks $e_y < \gamma$ where e_y is the extent in the y-direction of all the pieces put together in one break, and γ is the bounding limit in the y-direction.
2. In a particular break, for better results it is necessary that the pieces under consideration $\Delta(x_i, x_k) < \eta$, where $\Delta(x_i, x_k)$ indicates the difference between the x-coordinate of the i-th and k-th pieces and η is the tolerance difference.

In connection with the second point we can give the following proposition,[3].

PROPOSITION 2. *The greater η is the more waste is encountered.*

An important observation leads to the following proposition.

PROPOSITION 3. *Considering Ω_i already placed, there can possibly be four different M^1_{ij}.*

Let Ω_j to be placed adjacent to an already placed piece Ω_i. Since the orientation is fixed, i.e., R_j is defined with respect to an orthogonal coordinate system x,y there are only four different transformations i) reflection about the y-axis, ii) reflection about the x-axis, iii) reflection about the origin, iv) identity transformation. Therefore, there are four different relative positions of the piece Ω_j with respect to Ω_i. Any combination of the above mentioned four transformations gives one of the four possible positions corresponding to basic transformations above. Therefore, four and only four M^1_{ij} can be computed. Reflection about the y-axis will be called *flipping*. Reflection about the origin will be called *rotation*. Following these definitions, we can now rephrase the above transformations as follows: Transformation i) consists of one flipping, ii) consists of one flipping, one rotation, iii) consists of one rotation, and iv) is without flipping or rotation.

The algorithm consists of two main parts.

I. Preparation of MVIM. To form the incidence matrix we have to evaluate certain measures of optimality. These are

1. $M^1(\Omega_i, \Omega_k)$ for all $i, k \in I$.
2. $M^2(\Omega_i, \Omega_k)$ for those i,k for which $M^1 \leqslant a$, a is a predetermined small value, see below II.2.b.).
3. $R_i \cap R_k$ corresponding to min x_i^* where $x_i^* = max\,(x_i, x_k)$.

In addition to these measures, an ordering of the pieces by the area is made, namely,

4. $R_1 \geqslant R_2 \geqslant \ldots \geqslant R_n$.

II. Manipulating on MVIM. Once the incidence matrix is formed, we then start interlocking as follows.

1. To initiate the procedure the piece with the largest area is picked, say the i-th piece.
2. a) From the MVIM we look for the largest M^1_{ij} and take this as the pivot of the next step. Notice that these values are obtained by considering the i-th piece below the j-th piece across the width of the material, namely, in the positive direction of the y-axis.
   b) In case the interlocking of two pieces can not be judged by the measure of the first type, the measure of the second type, M^2_{ij} should be considered. The value of a may be determined from some experimentation. This is the case, for instance, where the piece is close to a rectangular shape. Then,

although the measure M_{ij}^1 for matching is almost zero, the top of the i-th piece fits perfectly to the bottom of the j-th piece. Then these two pieces should be interlocked assuming that I.3 is satisfied. Therefore, the second measure is more important for this type of figure.

c) Here, I.3 should be checked for the reason that there is not unnecessary buldging in the x-direction as given in Proposition 2.

3. Then the j-th row is considered and the largest M_{ij} is picked as the pivot and k-th piece is placed above the j-th piece which is already placed above i-th piece in the positive y-direction.
4. Each time a new piece is added $y_i^* \leqslant \gamma$ is also checked.
   a) If $y^* < \gamma$ continue to II.2.
   b) If $y^* = \gamma$ a break is formed.
   c) If $y^* > \gamma$ disregard the last placed piece and look for another with the property that $(y_k - M_{jk}/x_k) \leqslant \gamma - y^*$. If such a piece is not found, then a break is completed.
5. If a break is complete, the largest of the remaining pieces is picked and the algorithm returns to the step II.2.

SOME BASIC CONSIDERATIONS FOR FURTHER ALGORITHMS. Let G_n denote the complete planar graph on n vertices. Consider the specific representation of G_n in a plane, called the *alternating linear model.* This is obtained by taking a horizontal line and placing the vertices $\Omega_1, \Omega_2, \ldots, \Omega_n$ consecutively on the line. Considering the *directed* graph whose edges are always directed from a vertex with a smaller index to that with larger index, it is assumed that no two edges intersect. The following proposition holds true [*4*].

PROPOSITION 4. *Except for* Ω_1, Ω_{n-1} *and* Ω_n, *without intersecting any other edge, each vertex can only be linked to the following two vertices.*

This proposition defines the *directed two linked graph.* The proof is simple. For $n \leqslant 3$ the case is trivial for Ω_1, Ω_2 and Ω_3 are all excluded. For $n = 4$ it is obvious; for $n \geqslant 5$ by induction it can be shown that the proposition is correct. *Remark:* Ω_1 can be joined to all Ω_i, $i = 2,3,\ldots, n$ without intersecting any other edges, Ω_n cannot be linked forward to a vertex. Finally Ω_{n-1} can be linked to Ω_n only.

This leads to the following propositions.

PROPOSITION 5. *A vertex* Ω_i *can be linked to any consecutive vertex unless the vertex* Ω_{i-1} *is already linked.*

PROPOSITION 6. *If a two-linked graph exists, the vertex* Ω_{2i} *can also be linked to* $(2i + 2n)$*-th vertex,* $n = 1,2,\ldots$ *and the vertex* Ω_{2i+1} *can be linked to* $(2i+n)$*-th vertex,* $n = 1,2,\ldots$

For these propositions, we refer to a graph with certain properties which are i) directedness, ii) alternating linearity, iii) two-linked form. We now introduce the values attached to the edges. The above three properties still hold but in addition we have values M_{ij} as shown in Figure 4. The following theorem which can be stated is instrumental in discussion of Algorithms.

THEOREM. *If* $M_{i,i+1} \geqslant M_{i+1,i+2}$ *for all* $i = 1,2,\ldots, n$, *the maximum* $\sum_{i=1}^{n} M_{i,i+1}$, *is obtained by joining* Ω_i *to* Ω_{i+1}.

The corollary below devises a variation of the above theorem for graphs reaching a constraint which will be referred to as the *border constraints.*

COROLLARY. *If a link joining two consecutive vertices* Ω_i *and* Ω_{i+1} *is left out, the loss in the maximum measure is at least equal to* $M_{i,i+1}$.

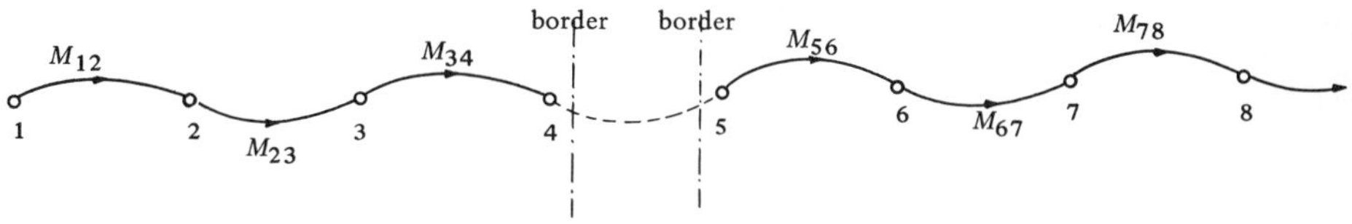

Figure 4

REFERENCES

1. R.C. ART, JR.: *An Approach to the Two-Dimensional Irregular Cutting Stock Problem*, IBM Cambridge Scientific Center Report No. 36.Y08, September 1966, 22 pp.
2. M.J. HAIMS: *On the Optimum Two-Dimensional Allocation Problem,* New York University, Department of Electrical Engineering, Technical Report No. 400-136, June 1966, 132 pp.
3. O. GUREL: *Marker Layout Problem Via Graph Theory, An Attempt for Optimal Layout of Irregular Patterns,* IBM New York Scientific Center Report No. 320-2921, January 1968, 42 pp.
4. O. GUREL: *Additional Considerations on Marker Layout Problem via Graph Theory,* New York Scientific Center Technical Report No. 320-2945, April 1968, 34 pp.

MULTIPLIER AND GRADIENT METHODS

MAGNUS R. HESTENES†
Department of Mathematics, University of California
Los Angeles, California

1. Introduction

About twenty years ago the author became interested in computational methods for optimal control problems*. This interest was stimulated by an attempt to compute the time optimal path of an airplane from take off to level flight at a prescribed postion and velocity. At that time large scale digital computing machines were not available. Computing had to be carried out by analog computers or by mechanical desk computers. An attempt was made to compute the time optimal path for an airplane by integrating the corresponding Euler-Lagrange equations on an analog computer (REAC). However the differential equations were unstable and the results were unsatisfactory. However a good estimate could be found by hand computation using special properties of the problem. This experience convinced the author that general procedures should be devised for obtaining solutions or for improving estimates of solutions. Accordingly the author experimented with three methods, namely, Newton's method, the gradient method and the method of penalty functions. Since he was restricted to the use of hand computation, the author considered only simple variational problems which possessed non-minimizing as well as minimizing extremals. It was found that

---

*See M. R. Hestenes. A general problem in the calculus of Variations with applications to paths of least time, Rand Corporation (1950). RM-100, ASTIA document number AD112382.
A. S. Mengel. Optimum Trajectories, Rand Corporation (1951), P-199.

Newton's method and the gradient method were very effective*.

The author however had difficulties with the method of penalty functions because of round off errors. To obtain any accuracy to the solution of the problem considered required carrying more significant figures than were convenient in hand computation. Although the method of penalty functions has been used with reasonable success in recent years, the author has always felt that an improvement of the method could be made. The purpose of this paper is to suggest a modification of the method of penalty functions which we shall call the method of multipliers. In addition we shall make some remarks concerning Newton's method, the method of gradients and conjugate gradients that may be useful.

2. Constrained and Unconstrained Minima

Before describing the method of multipliers it is instructive to recall a connection between constrained and unconstrained minima upon which the method is based. We shall consider only the simplest case in which a point x_0 affords a minimum to a real valued function $f(x) = f(x^1, \ldots, x^m)$ subject to a single constraint

$$g(x) = 0. \tag{2.1}$$

The extension to the case in which g is vector valued is immediate. We assume that f and g are of class C'' and that the gradient

$$g'(x) = \left(\frac{\partial g(x)}{\partial x^i}\right)$$

---

*M. R. Hestenes, Numerical methods for obtaining solutions of fixed endpoint problems in the calculus of variations, Project Rand Research Memorandum No. 102 (1949).

M. L. Stein, On methods for obtaining solutions of fixed endpoint problems in the calculus of variations, J. Research, National Bureau of Standards, Vol. 50 (1953), pp. 277-297, RP2418.

M. R. Hestenes, Iterative computational methods, communications on pure and applied mathematics, Vol. VIII (1955), pp. 85-96.

of g is not zero at x_0. Then there exists a multiplier λ such that, if we set $G = f + \lambda g$, we have

$$G'(x_0) = 0, \quad g(x_0) = 0 \tag{2.2}$$

$$G''(x_0,h) = \sum_{i,j=1}^{m} \frac{\partial^2 G}{\partial x^i \partial x^j} h^i h^j \geq 0 \tag{2.3a}$$

for all $h \neq 0$ such that

$$g'(x_0,h) = \sum_{i=1}^{m} \frac{\partial g(x_0)}{\partial x^i} h^i = g'(x_0) \cdot h = 0. \tag{2.3b}$$

Here $g'(x_0,h)$ is the first differential of g at x_0 and is the cartesian inner product of $g'(x_0)$ and h. Similarly $G''(x_0,h)$ is the second differential of G at x_0. The point x_0 will be said to be <u>nonsingular</u> in case

$$\begin{vmatrix} \dfrac{\partial^2 G}{\partial x^i \partial x^j} & \dfrac{\partial g}{\partial x^i} \\ \dfrac{\partial g}{\partial x^j} & 0 \end{vmatrix} \neq 0$$

at $x = x_0$. If x_0 is a nonsingular minimum point for f subject to $g = 0$, the equality in (2.3a) holds only if $h = 0$. This implies the existence of a positive number c such that

$$G''(x_0,h) + cg'(x_0,h)^2 > 0$$

for all $h \neq 0$. Setting

$$F = f + \lambda g + \frac{c}{2} g^2 = G + \frac{c}{2} g^2$$

it is seen that at $x = x_0$ we have

$$F'(x_0) = G'(x_0) = 0$$

$$F''(x_0,h) = G''(x_0,h) + cg'(x_0,h)^2 > 0 \quad (h \neq 0).$$

Here we have used the fact that $g(x_0) = 0$. In view of these relations we see that x_0 affords an unconstrained local minimum to F. This yields the following

THEOREM 1. <u>If x_0 is a nonsingular minimum point of f subject to $g = 0$, there exists a multiplier λ and a constant c such that x_0 affords an unconstrained local minimum to the function</u>

$$F = f + \lambda g + \frac{c}{2} g^2.$$

<u>Conversely if $g(x_0) = 0$ and x_0 affords a minimum to a function F of this type, then x_0 affords a minimum to f subject to $g = 0$.</u>

3. The Methods of Penalty Functions and the Methods of Multipliers

One of the popular methods of finding a constrained minimum point is the method of penalty functions. For the problem considered in the last section this method seeks a minimum point x_n of the function

$$f_n(x) = f(x) + \frac{n}{2} g(x)^2.$$

A limit point of the sequence $\{x_n\}$, if it exists, is then the solution x_0 to our problem. Moreover, in as much as

$$0 = f_n'(x_n) = f'(x_n) + ng(x_n)g'(x_n)$$

it is seen that if $g'(x_0) \neq 0$ then $\lambda_n = ng(x_n)$ converges to the corresponding multipliers λ for x_0. It is a simple matter to formulate conditions which insure the existence of a minimum point x_n for $f_n(x)$ on an open set S and the convergence of the sequence $\{x_n\}$ to a point x_0 in S which minimizes f on S subject to $g = 0$. Observe that

$$f_n(x_n) = f(x_n) + \frac{n}{2} g(x_n)^2 \leq f_n(x_0) = f(x_0). \tag{3.1}$$

If x_0 is a nonsingular solution there is, by Theorem 1, a constant c, a multiplier λ and a neighborhood N of x_0 such that

$$f(x_0) \leq f(x_n) + \lambda g(x_n) + \frac{c}{2} g(x_n)^2 \tag{3.2}$$

whenever x_n is in N. Combining (3.1) and (3.2) we see that

$$(n - c)g(x_n)^2 \leq 2\lambda g(x_n)$$

whenever x_n is in N. In the event that $f'(x_0) = 0$ we have $\lambda = 0$ since $g'(x_0) \neq 0$, by virtue of the nonsingularity of x_0. In this event $x_n = x_0$ if $n > c$ and x_n is in N. Thus, the method of penalty functions is very effective whenever $f'(x_0) = 0$ and should be reasonably effective when $f'(x_0)$ is near zero. However, in general this is not the case and the method becomes sensitive to round off errors in the term $ng(x)^2$. For large values of n it is difficult to obtain an appropriate numerical approximation of x_n and hence of x_0.

In order to circumvent the numerical difficulty that may arise in the method of penalty functions the author suggests a simple modification. This modified method is based on the theorem stated in the last section and will be called the method of multipliers. In this method we select a positive constant c and consider the function

$$F(x,\lambda) = f(x) + \lambda g(x) + \frac{c}{2} g(x)^2.$$

The constant c, if chosen suitably large, is held fast. Let λ_1 be an initial estimate of λ and select a minimum point x_1 of $F(x,\lambda_1)$. In general having obtained an estimate λ_n of λ we select x_n to minimize $F(x,\lambda_n)$. Observe that

$$F'(x_n,\lambda_n) = f'(x_n) + (\lambda_n + cg(x_n))g'(x_n) = 0.$$

This suggests that we select

$$\lambda_{n+1} = \lambda_n + c_n g(x_n)$$

where $0 < c_n \leq c$. Various rules can be given for selecting

c_n. For example we can choose $c_n = \gamma c$, where γ is a positive constant, normally ≤ 1. Or we can choose c_n such that $g(x_n)g(x_{n+1}) > 0$. It is not difficult to give criteria which will insure the convergence of the method for problems of this type.

In order to illustrate this method consider the special case in which

$$f(x) = \frac{1}{2} x^* Ax - \alpha b^* x, \qquad g(x) = b^* x$$

where A is a nonsingular symmetric matrix, b and X are column vectors with $b \neq 0$, b^* is the transpose of b, and α is a positive number. We assume that $x^* Ax > 0$ for all $x \neq 0$ such that $g(x) = b^* x = 0$. The point $x = 0$ minimizes f subject to $g = 0$ and $\lambda = \alpha$ is the corresponding Lagrange multiplier. Select c such that

$$x^* Ax + c(b^* x)^2 > 0$$

for all $x \neq 0$ and set

$$F(x,\lambda) = f + \lambda g + \frac{c}{2} g^2 .$$

The minimum point $\bar{x}$ of $F(x,\lambda)$ solves the equation

$$Ax - \alpha b + (\lambda + cb^* x)b = 0.$$

The solution takes the form

$$\bar{x} = \gamma A^{-1} b, \qquad \gamma = \frac{\alpha - \lambda}{1 + c\beta}, \qquad \beta = b^* A^{-1} b.$$

If one uses the method of multipliers with $\lambda_1 = 0$ and $\lambda_{n+1} = \lambda_n + cg(x_n)$ it is found that

$$x_n = \frac{\alpha}{(1 + c\beta)^n} A^{-1} b, \qquad \lambda_{n+1} = \alpha - \frac{\alpha}{(1 + c\beta)^n} .$$

Convergence is obtained if $|1 + c\beta| > 1$. If the method of penalty functions is used we have

$$x_n = \frac{\alpha}{1 + n\beta} A^{-1} b, \qquad ng(x_n) = \frac{\alpha n\beta}{1 + n\beta} .$$

Of course, one would not use the method of multipliers or of penalty functions for this problem, since the solution is easily obtained by the Lagrange multiplier rule. However this example gives some indication of the nature of the two methods in the general case provided that we are close to a solution.

The reader will find it instructive to consider the two dimensional cases in which

$$f(x,y) = x^2 - y^2 - y, \quad g(x,y) = y \quad \text{or} \quad g(x,y) = y + y^3$$

The method of multipliers has the advantage that the coefficient of g^2 need not be very large. It has the disadvantage that one needs to have an initial estimate of the multiplier λ. Perhaps a combination of the method of multipliers and the penalty function method would be most effective. Begin with the method of penalty functions so as to obtain an initial estimate of x_0 and from this deduce an estimate of λ. Then switch to the method of multipliers. The author has not had time to experiment with the method of multipliers for general functions but plans to do so in the near future.

4. Extensions to Variational and Optimal Control Problems.

The method of penalty functions has been applied to a large class of variational problems. It has been used, for example, to eliminate terminal constraints or isoperimetric constraints. More recently, it has been used by Balakrishnan* to eliminate dynamic constraints. In each case one can modify the method of penalty functions to obtain a corresponding method of multipliers. We shall give a heuristic description of how to formulate the method of multipliers for the simple nonlinear optimal control problem with fixed terminal and initial states.

The problem we shall consider is the following. Let ξ denote a pair

$$\xi : \quad x^i(t), \quad u^k(t) \qquad (0 \leq t \leq T)$$

---

*A. V. Balakrishnan, A new computing technique in optimal control and its application to minimal time flight profile optimization. Presented at the 2nd International Colloquium on Methods of Optimization, Novosibirsk, U.S.S.R., June 1968. To appear in Proceedings to be published by Springer-Verlag.

of state functions $x^i(t)$ and control functions $u^k(t)$ on a fixed interval $0 \leq t \leq T$. We shall consider ξ to be an arc in txu-space. We make the usual continuity and differentiability assumptions on $x(t)$ and $u(t)$. The class of arcs ξ whose elements $(t,x(t),u(t))$ lie in a prescribed region in txu-space will be denoted by $\mathfrak{A}$. We denote by $\mathfrak{B}$ the subclass of $\mathfrak{A}$ having prescribed initial and terminal states $x(0)$ and $x(T)$. Finally we denote by $\mathfrak{C}$ the class of all arcs ξ in $\mathfrak{B}$ satisfying the differential constraint

$$\dot{x}^i = f^i(t,x,u).$$

We suppose that there is a unique arc

$$\xi_0 : \quad x_0(t), \quad u_0(t) \qquad (0 \leq t \leq T)$$

in $\mathfrak{C}$ that minimizes a given integral

$$I(\xi) = \int_0^T L(t,x(t),u(t))dt.$$

This problem becomes a classical problem of Lagrange with one variable endpoint if we introduce the auxiliary state variable

$$y(t) = \int_0^t u(s)ds \qquad (0 \leq t \leq T)$$

so that $\dot{y}(t) = u(t)$.

It has been shown by the author* that if the arc ξ_0 satisfies certain standard sufficiency conditions for a strong relative minimum on $\mathfrak{C}$, there exist multipliers $p_i(t)$ and a function $c(t,x,\dot{x},u)$ such that ξ_0 affords a local minimum to the function

$$J = \int_a^b \{L + p_i(\dot{x}^i - f^i) + \frac{c}{2}|\dot{x} - f|^2\}dt$$

where i is summed over its range. The functions $p_i(t)$ are

---

*M. R. Hestenes, An indirect sufficiency proof for the problem of Bolza in nonparametric form, Transactions of the American Mathematical Society, Vol. 62 (1947), pp. 509-535.

the usual costate functions associated with ξ_0. In many cases c can be chosen to be a constant. In particular this is the case when one is concerned only with weak relative minima.

This result suggests the following method of multipliers. Having chosen c sufficiently large, hold c fast and proceed as follows: Let $p_q(t)$ be an estimate of $p(t)$ and let $J_q(\xi)$ be the integral obtained from J by setting $p(t) = p_q(t)$. We then seek a minimum ξ_q of $J_q(\xi)$ on $\mathcal{B}$. This problem is a classical minimum problem of the type considered by Tonelli and his school. Having obtained ξ_q, determine a new set of multipliers p_{q+1} by some reasonable rule. For example one can select

$$p_{q+1} = p_q + c(\dot{x} - f)$$

evaluated along ξ_q. Or one could let p_{q+1} be a solution along ξ_q of

$$\dot{p}_i = L_{x^i} - p_j f^j_{x^i}$$

with suitable initial or terminal conditions.

The author has not determined conditions under which this method would be effective. It is to be expected that ξ_0 exists and if suitably strong hypotheses are made, then ξ_q exists and converges to ξ_0. In the general case it is expected that one would have to enlarge the problem so as to include generalized curves and relaxed controls.

5. Newton's Method and Gradient Methods

In the preceding pages it was shown that problems with constraints often can be solved with the help of solutions of problems without constraints. This section will be devoted to methods for obtaining unconstrained minima. To this end let $F(x)$ be a real valued function on a normed linear space $\mathcal{E}$. We normally consider $\mathcal{E}$ to be Euclidian. We assume that F possesses first and second Frechet differentials $F'(x,h)$ and $F''(x,h)$. We then have the Taylor's formula

$$F(x + h) = P(x,h) + R(x,h) \tag{5.1a}$$

where

$$P(x,h) = F(x) + F'(x,h) + \frac{1}{2} F''(x,h). \tag{5.1b}$$

Newton's method for obtaining the minimum of F on an open set S of $\mathcal{E}$ can be described as follows: Having obtained an estimate x_n of the minimum point $\bar{x}$ of F on S select h_n so as to minimize the function $P(x_n,h)$ and use the formula

$$x_{n+1} = x_n + h_n$$

to obtain a new estimate of $\bar{x}$. This method converges quadratically to $\bar{x}$ under the usual hypotheses on $F''(x,h)$ if a suitable initial point x_0 is chosen. The point h_n satisfies the relation

$$F'(x_n,h) + F''(x_n,h_n,h) = 0 \quad \text{(h arbitrary)} \tag{5.2}$$

where $F''(x,k,h)$ is the bilinear form associated with $F''(x,h)$, namely, the differential of $F'(x,k)$ for fixed k. In the Euclidean case

$$h_n = -K_n F'(x_n) \tag{5.3}$$

where K_n is the inverse of the matrix $F''(x_n)$ of second derivatives of F at x_n. We have accordingly the iteration

$$x_{n+1} = x_n - K_n F'(x_n). \tag{5.4}$$

Quadratic convergence is assured if the matrix $F''(x_n)$ (and hence also K_n) is positive definite and the initial point x_0 is suitably chosen.

Newton's method has the following geometrical interpretation: Given the point x_n, approximate the level surface

$$F(x) = F(x_n)$$

by the ellipsoid

$$P(x_n, x - x_n) = F(x_n).$$

This ellipsoid is tangent to the level surface of F at x_n. Take the center x_{n+1} of this ellipsoid as the new estimate of the minimum point $\bar{x}$.

The difficulty encountered in Newton's method lies in the determination of the minimum point h_n of $P(x_n,h)$. In the finite dimensional case the matrix $F''(x_n)$ must be inverted. In infinite dimensional cases it involves the solution of a linear boundary value problem. For this reason it is often desirable to replace $P(x_n,h)$ by a simpler function

$$P_n(h) = F(x_n) + F'(x_n,h) + \frac{1}{2} Q_n(h)$$

where $Q_n(h)$ is a positive definite quadratic form. We then choose h_n to minimize $Q_n(h)$. The ellipsoid

$$P_n(x - x_n) = F(x_n) \tag{5.5}$$

is tangent to the level surface of F at x_n and its center yields the desired new estimate $x_{n+1} = x_n + h_n$ of $\overline{x}$. Again in the finite dimensional case the iteration takes the form (5.4) where K_n is the inverse of the matrix associated with Q_n.

If one selects Q_n to be of the form

$$Q_n(x) = c_n \|x\|^2$$

the surface (5.5) is a sphere. In this event $K_n = c_n^{-1} I$ and the iteration (5.4) is the usual gradient method. If $Q_n(h) = F''(x_n,h)$, we have Newton's method.

If K is an arbitrary positive definite matrix, the iteration

$$x_{n+1} = x_n - a_n KF'(x_n) \qquad (a_n > 0) \tag{5.6}$$

can be considered to be a gradient method. This iteration is obtained if we select

$$\langle x,y \rangle = (K^{-1}x,y)$$

as our inner product in place of the cartesian inner product (x,y). In this event $Q_n(x) = a_n^{-1}\langle x,x \rangle$. The gradient g of F relative to the new inner product $\langle x,y \rangle$ is given by the identity

$$F'(x,h) = \langle g,h \rangle. \tag{5.7}$$

Hence $g = KF'(x)$. The iteration (5.6) is equivalent to the usual gradient method in a suitably chosen coordinate system.

In the infinite dimensional case one should choose the inner product $\langle g,h\rangle$ such that $\langle h,h\rangle$ has the essential properties of $F''(x,h)$. For example, for the variational integral

$$F(x) = \int_a^b L(t,x(t),\dot{x}(t))dt$$

one should select

$$\langle g,h\rangle = g(a)h(a) + \int_a^b \dot{g}(t)\dot{h}(t)dt$$

or its equivalent as the inner product instead of the more familiar

$$\langle g,h\rangle = \int_a^b g(t)h(t)dt.$$

The reason for this choice will become self evident when one attempts to construct a gradient method for minimizing $F(x)$.

6. Rayleigh-Ritz and Conjugate Gradient Methods

The conjugate gradient method can be introduced in many ways. In this section we shall show that conjugate gradient and conjugate direction methods are variants of the Rayleigh-Ritz method. To this end let $\mathcal{E}$ be a finite or infinite dimensional real Hilbert space with (x,y) as its inner product and $\|x\| = (x,x)^{\frac{1}{2}}$ as its norm. Let A be a positive definite self adjoint bounded operator on $\mathcal{E}$. Then

$$(Ax,y) = (x,Ay), \quad m\|x\|^2 \leq (Ax,x) \leq M\|x\|^2$$

where m, M are suitably chosen positive constants. We seek a solution of the linear system

$$Ax = b \tag{6.1}$$

where b is a given element in $\mathcal{E}$. The solution $\bar{x} = A^{-1}b$ of this equation affords a minimum on $\mathcal{E}$ to the function

$$F(x) = \frac{1}{2}(Ax,x) - (b,x).$$

Observe that

$$F'(x,h) = (Ax - b,h). \tag{6.2}$$

The gradient of F at x is therefore

$$F'(x) = Ax - b. \tag{6.3}$$

The quantity $r = -F'(x) = b - Ax$ is called the residual at x and is also called the negative gradient of F at x.

If K is a second positive definite bounded self adjoint operator on $\mathcal{E}$, then

$$\langle x,y \rangle = (K^{-1}x,y) \tag{6.4}$$

is a second inner product topologically equivalent to the first. The negative gradient g of F at x relative to this new inner product is defined by the relation

$$F'(x,h) = -\langle g,h \rangle$$

for all h in $\mathcal{E}$. Hence

$$g(x) = Kr(x) = -KF'(x).$$

The generalized gradient method for solving (6.1) accordingly takes the form

$$x_{n+1} = x_n + a_n Kr_n \qquad (a_n > 0) \tag{6.5}$$

where $r_n = -F'(x_n)$ and a_n is a suitably chosen scale factor. The choice $K = A^{-1}$ would be the ideal choice for K. However, since A^{-1} is assumed to be unknown this choice is impossible. The conjugate gradient methods yield iterative methods for computing A^{-1}.

Before considering the Rayleigh-Ritz method it is convenient to recall a theorem on the minimization of F on a set $z + \mathcal{B}$, where z is a fixed point of $\mathcal{E}$, $\mathcal{B}$ is a linear subspace of $\mathcal{E}$ and $z + \mathcal{B}$ is the set of all points $x = z + y$, where y is in $\mathcal{B}$.

THEOREM 2. _A point_ $\bar{x} = z + \bar{y}$ _in_ $z + \mathcal{B}$ _minimizes_ F _on_ $z + \mathcal{B}$ _if and only if the negative gradient_ $g(\bar{x}) = -KF'(\bar{x})$ _is orthogonal to_ $\mathcal{B}$ _relative to_ (6.4) _or equivalently if and only if the residual_ $r(\bar{x}) = -F'(\bar{x})$ _is orthogonal to_ $\mathcal{B}$ _in the usual sense_.

In the general Rayleigh-Ritz method we select a basis $p_0, p_1, p_2, \ldots$ for $\mathcal{E}$. The linear subspace generated by $p_0, p_1, \ldots, p_{k-1}$ will be denoted by $\mathcal{B}_k$. If $\mathcal{E}$ is n-dimensional, then $\mathcal{B}_n = \mathcal{E}$. Let x_0 be a point in $\mathcal{E}$. For example, we may select $x_0 = 0$. Denote by x_k the minimum point of F on $x_0 + \mathcal{B}_k$. Then the sequence $\{x_k\}$ converges to the desired solution $\bar{x} = A^{-1}b$. Of course if $\mathcal{E}$ is n-dimensional then $x_n = A^{-1}b$. At each step x_k is an estimate of $\bar{x}$ and $F(x_k)$ is an estimate of the minimum value $F(\bar{x})$. In applications a wise choice of basis $\{p_j\}$ often yields good estimates $F(x_k)$ of $F(\bar{x})$ for small integers k.

The conjugate direction method is the special case of the Rayleigh-Ritz method in which the basis $\{p_j\}$ is chosen to be a conjugate basis in the sense that

$$(Ap_j, p_k) = 0 \qquad (j \neq k).$$

The advantage of this choice is that the point x_{k+1} is related to x_k by the simple formula

$$x_{k+1} = x_k + a_k p_k \tag{6.6a}$$

where

$$a_k = c_k/d_k, \quad d_k = (Ap_k, p_k), \quad c_k = (r_k, p_k) = \langle g_k, p_k \rangle \tag{6.6b}$$

$$r_k = -F'(x_k) = b - Ax_k, \quad g_k = Kr_k \, .$$

Moreover r_{k+1} can be computed by the formula

$$r_{k+1} = r_k - a_k A p_k \, . \tag{6.6c}$$

These formulas greatly simplify computations. It is easy to see that

$$(r_{k+1}, p_j) = \langle g_{k+1}, p_j \rangle = 0 \qquad (j \leq k) \tag{6.7a}$$

$$c_k = (r_j, p_k) = \langle g_j, p_k \rangle \qquad (j \leq k). \tag{6.7b}$$

In fact the formula for a_k can be obtained from (6.6c) and the relation

$$(r_{k+1}, p_k) = 0. \tag{6.8}$$

The conjugate direction method yields an explicit formula for the inverse A^{-1} of A. To see this we associate with each vector p the operator $\frac{pp^*}{(Ap,p)}$ which maps a vector x into the vector $p\frac{(p,x)}{(Ap,p)}$. We set

$$B_k = \sum_{j=0}^{k-1} \frac{p_j p_j^*}{d_j} \qquad (d_j = (Ap_j, p_j))$$

where $\{p_j\}$ is our conjugate basis. The operator

$$P_k = B_k A$$

has the property that

$$P_k p_j = p_j \; (j < k), \qquad P_k p_j = 0 \; (j \geq k).$$

It follows that if $\mathcal{E}$ is n-dimensional, then $B_n = A^{-1}$. If $\mathcal{E}$ is infinite dimensional then $\{B_k\}$ converges to A^{-1} in the sense that $\{B_k y\}$ converges to $A^{-1}y$ for each y in $\mathcal{E}$.

It is interesting to note that if we set

$$\Delta x_k = x_{k+1} - x_k = a_k p_k, \qquad \Delta F'_k = F'(x_{k+1}) - F'(x_k) = a_k A p_k$$

then the formula B_k can be put in the form

$$B_k = \sum_{j=0}^{k-1} \frac{\Delta x_j \Delta x_j^*}{(\Delta x_j, \Delta F'_j)} .$$

This formula is independent of the choice of the positive numbers $a_0, a_1, \ldots, a_{k-1}$. It follows that if one is only concerned with the computation of A^{-1}, the point x_k need not minimize F on $x_0 + \mathcal{B}_k$. It must however be on the line $x = x_{k-1} + \alpha p_{k-1}$.

By $A\mathcal{B}$ will be meant the class of all vectors $x = Ay$, where y is in $\mathcal{B}$. The orthogonal complement $\mathcal{C}$ of $A\mathcal{B}$ will be called the A-orthogonal complement of $\mathcal{B}$. We have $(Ay,z) = 0$ whenever y is in $\mathcal{B}$ and z is in $\mathcal{C}$. Given a point x, by a (negative) conjugate gradient of F at x on $\mathcal{C}$ relative to $\langle y,z \rangle$ will be meant a vector p in $\mathcal{C}$ such that

$$F'(x,h) = -\frac{1}{\beta}\langle p,h\rangle$$

holds for all h in KAC, where β is a positive number. We have introduced the constant β for convenience in computations. It emphasizes that we are interested in the direction of p and not its magnitude. It follows from this definition that if $r = -F'(x)$, then

$$(p - \beta Kr, z) = 0 \qquad (\text{all } z \text{ in } AC).$$

The vector $y = p - \beta Kr$ is therefore in $\mathfrak{B}$. We have accordingly the simple formula

$$p = \beta Kr + y$$

for the conjugate gradient of p of F at K,

The Rayleigh-Ritz method becomes a conjugate gradient method relative to K if at each step, p_k is the conjugate gradient of F at x_k relative to the A-orthogonal complement C_k of $\mathfrak{B}_k$. In this event we have the convenient formula

$$p_{k+1} = \beta_k Kr_{k+1} + b_k p_k, \qquad p_0 = Kr_0.$$

Here

$$b_k = -\beta_k \frac{(Ap_k, Kr_{k+1})}{d_k} = \beta_k \frac{(r_{k+1}, Kr_{k+1})}{c_k}$$

and β_k is an arbitrary positive number. In practice the choice $\beta_k = 1$ and $\beta_k = 1 - b_k$ are perhaps the preferred choices for β_k.

In the finite dimensional case any conjugate direction method is a conjugate gradient method with a suitable choice of K. In fact K can be chosen so that $\beta_k = 1$. A similar result undoubtedly holds in the infinite dimensional case.

7. Conjugate Gradient Algorithms

In the present section it will be convenient to use the symbol x^*y for the inner product (x,y). In a conjugate gradient algorithm, the conjugate basis $\{p_k\}$ is completely determined by the initial vector p_0, the positive definite operator K and the positive scale factor β_k for p_k. Starting with a vector $r_0 \neq 0$ and $p_0 = Kr_0$, $\beta_0 = 1$ a sequence $\{p_k\}$ of conjugate vectors is generated by the algorithm

$$s_k = Ap_k, \quad g_k = Kr_k \tag{7.1a}$$

$$r_{k+1} = r_k - a_k s_k, \quad p_{k+1} = \beta_k g_k + b_k p_k \tag{7.1b}$$

where

$$a_k = c_k/d_k, \quad d_k = p_k^* s_k, \quad c_k = p_k^* r_k = \beta_{k-1} g_k^* r_k \tag{7.1c}$$

$$b_k = -\beta_k \frac{s_k^* g_{k+1}}{d_k} = \beta_k \frac{r_{k+1}^* g_{k+1}}{c_k} = \frac{c_{k+1}}{c_k}.$$

The numbers a_k, a_k, c_k, d_k, β_k are positive. If $r_0 = -F'(x_0)$, the iteration

$$x_{k+1} = x_k + a_k p_k$$

yields a minimizing sequence for F. This sequence terminates in $m \leq n$ steps of $\mathcal{E}$ is of dimension n. The constant β_k in (7.1) is a scale factor for p_k. For example, we can choose β_k such that one has $\beta_k = 1$, $b_k = 1$ or $\beta_k = 1 - b_k$. This last relation is obtained by setting

$$\gamma_k = g_k^* r_k, \quad \beta_k = \frac{c_k}{c_k + \gamma_{k+1}}, \quad b_k = \frac{\gamma_{k+1}}{c_k + \gamma_{k+1}}. \tag{7.2}$$

We have the relations

$$c_k = p_k^* r_j \ (j \leq k), \quad p_k^* r_j = 0 \ (k < j) \tag{7.3a}$$

$$p_j^* A p_k = 0 \ (j \neq k), \quad r_j^* K r_k = 0 \ (j \neq k) \tag{7.3b}$$

$$r_j^* K s_k = 0 \ (j \neq k, k+1), \quad s_j^* K s_k = 0 \ (j + 1 < k). \tag{7.3c}$$

In addition

$$p_{k+1} = \lambda_k p_k - \mu_k KAp_k - \nu_k p_{k-1} \quad (\nu_0 = 0) \tag{7.4a}$$

where $\mu_k = \beta_k a_k$ is a scale factor and

$$\lambda_k = \frac{\beta_k}{\beta_{k-1}} + b_k = \mu_k \frac{s_k^* K s_k}{d_k}, \quad \nu_k = \frac{\beta_k b_{k-1}}{\beta_{k-1}} = -\mu_k \frac{s_k^* K s_{k-1}}{d_{k-1}}. \tag{7.4b}$$

The equations (7.4) can be used in place of (7.1) to generate the conjugate basis $\{p_k\}$. The equations here given can be obtained from the case $K = I$ by a transformation of variables.

Given p_0, K, $s_0 = Ap_0$ and $q_0 = Ks_0$ the conjugate sequence $\{p_k\}$ also can be generated by the algorithm

$$s_k = Ap_k, \quad d_k = p_k^* s_k, \quad e_k = q_k^* s_k \tag{7.5a}$$

$$p_{k+1} = p_k - \beta_k q_k, \quad \beta_k = \frac{d_k}{e_k} \tag{7.5b}$$

$$q_{k+1} = Ks_{k+1} + \alpha_k q_k, \quad \alpha_k = \frac{d_{k+1}}{d_k} = -\frac{s_k^* K s_{k+1}}{e_k}. \tag{7.5c}$$

Here α_k and β_k are determined by the relations

$$p_{k+1}^* s_k = 0, \quad q_{k+1}^* s_k = 0.$$

If we wish, we can introduce a scale factor ρ_k for q_k by replacing the last equation by

$$q_{k+1} = \rho_{k+1} K s_{k+1} + \alpha_k q_k, \quad \alpha_k = \frac{\rho_{k+1} d_{k+1}}{\rho_k d_k}$$

or by setting $s_k = \rho_k A p_k$, $d_k = \dfrac{p_k^* s_k}{\rho_k}$. This does not alter p_k. If $p_0 = Kr_0$, the iteration (7.5) is equivalent to (7.1) with $\beta_k + b_k = 1$. As described in the last section the sequence of matrices $\{B_k\}$ generated by the algorithm

$$B_0 = 0, \quad B_{k+1} = B_k + \frac{p_k p_k^*}{d_k} \tag{7.5d}$$

determines A^{-1} unless the algorithm terminates prematurely.

The iteration (7.5) can be put in another form. Starting with $p_0 \neq 0$, $M_0 = K$, $B_0 = 0$ we generate p_k, q_k, M_k, B_k as follows

$$s_k = Ap_k, \quad q_k = M_k s_k, \quad d_k = p_k^* s_k, \quad e_k = q_k^* s \tag{7.6a}$$

$$p_{k+1} = p_k - \beta_k q_k, \quad \beta_k = \frac{d_k}{e_k} \tag{7.6b}$$

$$M_{k+1} = M_k - \frac{q_k q_k^*}{e_k}, \quad B_{k+1} = B_k + \frac{p_k p_k^*}{d_k} . \tag{7.6c}$$

In this event we have

$$M_k s_j = 0 \ (j < k), \quad M_k s_j = Ks_j \ (j > k).$$

If the iteration does not terminate prematurely we have $M_n = 0$ if $\mathcal{E}$ is of dimension n and $\lim M_k x = 0$ for each x otherwise. Setting

$$H_k = M_k + B_k$$

and using the relation $B_k s_k = 0$ we see that the algorithm (7.6) yields the following algorithm. Starting with $p_0 \neq 0$ and $H_0 = K$ set

$$s_k = Ap_k, \quad q_k = H_k s_k, \quad d_k = p_k^* s_k, \quad e_k = q_k^* s_k \tag{7.7a}$$

$$p_{k+1} = p_k - \beta_k q_k, \quad \beta_k = \frac{d_k}{e_k} \tag{7.7b}$$

$$H_{k+1} = H_k - \frac{q_k q_k^*}{e_k} + \frac{p_k p_k^*}{d_k} . \tag{7.7c}$$

In the algorithms (7.6) and (7.7) one can replace s_k, d_k by $s_k = \rho_k Ap_k$, $d_k = p_k^* s/\rho_k$ $(\rho_k > 0)$ without altering p_{k+1}, M_{k+1}, B_{k+1}, or H_{k+1}.

In general the sequence $\{x_k\}$ defined by the recursion formula

$$x_k = x_0 - B_k F'(x_0) \quad \text{or} \quad x_k = x_0 - H_k F'(x_0)$$

is a minimizing sequence for F. This is always true if

$p_0 = -KF'(x_0)$. If no round off errors occur the iteration terminates in $m \leq n$ steps if $\mathcal{E}$ is of dimension n.

We shall give one final algorithm for generating a conjugate basis. This algorithm is equivalent to the preceding ones. We shall express the result in terms of the original function F to be minimized. Having chosen an initial point x_0 and the operators $M_0 = K$, $B_0 = 0$ we iterate as follows

$$p_k = -M_k F'(x_k), \quad \rho_k > 0, \quad \rho_k \text{ arbitrary} \tag{7.8a}$$

$$x_{k+1} = x_k + \rho_k p_k, \quad s_k = F'(x_{k+1}) - F'(x_k) \tag{7.8b}$$

$$q_k = M_k s_k, \quad e_k = q_k^* s_k, \quad d_k = \frac{p_k^* s_k}{\rho_k} \tag{7.8c}$$

$$M_{k+1} = M_k - \frac{q_k q_k^*}{e_k}, \quad B_{k+1} = B_k + \frac{p_k p_k^*}{d_k}. \tag{7.8d}$$

The relations (7.8b) can be replaced by

$$x_{k+1} = x_0 + \rho_k p_k, \quad s_k = F'(x_{k+1}) - F'(x_0) \tag{7.8b'}$$

if one so desires but we shall not do so here. The optimal choice for ρ_k is the minimum point $\rho = a_k$ of $F(x_k + \rho p_k)$. This algorithm with $\rho_k = a_k$ has been given by Kelley and Myers. If we select $\rho_k = a_k$ and replace M_k by $H_k = M_k + B_k$ we obtain Davidon's method as given by Fletcher and Powell. In these two cases the sequence $\{x_k\}$ is a minimizing sequence for F. In all cases the sequences $\{y_k\}$ or $\{z_k\}$ defined by

$$y_k = x_0 - B_k F'(x_0), \quad z_k = x_0 - H_k F'(x_0)$$

are minimizing sequences for F. In the n-dimensional case, there is an integer $m \leq n$ such that $y_m = z_m$ is the solution to our problem.

In the n-dimensional case the algorithm (7.8) with n-steps applied to an arbitrary function F can be looked upon as one Newton iteration. In particular if (7.8b') is used in the iteration the matrix B_n is an estimate $B(x_0)$ of the inverse of $F''(x_0)$. A repetition of the algorithm gives the sequence

$$\bar{x}_{k+1} = \bar{x}_k - B(\bar{x}_k)F'(\bar{x}_k), \quad \bar{x}_0 = x_0$$

as a gradient method. Of course at any stage one can use $B(\bar{x}_k) = B(\bar{x}_{k-1})$ instead of computing $B(\bar{x}_k)$ by the algorithm (7.8).

The possibility of using an arbitrary scale factor ρ_k in (7.8) was suggested by a statement in the invited address by B. Pscenichnig of USSR to the effect that he had devised a similar algorithm having this property.

References on Conjugate Gradient and Davidon's Methods

Hestenes, M. R. and Strefel, E., Method of conjugate gradients for solving linear systems, J. Research Nat. Bur. Standards, Vol 49 (1952), pp. 409-436. RP2379.

Hestenes, M. R., The conjugate gradient method for solving linear systems, Proceedings of Sixth Symposium in applied mathematics, Vol. VI (1956), pp. 83-102 Mathematical Society.

Hayes, R. M., Iterative methods for solving linear problems in Hilbert space, contributions to the solutions of systems of linear equations and the determination of Ligen-values, National Bureau of Standard Applied Mathematics Series, No. 39 (1954). U.S. Govt. Printing Office, Washington, D.C.

Fletcher, R. and Powell, M. J. D., A rapidly convergent descent method for minimization, Comput. J., Vol. 6 (1964), pp. 163-168.

Myers, G. E., Properties of the conjugate-gradient and Davidon Methods, Journal of Optimization Theory and Applications, Vol. 2 (1968), pp. 209-219.

Horwitz, L. B. and Sarachick, P. E., Davidon's method in Hilbert space, SIAM Journal on Applied Mathematics, Vol. 16 (1968), pp. 676-695.

Further references can be found in these papers.

† The preparation of this paper was sponsored by the U. S. Army Research Office under Grant DA-31-124-ARO(D)-355. Reproduction in whole or in part is permitted for any purpose of the United States Government.

GENERALIZED PROGRAMMING SOLUTION OF OPTIMAL CONTROL PROBLEMS*

G. Stephen Jizmagian
Arthur D. Little, Inc.
San Francisco, California

1. Introduction

In this paper, we use newly developed mathematical programming techniques to provide a computational method for solving large scale, continuous time optimal control problems while retaining the continuous times aspects of the original problem. The use of generalized linear programming (1), (2), (6) and specialized parametric linear and quadratic programming (3) permit the solution of the continuous time problem without the use of approximating difference equations or discrete time methods.

The method presented here is suitable for optimal control problems where very accurate switching times for control changes are desirable. This method is also suitable for providing an optimal value of the performance index for verifying the solutions derived for discrete time approximations of the continuous time problem.

2. Class of Problems Solvable by These Methods

Those control problems solvable by these methods include all problems for which the state equations, differential equations, are linear in the state and control and defined by the following set of equations,

$$\frac{dx}{dx} = \dot{x}(t) = Fx(t) + Gu(t), \tag{1}$$

where $x(t) \varepsilon E^n$ is the vector of state variables at time t and F and G are the system matrices.

*This work was performed at Stanford University and partially supported by Nonr-225(83) and Nonr-225(53) (NR-042-002), Joint Services contracts monitored by the Office of Naval Research.

The other restrictions on the classes of control problems adaptable to this solution procedure are those for which the initial and final state constraints are defined by convex sets in E^n, i.e.,

$$x(o) \varepsilon S_0 \text{ and } x(T) \varepsilon S_T,$$

where S_0 and S_T are convex sets (including fixed points) and T is the final time. The control constraints must also be represented by a convex polyhedral set of admissible control vectors, i.e., $u(t) \varepsilon U$ where U is a convex polyhedral set in E^m.

Given these above restrictions, we can optimize any continuous time problem with the following classes of loss functionals,

$$\ell(x,u) = f_o'x + g_o'u + \ell(u), \tag{2}$$

$$\text{where } \ell(u) = \begin{cases} 0 \\ \sum_i |u_i(t)| \\ u(t)' \, Qu(t) \end{cases} \tag{3}$$

where f_o' and g_o' are the transpose of vectors f_o and g_o, and Q is a positive semidefinite matrix, and the performance index, J, expressed by,

$$J = \int_0^T \ell(x,u) \, dt. \tag{4}$$

3. Generalized Linear Programming

We will use the Dantzig-Wolfe generalized programming procedure for the basis of our solution technique. A generalized program can be expressed as follows.

Find a vector P in a convex set C in E^n, such that the scalar λ is maximized and that the linear equations,

$$U_o \lambda + P = S, \tag{5}$$

are satisfied, where U_o is a fixed given vector and S is some given vector. (Note that S need not be fixed but may itself be a member of a convex set.)

The solution procedure for a generalized program is to have initially on hand n vectors, P^i , such that the following linear program has a non-degenerate, unique solution, (a method for obtaining these vectors is analogous to the following procedure) in the variables μ and λ.

$$\begin{aligned} &\text{Max } \lambda \\ &\text{Subject to } \quad U_0\lambda + P^1\mu_1 + \ldots + P^n\mu_n = S \\ &\qquad\qquad\qquad\qquad \mu_1 + \ldots + \mu_n = 1 \\ &\qquad\qquad\qquad\qquad \mu_i \geq 0 \end{aligned} \tag{6}$$

The dual variable, Π, to the linear program is then used to solve a subproblem,

$$\text{Find} \quad \delta = \min_{P\varepsilon C} \Pi' \begin{pmatrix} P \\ 1 \end{pmatrix} \tag{7}$$

If $\delta \leq 0$, the above solution to (6), i.e.,

$$P = \sum_i P^i\mu_i, \tag{8}$$

is also a solution to the generalized program. If $\delta < 0$, the vector P^{n+1} which generates δ is then added to (6) and the augmented linear program is solved.

After k iterations of the subproblem, the general iteration is to solve the linear program,

$$\begin{aligned} &\text{Max } \lambda \\ &\text{Subject to} \\ &U_0\lambda + P^1\mu_1 + \ldots + P^n\mu_n + P^{n+1}\mu_{n+1} + \ldots + P^{n+k}\mu_{n+k} = S \\ &\qquad \mu_1 + \ldots + \mu_n + \mu_{n+1} + \ldots + \mu_{n+k} = 1 \\ &\qquad\qquad \mu_i \geq 0, \end{aligned} \tag{9}$$

determine the dual variable, Π^k, to Eq. (9), and solve the subproblem,

$$\text{Find} \quad \delta^k = \min_{P\varepsilon C} \Pi^{k'} \begin{pmatrix} P \\ 1 \end{pmatrix} \tag{10}$$

If $\delta \leq 0$, the problem is solved, if not, augment Eq. (9) by P^{n+k+1} which produces and continue

The procedure has the properties that Π^k converges to a value $\Pi^* \neq 0$ such that,

$$0 = \Pi^* P^* \leq \Pi^* P, \ \forall P\varepsilon C, \text{ and} \tag{11}$$

P^* is a solution to the generalized program.

4. Conversion of Control Problems to Generalized Programs

For simplicity, we will consider fixed end point problems, and without loss of generality, assume the initial state vector is at the origin.

Let us now augment the state of the system so that the state zero or the first component of the vector

$$\bar{x}(t) = \begin{bmatrix} x_0(t) \\ x(t) \end{bmatrix}, \tag{12}$$

represents the value of the performance index at time t. The augmented set of differential equations is,

$$\begin{aligned} \dot{x}_0(t) &= \ell(x,u) = f_0'x + g_0'u = \ell(u) \\ x_i(t) &= f_i'x + g_i'u \qquad i = 1, \ldots, n, \end{aligned} \tag{13}$$

where f_i and g_i are the ith rows of F and G respectively. We can write (13) in compact matrix form as,

$$\dot{\bar{x}}(t) = \bar{F}\bar{x} + \bar{G}u + e_0\ell(u), \tag{14}$$

where

$$\bar{F} = \begin{pmatrix} 0 & \vdots & f_0' \\ \cdot & \vdots & \cdot \\ 0 & \vdots & F \end{pmatrix}, \quad \bar{G} = \begin{pmatrix} g_0' \\ \cdot \; \cdot \; \cdot \\ G \end{pmatrix}, \quad \text{and}$$

e_0 is an n+1 unit vector with a 1 in the first component. Assuming that the vector, $\bar{x}(0)$, is at the origin,

$$\bar{x}(t) = \int_0^T e^{\bar{F}(T-t)}\,\bar{G}u(t)\,dt + e_0\int_0^T \ell(u)dt. \tag{15}$$

Let us now define,

$$P = \int_0^T e^{F(T-t)}\,Gu(t)dt\,, \quad \text{and} \tag{16}$$

$$\bar{P} = \int_0^T e^{\bar{F}(T-t)}\,\bar{G}u(t) + e_0\int_0^T \ell(u)dt, \tag{17}$$

then

$$\bar{P} = \begin{pmatrix} p_0 \\ P \end{pmatrix} \tag{18}$$

where p_0 is the value of the performance index, J, when using the control function, u(t), generating the vector, P.

Let the vector, S, be the fixed final desired state and,

$$\bar{S} = \begin{pmatrix} 0 \\ S \end{pmatrix} \tag{19}$$

If we let $U_0 = e_0$ and $\lambda = -J$, then the optimal control problem is formulated as the following generalized program,

$$\begin{aligned} &\text{Max } (\lambda) \\ &\quad U_0\lambda + \bar{P} = \bar{S} \\ &\quad \bar{P} \in \bar{C}, \end{aligned} \tag{20}$$

where

$$\bar{C} = \left\{ \bar{P} = \begin{pmatrix} p_0 \\ P \end{pmatrix} \;\middle|\; \bar{P} = \int_0^T e^{\bar{F}(T-t)}\,\bar{G}u(t)dt + e_0\int_0^T \ell(u)dt, \quad u(t)\varepsilon U,\ t\varepsilon[o,T],\ U, \text{ a convex polyhedral set} \right\}.$$

Thus $\bar{C}$ is known to be the convex.

The set of equations, (20), imply that the vector, P, chosen provides a feasible solution to the control problem, i.e., an admissible control which brings the system to a desired final state in time T. The maximization of λ implies the minimization of the first component of $\bar{P}$, being p_0 and yields an optimal solution of the control problem.

We will now describe the subproblem of the generalized program (20) for each of the classes of loss functionals considered. In general the subproblem of the generalized program, after any iteration, k, is,

$$\underset{\bar{P}\varepsilon\bar{C}}{\text{Min}}\ \Pi^{k'}\begin{pmatrix}\bar{P}\\1\end{pmatrix} = \underset{\bar{P}\varepsilon\bar{C}}{\text{Min}} \left[\underline{\Pi}^{k'} \left(\int_0^T e^{\bar{F}(T-t)}\bar{G}u(t) + e_0\ell(u) \right) dt + \Pi^k_{n+1} \right],$$

where $\Pi^k = (\underline{\Pi}^k, \Pi^k_{n+1})$ is an n+2 vector.

By realizing that $\underline{\Pi}^k$ is a constant vector and that the minimization is over the choice of $u(t)\varepsilon U$ for $t\varepsilon[o,t]$, the subproblem becomes,

$$\underset{u(.)}{\text{Min}} \int_0^T \left(\underline{\Pi}^{k'} e^{\bar{F}(T-t)}\bar{G}u(t) + \underline{\Pi}^{k'} e_0\ell(u) \right) dt, \text{ or}$$

since Π^k_o can be shown to be equal to 1, and since the integral is minimized when the integrand is a minimum for every value of $t\varepsilon[o,T]$, the subproblem is,

$$\begin{aligned} &\text{Min } \underline{\Pi}^{k'} e^{\bar{F}(T-t)}\bar{G}u(t) + \ell\,(u(t)) \\ &\text{subject to } u(t)\varepsilon U, \text{ for } t\varepsilon\ [o,T]\ . \end{aligned} \tag{21}$$

If we designate the vector,

$$\gamma\ (t) \equiv \underline{\Pi}^{k'} e^{\bar{F}(T-t)}\bar{G}\ , \tag{22}$$

the subproblem becomes,

$$\begin{array}{l} \text{Min } \gamma^k(t)'u(t) + \ell\ (u(t)) \\ \text{subject to } u(t)\varepsilon U,\ t\varepsilon[o,t]\ . \end{array} \tag{23}$$

If we remember that any convex polyhedral set U, can be expressed (perhaps with a change in variables necessary) by

$$U = \{u | Au \leq b,\ u \geq 0\}\ ,$$

we now show that the subproblem (23) is a parametric programming problem for the various functions $\ell(u)$ mentioned previously.

The system (20) assures feasibility of the control problem while minimizing the objective over all control functions generated by the subproblem. The subproblem to the master program consists of finding a new admissible control that will improve on the current value of the objective function when added to the current restricted master (9). The subproblem is analogous to Pontryagin's maximum principle (4) when the vector solution of the dual to (9) is assumed to be the solution to the adjoint equations. Thus, the algorithm maintains a feasible control while using the Hamiltonian to obtain improvements in the objective value.

The first case is when the loss criterion is a linear functional, or when $\ell(u) = 0$. In this case the subproblem can be solved by the solution of the following parametric linear program,

$$\begin{array}{ll} \text{Min } \gamma(t)'u & \\ \text{Subject to } & Au \leq b \\ & u \geq o \\ & t\varepsilon\ [0,T] \end{array} \tag{24}$$

Since the vector $\gamma(t)$ has the property that each component is a member of the class of solutions of constant coefficient, homogeneous, linear differential equations, the parametric linear program (24) can be solved by techniques developed in (3). This parametric linear programming algorithm is an extension of the revised simplex method and uses an internal scheme based on the nonlinearity in t to solve the degeneracy problem that arises whenever a change in basis occurs. The parametric programming algorithm provides a solution, $u^*(t)$, which is optimal for the problem (24) for the continuum defined by the interval, $[0,T]$. The function $u^*(t)$ is also known to have a piecewise constant solution with a finite number of discontinuities in any finite interval, $[0,T]$.

The second case of interest is the minimum fuel problem, i.e.,

$$\ell(u) = \Sigma|u_i|\ .$$

By adding the following variables,

$$u_i = u_i' - u_i'', \; u_i', \; u_i'' \geq 0$$

$$\text{and letting } |u_i| = u_i' + u_i'',$$

the subproblem again becomes a parametric linear program,

$$\text{Min } \gamma(t)'u' - \gamma(t)'u'' + \Sigma u_i' + \Sigma u_i''$$

$$\text{subject to } Au' - Au'' \leq b$$
$$u_i', \; u_i'' \geq 0 \; .$$

The solution of the linear program for any t has the property that u_i' and u_i'' are not both positive for all i. Thus the solution $u^*(t)$ of the subproblem is again piecewise constant with a finite number of discontinuities for any finite interval.

The last case applies to loss functionals quadratic in the control. (We assume Q is p.s.d.) In this case, the subproblem requires the solution of a parametric quadratic programming problem. This problem is solvable in a finite number of steps using an algorithm developed in (3) based on the Dantzig-Cottle (5) complementary pivot algorithm for quadratic programs.

Note that the optimal value of the dual variable to the generalized program is the optimal value of the adjoint vector at the final time.

5. Feasibility Phase

A difficult (and at times the most important) aspect of a control problem is the generation of a feasible solution to the constraints. A phase I method of generalized programming can be used to find a feasible solution for the linear system control problems discussed previously.

The phase I generalized program is used to find a vector, $P \varepsilon C$, which provides a feasible solution to the linear vector equations, P = S, where S is a fixed vector. The generalized program formulation is,

$$\begin{aligned} \text{Min } w = \Sigma y_i^+ + \Sigma y_i^- \\ P\mu + Iy^+ + Iy^- = S \\ \mu = 1 \\ y^+, \; y^- \geq 0 \end{aligned} \qquad (25)$$

If a feasible solution exists, a solution to (25) is found iff w = 0 at any stage.

We will investigate two types of feasible control problems i) where feasibility is not known to exist for S and ii) when feasibility exists for an ε neighborhood about S.

For the first case, we set the right hand side of (25) at the given vector S and solve the generalized program. The following theorem gives a sufficient condition for infeasibility of the control problem for a given S.

Theorem 1: If at any stage, k, of the generalized program, (25), the value of $w^k + \delta^k > 0$, the original control problem is infeasible.

Proof: Consider the master program, at the kth stage, as

$$\begin{aligned} \text{Max } U_0\lambda + \bar{P}^1\mu^1 + \ldots + \bar{P}^k\mu_k + \bar{I}y^+ - \bar{\bar{I}}y^- - \bar{S}\nu &= 0 \\ \mu_1 + \ldots + \mu_k &= 1 \\ \nu &= 1 \\ y_i^+,\ y_i^-,\ \mu_i \geq 0, \end{aligned} \tag{26}$$

where $\bar{P}^i = \begin{pmatrix} 0 \\ P^i \end{pmatrix}$; $\bar{S} = \begin{pmatrix} 0 \\ S \end{pmatrix}$; $\bar{I} = \begin{bmatrix} 1 & 1 \ldots 1 \\ \cdot & \cdot \quad \cdot \\ & I \end{bmatrix}$; $\bar{\bar{I}} = \begin{bmatrix} -1 & -1 \ldots -1 \\ \cdot & \cdot \quad \cdot \\ & I \end{bmatrix}$.

Thus $\lambda^k = w^k$ and the dual variable to problem (26) is

$$\bar{\Pi}^{k'} = (\Pi_0^k, \Pi^{k'}, \Pi_{n+1}^k, \Pi_{n+2}^k).$$

By the duality theorem of linear programming and using the dual to (26),

$$\lambda^k = \Pi_{n+1}^k + \Pi_{n+2}^k .$$

Also
$$\delta^k = \min_{P \epsilon C} \bar{\Pi}^{k'} \begin{pmatrix} 0 \\ P \\ 1 \\ 0 \end{pmatrix} = \min_{P \epsilon C} \Pi^{k'} P + \Pi_{n+1}^k .$$

Since $\bar{S}$ is always in the basis of (26), $\Pi^{k'} \begin{pmatrix} -\bar{S} \\ 0 \\ 1 \end{pmatrix} = 0$,

which implies $\Pi^{k'}(-S) = -\Pi_{n+2}^k$. (27)

By hypothesis,

$$0 < \delta^k + w^k = \min_{P \epsilon C} \Pi^{k'} P + \Pi_{n+1}^k + w^k \leq \Pi^{k'} P + \Pi_{n+1}^k + w^k$$

for any $P \epsilon C$.

Since
$$w^k = -\lambda^k = -\Pi_{n+1}^k - \Pi_{n+2}^k,$$

$0 < \delta^k + w^k \leq \Pi^{k'} P - \Pi_{n+2}^k$, and by (27)

$0 < \Pi^{k'} P - \Pi^{k'} S$, or

$$0 < \Pi^{k'}(P-S) \text{ for all } P.$$

Thus $\Pi^k \neq 0$ and $P-S \neq 0$ for all P.
This implies that there is no admissible control function, u(t), which can generate a feasible solution to the control problem.

Q. E. D.

On the other hand, when $w^k = 0$ (or $w^k < \varepsilon$, where ε is a very small positive number), the control, $u^*(t)$,

$$u^*(t) = \Sigma \mu_i^k u^i(t),$$

where $u^i(t)$ generate the columns P^i in the master program and μ_i^k is a solution to the master program of the kth iteration, provides a feasible solution to the optimal control problem.

As can be seen from the master program, (26), of the feasibility phase, the subproblem for phase I of the generalized programming formulation of the control problem is a parametric linear program of the type described previously.

When a feasible solution is known to exist for a given S (final end point) and some finite dimensional neighborhood about S, an alternate phase I procedure which converges to an exact feasible solution in a finite number of steps is provided in Ref. (3) and outlined here. A generalized program identical to (25) must be solved for n+1 points S^i (where the state space has dimension n), where each S^i is a small distance from S in a pre-chosen direction so that S^i is in the feasible neighborhood of the control problem. Each generalized program can be terminated when

$$0 \leq w^k < \varepsilon,$$

where ε is some small number depending on the size of the known feasible neighborhood. Thus, termination is possible in a finite number of steps and a feasible control for the optimal control problem is easily constructed from the solution to the generalized programs for each S^i.

6. Optimality Phase

Once the phase I procedure is completed, the optimization phase of the optimal control problem must be initiated. Although finite convergence is not guaranteed for the optimization phase, the solution converges monotonically towards the optimum objective value, and provides at every stage a feasible solution and a bound on how far in objective value the current solution differs from an optimal solution.

Since the dynamic system is linear in state and control, the equations relating P^i and S in the generalized program insure that the control chosen is a feasible control. The bound in objective value is shown by the following theorem (3), (1).

Theorem 2: during any (k^{th}) iteration of the optimization phase of the generalized program, the optimal value of the cost functional, $J(u^*)$, satisfies the following inequalities.

$$J^k(\bar{u}) + \delta^k \leq J^k + \delta^k \leq J(u^*) \leq J\ (u^*) \leq J^k(\bar{u}) \leq J^k = -\lambda^k \quad (28)$$

where $\bar{u}(t) = \sum_{i=1}^{k} \mu_i^k u^i(t)$, and $u^i(t)$ generate the P^i in the master program, μ_i^k and λ^k are the solutions to the kth stage of the master program; and J^k is defined by the extreme right hand equality of (28).

Proof: Consider the kth stage master program to the generalized program (equivalent to (20)):

$$\begin{aligned} &\text{Max } \lambda \\ &U_0\lambda + \bar{P}^1\mu_1 + \ldots + \bar{P}^k\mu_k - S\nu = 0 \\ &\mu_1 + \ldots + \mu_k = 1 \\ &\nu = 1 \\ &\mu_i \geq 0 \end{aligned} \quad (29)$$

The solution to (29) is λ^k and by the duality theorem of linear programming,

$$\lambda^k = \Pi_{n+1}^k + \Pi_{n+2}^k,$$

where $\bar{\Pi}^{k'} = (\Pi_0^k, \Pi^{k'}, \Pi_{n+1}^k, \Pi_{n+2}^k)$ is the dual to (29). Since $\Pi_0^k = 1$, the subproblem has the solution,

$$\delta^k = \min_{u(.)} \left\{ J(u) + \Pi^{k'}P + \Pi_{n+1}^k \right\} ;$$

thus, for the value u^*,

$$\delta^k \leq J(u^*) + \Pi^{k'}P^* + \Pi_{n+1}^k, \text{ and}$$

$$-\lambda^k + \delta^k = J^k + \delta^k \leq J(u^*) + \Pi^{k'}P^* + \Pi_{n+1}^k - \Pi_{n+1}^k - \Pi_{n+2}^k,$$

or

$$J^k + \delta^k \leq J(u^*) + \Pi^{k'}P^* - \Pi_{n+2}^k.$$

$$\text{Since } \bar{\Pi}^{k'} \begin{pmatrix} 0 \\ -S \\ 0 \\ 1 \end{pmatrix} = -\Pi^{k'}S + \Pi_{n+2}^k = 0,$$

$$J^k + \delta^k \leq J*u^*) + \Pi^{k'}(P^*-S).$$

If u^* is the optimal control, u, for all t, then P^* is feasible and $P^* = S$. Thus,

$$J^k + \delta^k \leq J*u^*) \leq J^k(\bar{u}),$$

where $J^k(\bar{u})$ is the current solution to the optimal control problem and $\bar{u}$ is a feasible control, and the right hand inequality immediately follows. Since $J(u)$ is convex in u,

$$J^k(\bar{u}) \leq J^k = \sum_{i=1}^{k} \mu_i J(u^i).$$

Therefore, the inequalities (28) must hold.

Corollary 1: When $\delta^k = 0$, $J^k(\bar{u}) = J^k = J(u^*)$.
Proof: The equalities immediately follow from (28).

Although δ^k does not necessarily increase monotonically to 0, it does so for a subsequence of k. Thus the best bound from previous iterations should be retained until a better bound is attained. The current value of δ^k (at the kth iteration) may be used as a stopping condition for termination of the optimization phase. By observing the value $\delta^k/J^k(\bar{u})$, we can determine the maximum percentage decrease in objective value for the optimal solution over the current solution. Note that we are always assured that the current solution, $\bar{u}(t)$, is feasible for the original control problem.

7. Summary of Results

The author has shown in (3) that the parametric linear program described by (24) has a solution in u(t) which is piecewise constant with a finite number of discontinuities over any finite interval in t. It was also shown that any optimal solution to (20) contains a combination of at most n+1 columns, P^i. Thus the following theorem is made possible.

Theorem 3: For the linear loss case and the minimum fuel case, where a feasible control exists, an optimal control, $u^*(t)$, exists which is piecewise constant and has a finite number of discontinuities in any finite interval of t.
Proof: The subproblem for the linear loss and minimum fuel case is a parametric linear program with the above mentioned properties. The optimal control found by generalized programming is a combination of at most n+1 admissible controls with the piecewise constant property. Thus an optimal control exists with the above property.

Q. E. D.

It should be noted that no assumption of a "general position principle" (Pontryagin (4)) is made on the system matrices. It has also been shown (3) that the subproblem to the generalized program, when Π^k is an optimal value of the dual to the generalized program, is equivalent to the maximum principle of Pontryagin (4).

It should also be noted that the algorithm described here is adaptable, though not restricted, to hybrid computing techniques. The fundamental matrix, used in the generation of $\gamma(t)$ of the subproblem and again in the generation of P^i given the function $u^i(t)$, may be realized by an analog computer, while the linear programming solutions and linear algebra must be performed on a digital computer.

The main advantage to this algorithm is that it can provide a very accurate solution to a continuous time problem of large dimension due to the use of mathematical programming techniques. It has been demonstrated in (3) for a minimum fuel problem, that a discrete model of a million increments would have to be made to acquire the same accuracy provided by the generalized programming algorithm.

References

(1) Dantzig, G. B., Linear Programming and Extensions, Princeton University Press, (1966).

(2) Dantzig, G. B., "Linear Control Processes and Mathematical Programming," J. SIAM Control, Vol. 4, (1966).

(3) Jizmagian, G. S., "Generalized Programming Solution of Continuous Time Linear System Optimal Control Problems," Ph.D. Thesis, Stanford University, Stanford, California, (1968).

(4) Pontryagin, L. S., V. G. Boltyanskii, R. V. Gamkrelidze, and E. F. Mishenko, The Mathematical Theory of Optimal Processes, Interscience, (1962).

(5) Dantzig, G. S., and R. W. Cottle, "Complementary Pivot Theory of Mathematical Programming," Linear Algebra and Its Applications 1, (1968).

(6) Van Slyke, R. M., "Mathematical Programming and Optimal Control," Ph.D. Thesis, University of California, Berkeley, (1965).

PENALIZATION TECHNIQUES FOR OPTIMAL CONTROL PROBLEMS GOVERNED BY PARTIAL DIFFERENTIAL EQUATIONS

P.KENNETH*, M.SIBONY**, J.P.YVON*

* Institut de Recherche d'Informatique et d'Automatique (I.R.I.A.), 78 - Rocquencourt, France.
** Université de Paris, Faculté des Sciences, Paris, France.

Introduction. The concept of penalty functions was introduced by R.Courant (1). The idea of accounting for the dynamics of the system via penalty terms was suggested to us by J.L.Lions (2). A further contribution in this direction is due to A.V.Balakrishnan (3). We begin with the theory of penalization for convex programs on a Hilbert space, basing ourselves on the work of E.J.Beltrami (4), and furnish the necessary extensions and generalizations which enable us to treat optimal control problems governed by partial differential equations (see also A.Bensoussan, P.Kenneth (5)). Finally, we apply the procedure to a particular example and exhibit the numerical results obtained.

Theory. Let W be a Hilbert space, and consider the $m+1$ functionals $J(v)$, $g_1(v), \ldots, g_m(v)$, defined on W, with the following properties :

$J(v)$ is lower semi-continuous (l.s.c.), (1)

$J(v)$ is strictly convex, (2)

$J(v) \to +\infty$ as $\|v\| \to \infty$ (3)

$g_j(v)$ is convex, $j = 1,\ldots,m$; $g_j(v) \geq 0$, $j = 1, \ldots, r$, (4)

$g_j(v)$ is l.s.c. , $j = 1,\ldots,m$. (5)

Define the set $X \subset W$:

$$X = \left\{ v \in W \;\middle|\; \begin{array}{ll} g_j(v) = 0 , & j = 1,\ldots,r \\ g_j(v) \leq 0 , & j = r+1,\ldots,m \end{array} \right\} (0 \leq r \leq m) . \tag{6}$$

Introduce the functions $H_j : W \to R$, defined by

$$H_j \equiv 1 \text{ , for } j = 1,\ldots,r \tag{7}$$

$$H_j(v) = \begin{cases} 1 , \text{ if } g_j(v) > 0 \\ 0 , \text{ if } g_j(v) \leq 0 \end{cases} \text{, for } j = r+1,\ldots,m \tag{8}$$

$$\text{Let } g(v) = \sum_{j=1}^{m} H_j(v)\, g_j^2(v) . \tag{9}$$

The functional $g(v)$ is non-negative, and, by hypotheses (4) and

(5), it is convex and l.s.c.
We have

$$X = \{ v \in W \mid g(v) = 0 \}. \tag{10}$$

The problem is to find $u \in X$, such that

$$J(u) = \inf_{v \in X} J(v) . \tag{11}$$

By hypotheses (1),(2) and (3), and since X is a closed convex subset of W, there exists a unique $u \in X$ satisfying (11) (We assume $X \neq \emptyset$).

For $\varepsilon > 0$, let

$$J_\varepsilon(v) = J(v) + \tfrac{1}{\varepsilon} g(v) . \tag{12}$$

For each $\varepsilon > 0$, there exists a unique element u_ε such that

$$J_\varepsilon(u_\varepsilon) = \inf_{v \in W} J_\varepsilon(v) . \tag{13}$$

We are interested in the behaviour of the sequence u_ε as $\varepsilon \to 0$. Thus, the idea of penalization is to replace the problem of the minimization of $J(v)$ on X by the problem of the minimization of $J_\varepsilon(v)$ on the whole space W. That is, to replace a minimization problem with constraints by a sequence of minimization problems without constraints.

Theorem (1). Let $J(v)$, $g_j(v)$, $j = 1,\dots,m$, satisfy hypotheses (1) - (5). Then the sequence u_ε defined by (12) and (13) converges weakly to a unique $u \in X$ verifying (11).

The following corollary is useful for the application to optimal control problems.

Corollary(1). Let $J(v)$, $g_j(v)$, $j=1,\dots,m$, satisfy hypotheses (1),(2),(4) and (5). Suppose there exists $\lambda > 0$ such that $J(v) + \frac{1}{\lambda} g(v) \to +\infty$ as $\| v \| \to \infty$. Suppose there exists a unique $u \in X$ satisfying (11). Then, for all $\varepsilon > 0$, $\varepsilon \leq \lambda$, there exists a unique element u_ε satisfying (13), and the sequence u_ε converges weakly to u, as $\varepsilon \to 0$.

For strong convergence, sufficient conditions are given by Corollary (2). Let $a(v,w)$ be a continuous bilinear functional on $W \times W$, with the property that there exists $\alpha > 0$ such that $a(v,v) \geq \alpha \| v \|_W^2$ for all $v \in W$. Let $L(v)$ be a continuous linear functional on W. If, in addition to the hypotheses of corollary (1) for all $v \in W$, $J(v) + \frac{1}{\lambda} g(v) \geq a(v,v) - 2L(v)$; Then the sequence u_ε converges strongly to u, as $\varepsilon \to 0$.

The proofs of theorem (1) and corollaries (1) and (2) are given in (6).

Remark (1). Suppose X' is another closed convex set belonging to W, and $X' \cap X \neq \emptyset$. Then, under the hypotheses of corollary (2), $u_\varepsilon \in X'$ such that $J_\varepsilon(u_\varepsilon) = \inf_{v \in X'} J_\varepsilon(v)$ converges strongly to u, minimizing $J(v)$ on $X \cap X'$.

We now introduce a different approach which enables us to treat certain non linear control problems.

Let W be a uniformly convex (reflexive) Banach space, and W' its dual space. Let $J(v)$ satisfy (1)(2) and (3). In addition, $J(v)$ is Gateaux-differentiable ($J' : W \to W'$), and J' satisfies: For all $v, w \in W$, the mapping $t \to (J'(v - tv + tw), v - w)$ (14) is continuous for $t \in [0,1]$ (hemicontinuity), and

$$(J'(v) - J'(w), v - w) \geq (\varphi(\|v\|) - \varphi(\|w\|)(\|v\| - \|w\|), \quad (15)$$

for all $v, w \in W$; where $\varphi : R^+ \to R$ is strictly increasing and such that $\lim_{r \to \infty} \varphi(r) = +\infty$.

Let $B : W \to W'$, be a hemicontinuous operator such that $(Bv - Bw, v - w) \geq 0$, for all $v, w \in W$ (Monotone).

Define $X = \{ v \in W \mid Bv = 0 \}$ (16)

<u>Theorem</u> (2). Let $J(v)$ satisfy (1)(2),(3),(14) and (15). Let X he defined by (16). Then

(a) There exists a unique $u \in X$ such that

$$J(u) = \inf_{v \in X} J(v) .$$

(b) For all $\varepsilon > 0$, the equation

$$J'(v) + \frac{1}{\varepsilon} Bv = 0 \quad (17)$$

admits a unique solution $u_\varepsilon \in W$.

(c) u_ε tends strongly to u , as $\varepsilon \to 0$.

The proof of theorem (2) is given in (<u>7</u>) .

<u>Applications</u> . As an exemple of the application of penalization techniques to optimal control problems, we consider the following.

Let Ω be a bounded open set in R^n with regular boundary Γ . $T \in]0, +\infty[$, $Q = \Omega \times]0,T[$, $\Sigma = \Gamma \times]0,T[$.

$V = H^1(\Omega)$; $\mathcal{U} = L^2(\Sigma)$, (control space). Let $A(t)$ be a differential elliptic operator of the second order, satisfying : there exist $\alpha, \beta > 0$ such that $(Ay,y) + \beta \|y\|^2_{L^2(\Omega)} \geq \alpha \|y\|^2_V$, for all $y \in V$ and $t \in]0,T[$.

We consider the system description :

$$\begin{aligned} &\frac{\partial y}{\partial t} + A(t)y = f \quad , \quad f \in L^2(Q) \\ &\frac{\partial y}{\partial \nu_A} = v \quad , \text{ on } \Sigma \; , \quad v \in L^2(\Sigma) \\ &y(x,0) = y_0(x) \quad , \quad y_0 \in L^2(\Omega) \; . \end{aligned} \quad (18)$$

($\frac{\partial}{\partial \nu_A}$ denotes the "normal derivative in accordance with A ". See J.L.Lions, E.Magenes (<u>8</u>), for a precise definition).

Let

$$J(v) = \int_0^T \int_\Omega | y(x,t;v) - z_d(x,t) |^2 \, dxdt + \gamma \|v\|^2_{\mathcal{U}} \quad , \quad (19)$$

where γ is a positive constant and $z_d(x,t) \in L^2(Q)$ is given.

The problem is to find $u \in \mathcal{U}_{ad}$, such that

$$J(u) = \inf_{v \in \mathcal{U}_{ad}} J(v) , \tag{20}$$

where $\mathcal{U}_{ad}$ is a closed convex subset of $\mathcal{U}$.

This problem has a unique solution (cf. J.L.Lions (2)) .

We want to consider the system equations, boundary-initial conditions, Eqs.(18), as constraints expressible in the form (10) or (16). For this purpose, we define the Hilbert space

$$Y = \left\{ y \in L^2(0,T;V) \mid \frac{\partial y}{\partial t} + Ay \in L^2(Q) \; ; \frac{\partial y}{\partial \nu_A} \in L^2(\Sigma) \right\} , \tag{21}$$

with the norm

$$\| y \|_Y = \left(\|y\|^2_{L^2(0,T;V)} + \left\| \frac{\partial y}{\partial t} + Ay \right\|^2_{L^2(Q)} + \left\| \frac{\partial y}{\partial \nu_A} \right\|^2_{L^2(\Sigma)} \right)^{\frac{1}{2}} . \tag{22}$$

Then $W = Y \times \mathcal{U}$, with elements (y,v). (23)

Let $X_1 = \{ (y,v) \in W \mid y,v \text{ satisfy } (18) \}$ (24)

and $X_2 = Y \times \mathcal{U}_{ad}$. (25)

Then, the (closed, convex) constraining set is

$$X = X_1 \cap X_2 . \tag{26}$$

In the case in which it is feasible (computationally) to "project" on X_2(e.g.linear constraints), we consider

$$\begin{aligned} J_\varepsilon (y,v) = {} & \| y - z_d\|^2_{L^2(Q)} + \gamma \|v\|^2_{\mathcal{U}} + \frac{1}{\varepsilon_1}\left\|\frac{\partial y}{\partial t} + Ay - f\right\|^2_{L^2(Q)} \\ & + \frac{1}{\varepsilon_2}\left\|\frac{\partial y}{\partial \nu_A} - v\right\|^2_{L^2(\Sigma)} + \frac{1}{\varepsilon_3}\|y(.,0) - y_0\|^2_{L^2(\Omega)} , \end{aligned} \tag{27}$$

and seek the sequence of couples $(y_\varepsilon , u_\varepsilon)$ (for each ε, $\varepsilon \to 0$) minimizing J_ε on X_2 . In accordance with remark (1), we obtain the strong convergence of $(y_\varepsilon , u_\varepsilon)$ to the desired solution $(y(u),u)$ of (20) .

Remark (2) . For an iterative minimization method well suited to treat the above problem see M.Sibony (9) .

In general, we are concerned with the case

$$\mathcal{U}_{ad} = \{ v \in \mathcal{U} \mid h(v) = 0 \} , \tag{28}$$

where $h(v)$ is of the form given in (9) .

X may be written

$$X = \{ w \in W \mid g(w) = 0 \} , \tag{29}$$

where

$$\begin{aligned} g(y,v) = {} & \left\|\frac{\partial y}{\partial t} + Ay - f\right\|^2_{L^2(Q)} + \left\|\frac{\partial y}{\partial \nu_A} - v\right\|^2_{\mathcal{U}} \\ & + \|y(.,0) - y_0\|^2_{L^2(\Omega)} + h(v) . \end{aligned} \tag{30}$$

Thus, defining $J(y,v) = \| y - Z_d \|^2_{L^2(Q)} + \gamma \| v \|^2_{\mathcal{U}}$, we may apply corollary (2).

Remark (3). In the framework of theorem (2), we have $B = g'(w)$.

Numerical Example . The example we have treated is of the form (18), (19) in one-dimensional x - space :

$$\frac{\partial y}{\partial t} - \frac{\partial^2 y}{\partial x^2} = f \ , \quad 0<x<1 \ , \quad 0<t<T \ (=1) \tag{31}$$

$$- \frac{\partial y}{\partial x}(0,t) = v(t) \ ; \ \frac{\partial y}{\partial x}(1,t) = 0 \ , \quad 0<t<T$$

$$y(x,0) = y_0(x) \ , \quad 0<x<1 \ .$$

$$\text{with } J(v) = \int_0^T \int_0^1 |y(x,t;v) - Z_d(x,t)|^2 dx\, dt + \gamma \int_0^T |v(t)|^2 dt. \tag{32}$$

$$\text{Here, } J_\varepsilon(y,v) = \int_0^T \int_0^1 |y(x,t) - Z_d(x,t)|^2 dx\, dt + \gamma \int_0^T |v(t)|^2 dt$$

$$+ \frac{1}{\varepsilon_1} \int_0^T \int_0^1 \left| \frac{\partial y}{\partial t}(x,t) - \frac{\partial^2 y}{\partial x^2}(x,t) - f(x,t) \right|^2 dx\, dt$$

$$+ \frac{1}{\varepsilon_2} \int_0^T \left| \frac{\partial y}{\partial x}(0,t) + v(t) \right|^2 dt + \frac{1}{\varepsilon_3} \int_0^T \left| \frac{\partial y}{\partial x}(1,t) \right|^2 dt$$

$$+ \frac{1}{\varepsilon_4} \int_0^1 |y(x,0) - y_0(x)|^2 dx \ . \tag{33}$$

We have considered two cases, without and with constraints on the control, respectively. In the first case ($\mathcal{U}_{ad} = \mathcal{U}$), Z_d, f, γ , y_0 , were determined so as to yield the optimal control

$$u(t) = 0.5(1 - t) \ , \tag{34}$$

and the corresponding state

$$y(x,t) = 0.25(x^2 - 2x + 5)(1 - t) + 1 \ . \tag{35}$$

In the second case, we chose

$$\mathcal{U}_{ad} = \{ v \in L^2(0,1) \mid v(t) \geq 0.25 \text{ a.e.} \} \ , \tag{36}$$

and thus minimize

$$J_\varepsilon(y,v) + \frac{1}{\varepsilon_5} \int_0^T H(v(t))(v(t) - 0.25)^2 dt \tag{37}$$

with

$$H(v(t)) = \begin{cases} 0 \ , & \text{if} \quad v(t) \geq 0.25 \\ 1 \ , & \text{if} \quad v(t) < 0.25 \end{cases} \tag{38}$$

Numerical Results . Some numerical results have been obtained for the above examples. The state and control functions were approximated by step functions. The derivatives (in x and t) were taken in the sense of finite differences. For all details concerning the convergence of the discretization scheme, we refer to J.P. Yvon (10). In this manner, the penalized functionals (33) and (37) take the form of functions on R^n, which were minimized by the conjugate gradient method.

For a given set of ε's and a discretization step of one tenth in both x and t coordinates $(h = k = 1/10)$, the results are exhibited in Fig. 1 . In Fig. 2, we illustrate further results pertaining to the unconstrained case (33), for various discretization steps. A comparison of the relative error on the state (for the unconstrained case with fixed discretization steps) for various ε's is given in Fig. 3.

The numerical results we have obtained indicate the feasibility of treating optimal control problems governed by partial differential equations by penalization techniques. If is our belief, that the major remaining work is the improvement of finite-dimensional minimization procedures necessary for the method, since we must in general deal with functions of a large number of variables.

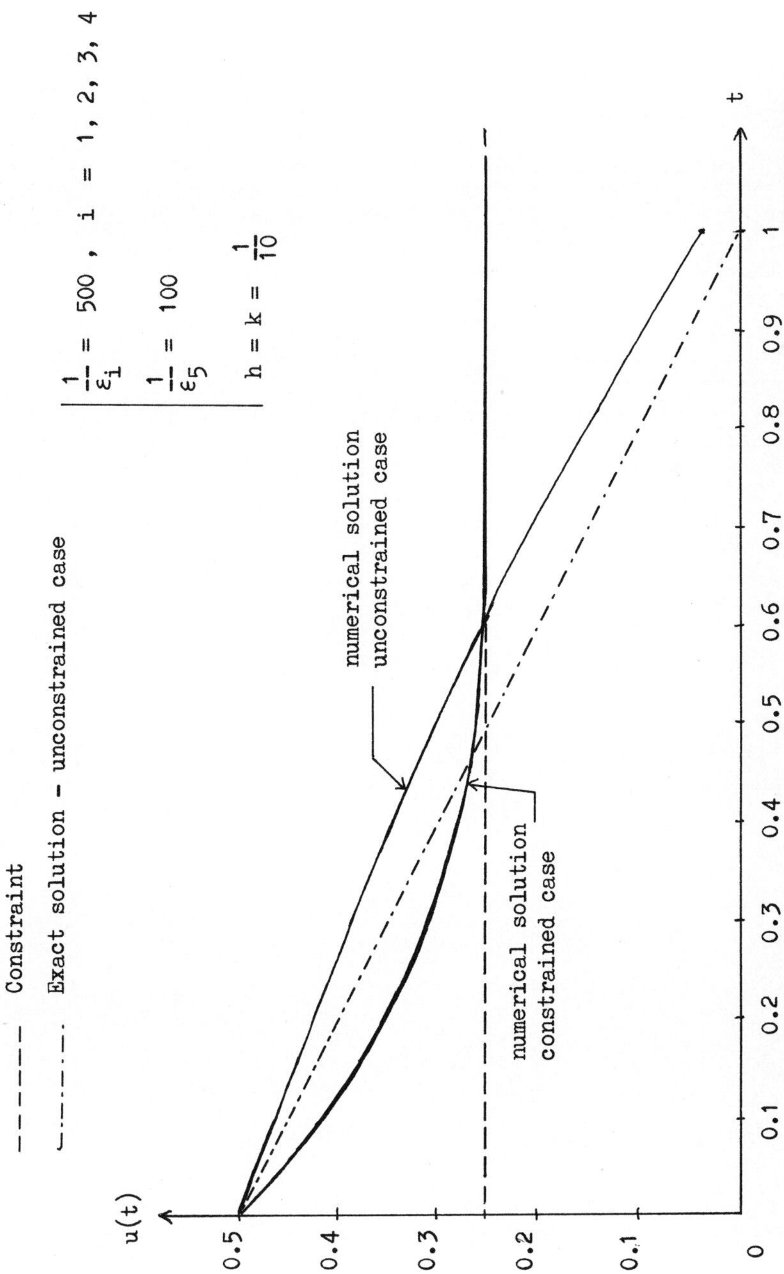

Constraint
Exact solution - unconstrained case
$\frac{1}{\varepsilon_i} = 500$, $i = 1, 2, 3, 4$
$\frac{1}{\varepsilon_5} = 100$
$h = k = \frac{1}{10}$
numerical solution unconstrained case
numerical solution constrained case
u(t)
t
0.5
0.4
0.3
0.2
0.1
0
0.1
0.2
0.3
0.4
0.5
0.6
0.7
0.8
0.9
1

Fig. 1

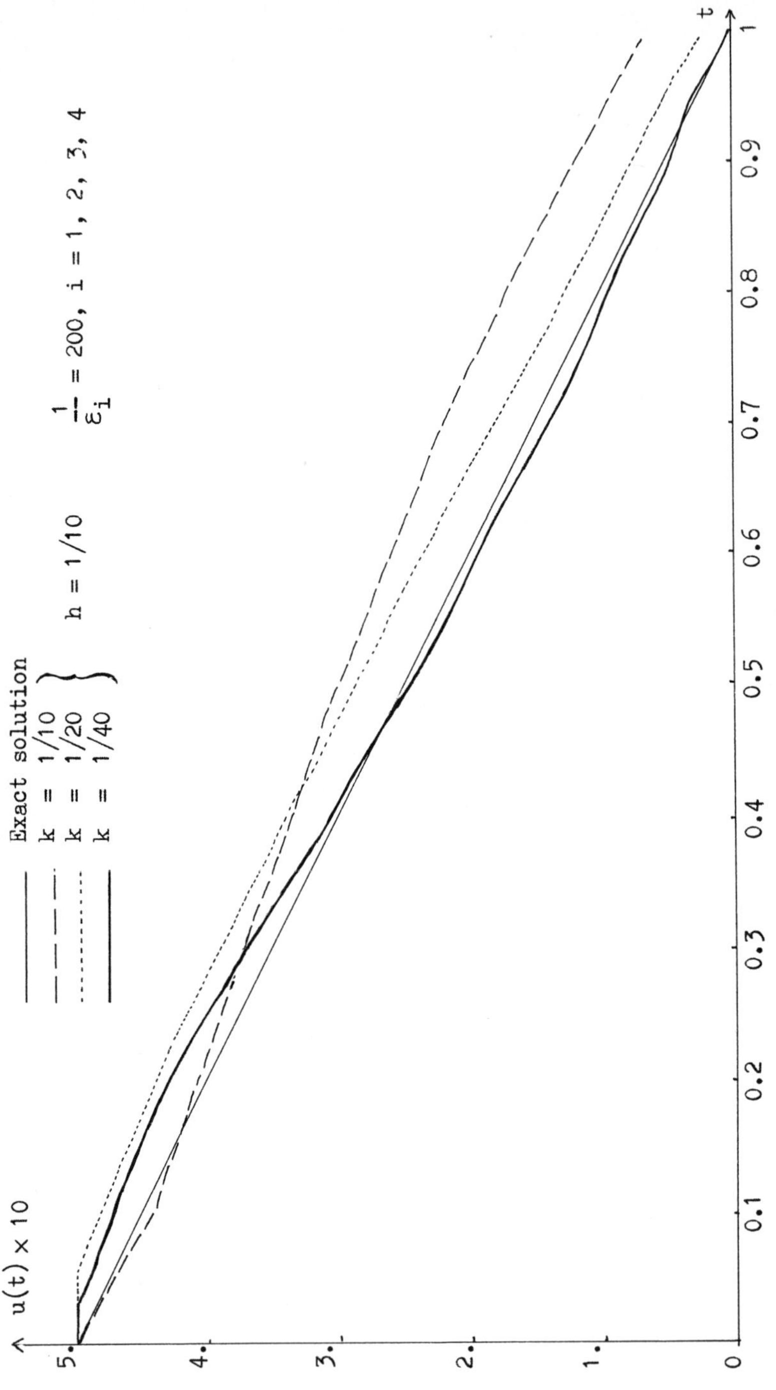

Fig.2. Control - Unconstrained Case.

$$\varepsilon = \varepsilon_i,\ i = 1,\ 2,\ 3,\ 4.$$

$$h = 1/10$$

$$k = 1/40$$

$$\delta(t) = h \sum_{j=0}^{10} \frac{\left| y_j(t) - S_j(t) \right|}{\left| S_j(t) \right|}$$

$$S_j(t) = S(jh, t) = \text{exact solution.}$$

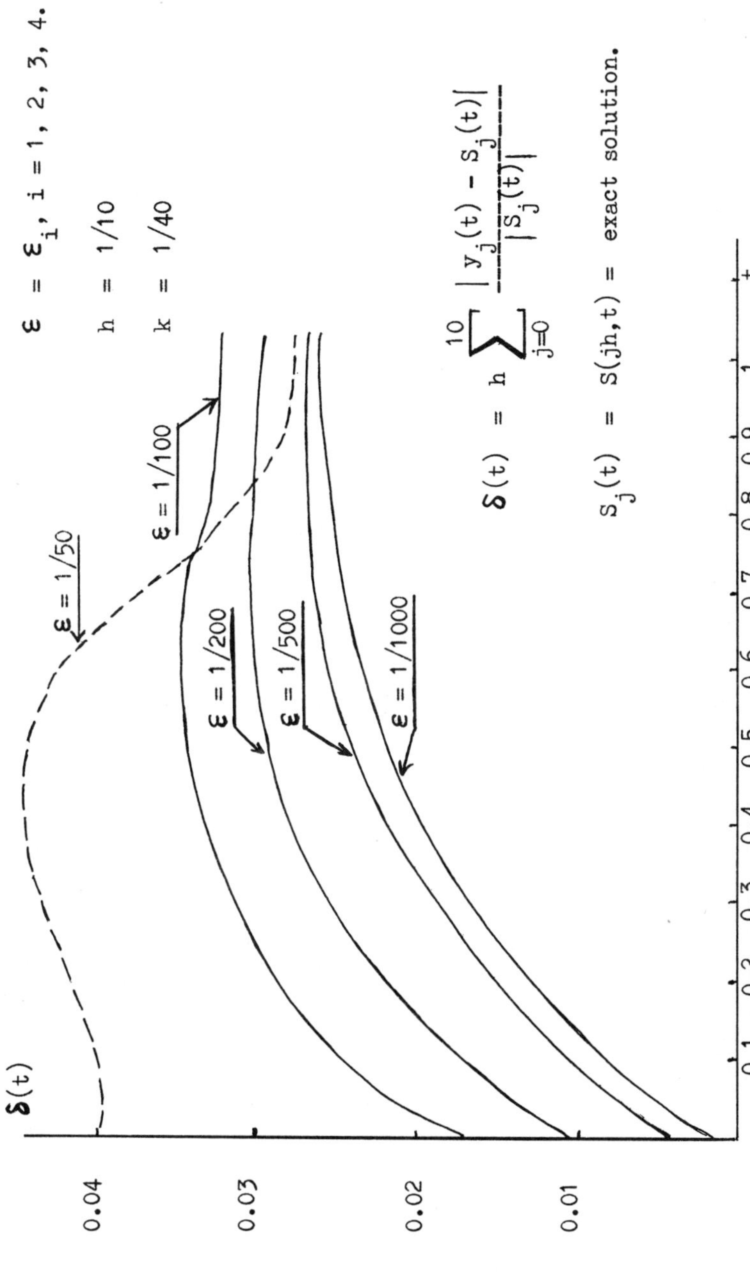

Fig. 3. Error on the State. Unconstrained Case

REFERENCES

(1) R. COURANT	Bull. Am. Math. Soc., 49, 1-23 (1943).
(2) J.L.LIONS	"Contrôle Optimal de Systèmes gouvernés par des Equations aux Dérivées Partielles" Dunod, Paris, 1968.
(3) A.V.BALAKRISHNAN	SIAM J. Control, 6, 149-173 (1968).
(4) E.J.BELTRAMI	J.Computer and System Sciences, 1, 323-329 (1967).
(5) A.BENSOUSSAN and P.KENNETH	Revue d'Informatique et de Recherche Opérationnelle, 13 (1969).
(6) P.KENNETH, M.SIBONY and J.P.YVON	Cahiers de l'I.R.I.A. (to be published).
(7) M.SIBONY	Contrôle des Systèmes gouvernés par des Equations aux Dérivées Partielles (to be published).
(8) J.L.LIONS and E.MAGENES	"Problèmes aux limites non-homogènes et Applications" Dunod, PARIS, 1968
(9) M.SIBONY	Thesis, Paris (to be published).
(10) J.P.YVON	Cahiers de l'I.R.I.A.(to be published)

SEQUENTIAL DECISIONS WITH RANDOMLY MANY STAGES: SIMULATION RESULTS

Allen Klinger
Department of Engineering
University of California
Los Angeles, California

1. Introduction

This paper discusses a special structure in dynamic programming in which a series of sequential decisions is made at random points in time which are generated by a Poisson process. In this model, decisions in no way affect subsequent random decision times (this, and other simplifications discussed below, facilitates computation of the optimum return functions). The result is a structure with random "planning horizon," a case intermediate between the finite and infinite stage models. At any given decision time the number of future decision times is a Poisson variable; the expected number of decisions or stages which will occur in the future is known at each decision time: this information characterizes the Poisson process governing arrivals of random decision times. The decisions themselves are restricted in nature. We consider discrete inventory expenditure decisions with expected returns given by known probabilistic properties of the elements in stock.

Section 2 describes a particular problem with randomly many stages and its recursive formulation. Section 3 compares the solution and strategy functions to theoretical results. Section 4 describes simulation experiments and their bearing on sensitivity.

2. The Problem and the Recursive Formulation

A system analysis problem which occurs in many contexts involves apportioning a fixed number of units among a random number of "calls." When success of the system in handling a given call can be enhanced by use of more units the problem becomes one of striking a balance between better performance at a given call and retaining ability to deal with future decision stages. The particular problem of this paper is of this form where individual units function ("success") at random with the same probability. Here we need to find decision rules to maximize returns attainable with n units of inventory, p=1-q unit success probability, and x=m(t) expected Poisson decision-stages in (0, t), given m continuous and all random events mutually independent. Several return criteria were examined in (1). The simulation results presented here are for overall system effectiveness in terms of probability that at least one unit succeeds at each random decision stage which occurs, consequently, the following deals solely with the optimum return criterion $P_n^*(t)$, the maximum probability at least one allotted unit succeeds at every Poisson arrival in (0, t). This criterion satisfies (1) the recursive relationship

$$P_n^*(t) = e^{-m(t)} + \int_0^{m(t)} \max_{i=1(1)n} \left\{ (1-q^i) P_{n-i}^*(\tau) \right\} e^{-[m(t)-m(\tau)]} dm(\tau) \tag{1}$$

That is, $e^{-m(t)}$, the probability of no decision-stages in (0, t) plus an expectation over τ, the time the first decision was required as "time-remaining" decreased from t. Of course, $1-q^i$ is the probability of at least one success in i trials. Hence the bracketed term is a combination of "single-stage-return" and best future return from a new state. Thus the recursion relation is of the renewal or optimality principle form. The initial condition

$$P_0^*(t) = e^{-m(t)} \tag{2}$$

is assumed.

Although time-dependence of the mean number of decision stages introduces generality in the distribution function for their arrival times, the maximum probability $P_n^*(t)$ depends on t only through the expected number of stages x=m(t), (1). Hence the condensed expressions

$$P_n^*(t) = e^{-x} \Phi(n, x) \tag{3}$$

$$\Phi(n, x) = 1 + \int_0^x \max_{i=1(1)n} \{(1-q^i) \Phi(n-i, y)\} dy \tag{4}$$

$$\Phi(0, x) = 1 = \Phi(n, 0) \tag{5}$$

The strategy functions $\Psi(n, x)$ are step functions: they are defined pointwise as the smallest integer that attains the maximum in the integrand of Eq. (2). Approximate numerical integration solutions of Eq. (3) are presented in (2); they indicate that $\Psi(n, x)$ is a monotonic nonincreasing function of x.

The set of strategy functions comprise a decision rule for the random number of stages. If the first decision is at T_L, the stock at the next decision (time T_{L-1}) is $n - \Psi(n, m(T_L)) = N_{L-1}$. Here capital Roman letters are random variables: thus there are L decision stages on (0, t), at times $T_i (i=1, \ldots, L)$, with random state N_{L-1} units of inventory resulting from the decision at T_L. The next decision uses the function $\Psi(N_{L-1}, \bullet)$.

3. Comparisons with Theoretical Results

From the preceding it is clear that the recursive equations solve a special type of discrete inventory allocation problem. Highly accurate approximate solutions of these equations were obtained by numerical integration (1). Comparison with related theoretical work (3) - (8) shows that the key simplifying step is choice of a criterion requiring "at least one" unit at each stage to accrue return. This effectively restricts the decision variable domain to exclude zero, yielding optimal return functions which satisfy simpler recurrence relations than the functional equations appearing in (3) - (8).

Several aspects of the problem of Section 2 are encompassed by the earlier theoretical literature. The analysis in (3) "The Inventory Problem" (2. Case of One Time Interval, p. 189) includes our problem as a special case with no "reorder decision" (in our case stock decreases in applications) and no "allot-zero-inventory decision." Likewise the theoretical framework of (8) where decision stages are generated by a renewal process, is sufficiently general to include the "random number of stage" and "stage-decision impinges on actual number of stages" aspects of this problem. (Special state transition probabilities and renewal time probability distributions would have to be used.) The finite-time case functional equation (8), pp. 943-944, Eqs. (10) and (11) relates most closely to the results given here. However, no numerical solutions are presented in (8), and it is clear that the model of this paper is preferable for computations.

One further aspect of the theoretical literature should be mentioned. As the mean number of decisions, $x \to \infty$, use of the optimal strategy functions will almost surely lead to the state "failure for the overall decision process" for some time in $(0, t)$ whatever n may be. This will occur either by stage failure — all allotted units fail at some stage — or stock depletion — no inventory remains but an additional decision is required:

$$N_R = 0, \quad 1 < R \leqq L, \quad 0 < T_R \leqq t \tag{6}$$

Hence it should be possible to put our model into the framework of (6) and apply a result there (Theorem 4, (d): pp. 722, 723) to the more cumbersome model which will be obtained. That result applied "when there is a single terminal stage s^* which is certain to be reached eventually, no matter where we start or which policy we use, and which can never be left once reached" ((8), p. 725) — exactly our case.

4. Simulation Experiments

One key question about the model presented here which could best be answered by stochastic simulation experiments (Monte Carlo methods) was "How sensitive are the computed maximum success probabilities $P_n^*(x)$ to variations in the parameters?" The results of this section concern sensitivity to misestimation of x, the parameter which represents "nature;" q and n are presumably under the control of the decision-maker. Throughout the following a homogeneous Poisson process is assumed $\left(x = m(t) = \lambda t\right)$.

The experiments were based on the strategy functions Ψ calculated from the recursive expressions. The procedure used a discrete approximation to the continuous time model based on a fine partition of the time axis. In all cases the initial time was $t = 10$ and intervals of length $\Delta t = 0.01$ were used. Likewise throughout the following $q=p=0.5$, and $x=5$. Time was decreased according to

$$t_i = t - i \bullet \Delta t \quad , \quad i = 1(1)1000 \tag{7}$$

Here 1000 independent choices of a random variable representing "decision-required" or "no decision required" at time t_i were made. The outcomes corresponded to Bernoulli trials with decision-required-probability

$$x \cdot \frac{\Delta t}{t} = 0.005 \tag{8}$$

With these values the Poisson theorem applies, the Poisson process is closely approximated by the binomial, and the sequence of Bernoulli trials we generate simulates the continuous model presented here ((9), pp. 71-74).

One trial of an experiment to estimate $P_n^*(x)$ applied the decision specified by Ψ at times where a "decision required" random outcome had occurred. At such a time a second Bernoulli trial was simulated. The success probability was $(1-q^i)$ with i given by Ψ, the current inventory N, and the decision time T. An experiment consisted of approximately 500 trials. The number of trials which achieved the goal "reach t=0 with success at each stage where a decision is required" divided by the total number of trials gave our estimate of $P_n^*(x)$, $\hat{P}_n(x)$. We will refer to achieving this goal as "overall success." Sensitivity experiments employed Ψ for values $\hat{x}$ different from x, with decision arrivals of mean number x generated as above. In these experiments the estimate of overall success probability is denoted by $\hat{P}_n(\hat{x})$. The experiments were performed on a system 360 computer using a FORTRAN code and a standard random number generator. We made no provision for repeating the various trials by recording the observed random numbers. Any variations in the actual sequence from the ideal uniform distribution were accepted as within the error caused by using a discrete approximation to the continuous model. Hence the results should be regarded as "crude Monte Carlo estimates." Nevertheless as Table 1. shows, good agreement between the approximate numerical integration calculated values P_n^* and our simulation estimates $\hat{P}_n$ was observed for x=5, n=5(5)20. The sensitivity results are presented in the following series of four figures. Figures 1 and 3 include an additional estimate: $\hat{P}_n$ from a uniform allocation of one unit at each decision stage. This statistic was easily computed with the basic simulation program: it is displayed here because variations in the plotted values show the effect of run-to-run fluctuations in the random number generator. (For a given n and x there is a definite value of success probability from a uniform strategy: the analytic expression for this value appears in (1), p. 175.) Such fluctuations can cause anomalies in the sensitivity results.

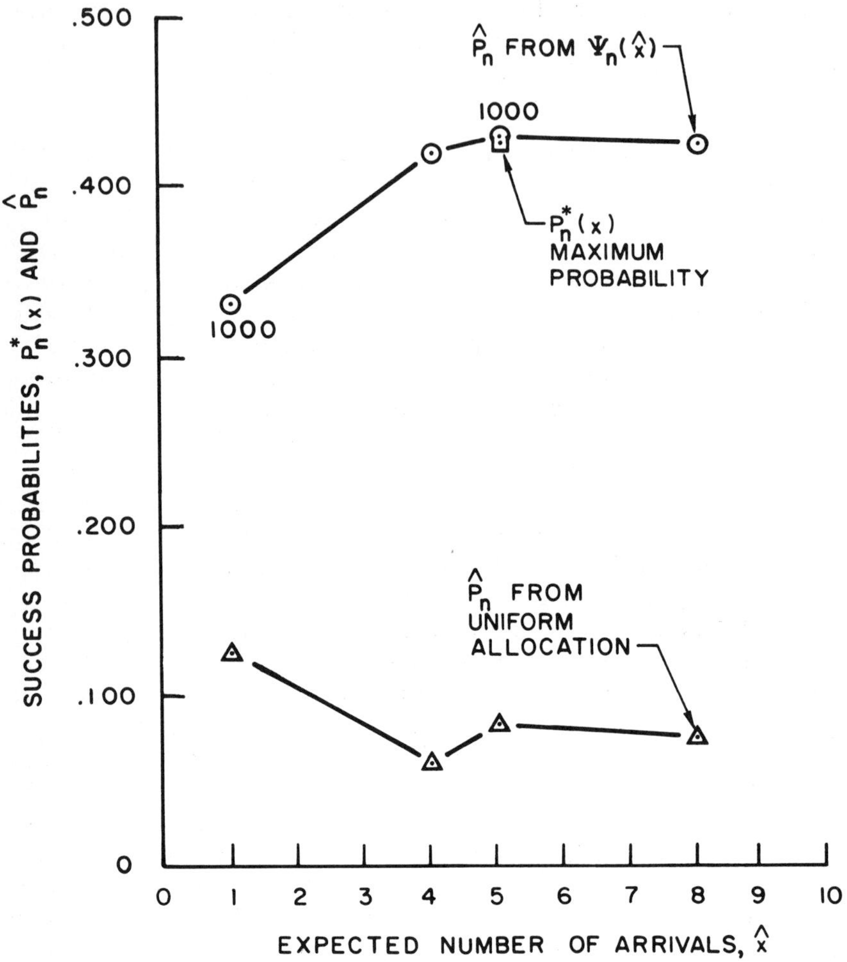

Number of units available, n = 15
Actual expected arrivals, x = 5
Experimental points based on 500 trials or number displayed

Fig. 1. Success Probability Versus Expected Number of Arrivals: n=15.

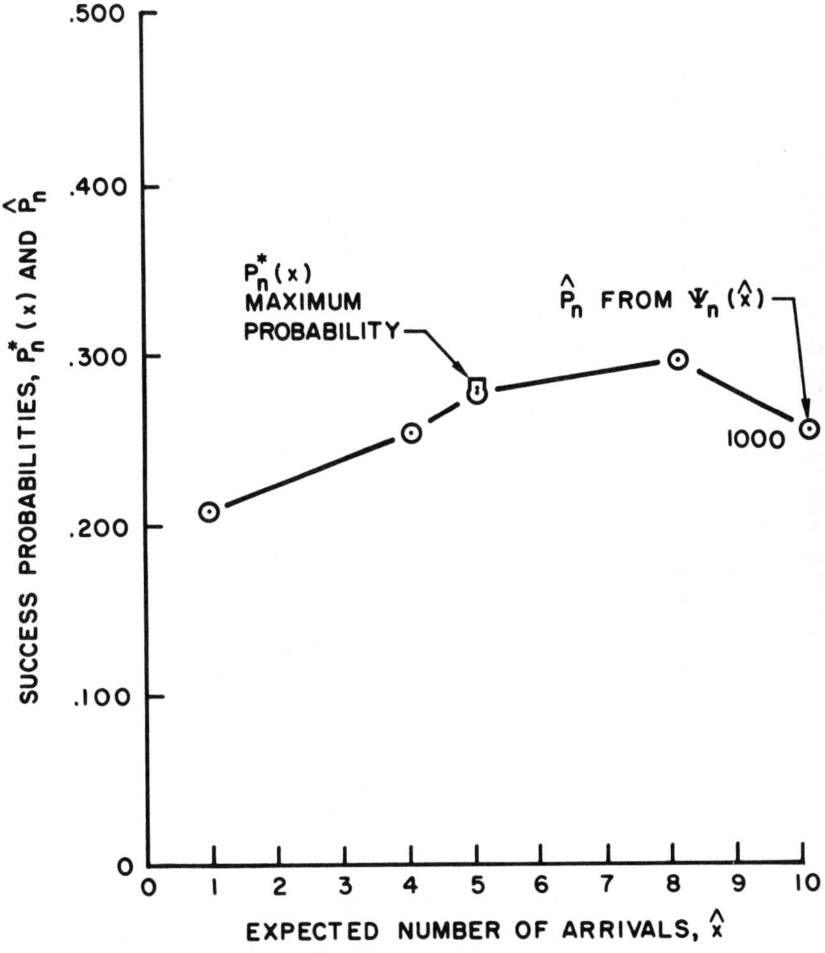

Number of units available, n = 10
Actual expected arrivals, x = 5
Experimental points based on 500 trials or number displayed

Fig. 2. Success Probability Versus Expected Number of Arrivals: n=10.

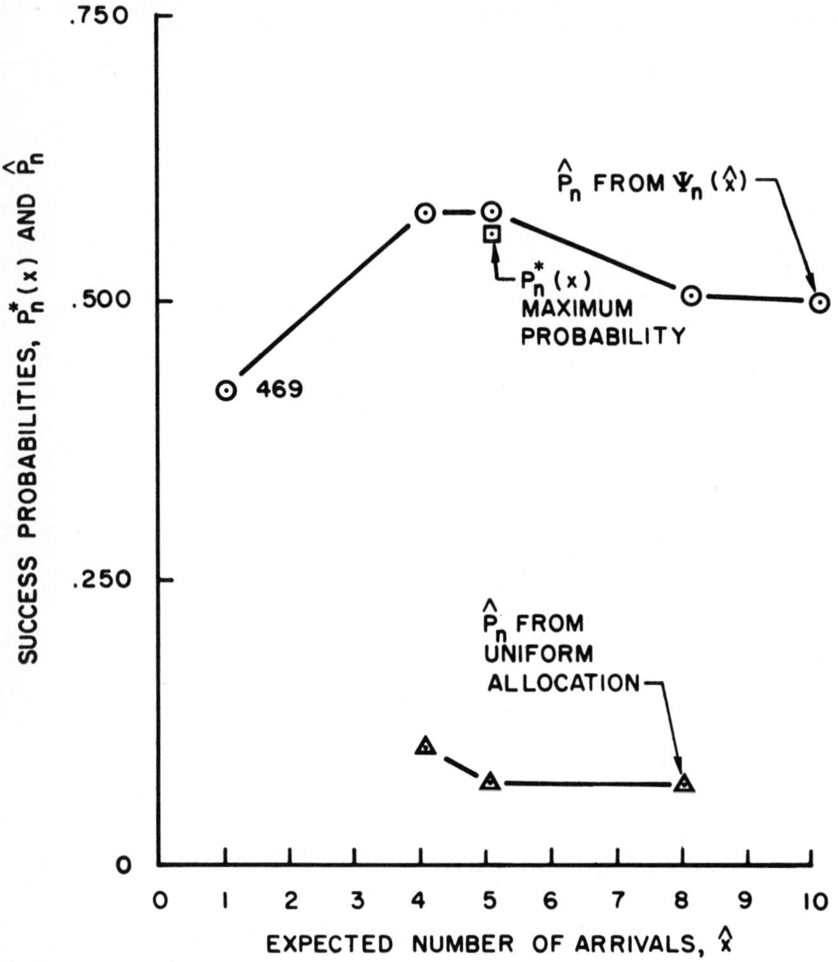

Number of units available, n = 20
Actual expected arrivals, x = 5
Experimental points based on 500 trials or number displayed

Fig. 3. Success Probability Versus Expected Number of Arrivals: n=20.

Table 1. A Comparison of the Maximum Success Probabilities $P_n^*(x)$ and $\hat{P}_n(x)$

$x = 5$ $\quad q = p = 0.5$

n	CALCULATED $P_n^*(x)$	SIMULATED $\hat{P}_n(x)$	NO. TRIALS
5	.1224	.108	1500
10	.2762	.274	500
15	.4296	.434	1000
20	.5609	.578	500

In Figure 2 there is a larger $\hat{P}_n$ at $\hat{x}=8$ than at $x=x=5$; this is unlikely and probably due to some source of statistical error. The general nature of the sensitivity results is to confirm that misinformation about the expected number of decision stages degrades performance but that the degradation is not severe. Thus Figure 4 shows at worst a loss of 25% from the maximum success probability $P_n^*(x)$ caused by an 80% error in $\hat{x}$ ($\hat{x}=1$, $x=5$).

5. Conclusion

We have described a special problem with randomly many stages and a recursive solution to the problem. The relation of our work to theoretical papers in sequential decision and inventory allocation has been considered. A series of simulation experiments which were carried out to determine the sensitivity of our model to lack of perfect information were described. Results showing moderate degradation from the maximum possible return which can be achieved with a given inventory were presented for some specific parameter values.

Acknowledgment

This work was partially supported by the Air Force Office of Scientific Research under Grant 68-1408, and the University of California, Los Angeles, under Academic Senate Research Grant 2485. Computer programs were coded and run by Robert Clark.

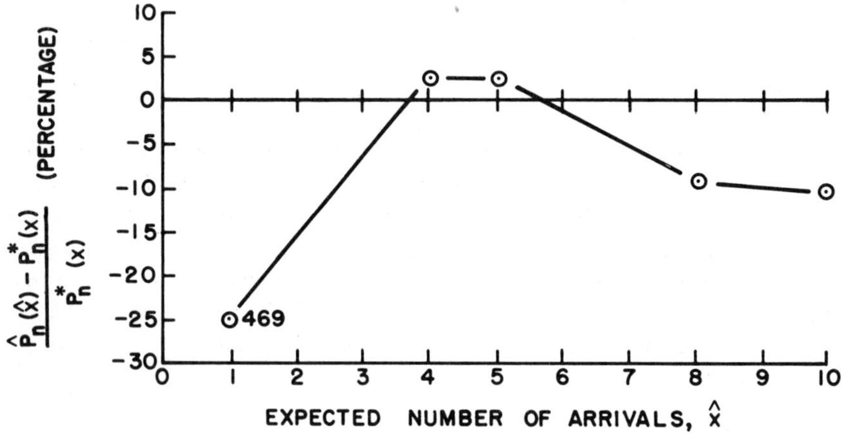

Number of units available, n = 20
Actual expected arrivals, x = 5
Experimental points based on 500 trials or number displayed

Fig. 4. Percent Difference to Maximum Success Probability Versus Estimated Number of Decision Stages.

REFERENCES

1. Klinger, A. and T. A. Brown, "Allocating Unreliable Units to Random Demands," Stochastic Optimization and Control, Ed. by H. F. Karreman, John Wiley and Sons, Inc., New York, 1968, pp. 173-210.

2. Klinger, A., "Stochastic Allocation and System Analysis," submitted to IEEE Transactions on System Science and Cybernetics, 1968.

3. Dvoretzky, A., J. Kiefer, and J. Wolfowitz, "The Inventory Problem: I, Case of Known Distributions of Demand," Econometrica 20, 1957, pp. 187-222.

4. Bellman, R. E., Dynamic Programming, Princeton University Press, 1957.

5. Howard, R. A., Dynamic Programming and Markov Processes, Technology Press and Wiley, New York, 1960.

6. Blackwell, D., "Discrete Dynamic Programming," Ann. Math. Stat. 33, 1962, pp. 719-726.

7. Bellman, R. E. and S. E. Dreyfus, Applied Dynamic Programming, Princeton University, 1962.

8. Jewell, W. S., "Markov-Renewal Programming I and II," Operations Research, Vol. 11, No. 6, 1963, pp. 938-948, 949-971.

9. Papoulis, A., Probability, Random Variables, and Stochastic Processes, McGraw-Hill Book Company, New York, 1965.

APPROXIMATE SEARCH FOR FIXED POINTS

Harold W. Kuhn
Princeton University
Princeton, New Jersey

1. Introduction

The Brouwer Fixed-Point Theorem is, in many ways, a perfect example of a result from pure mathematics that has found application in many different contexts. Its hypotheses are few and its conclusion is easy to understand. The beauty of the theorem is enhanced by an elegant proof due to Knaster, Kuratowski, and Mazurkiewicz (1), which derives the result from a purely combinatorial lemma discovered by Sperner (2). However, as satisfying as this demonstration is, it is non-constructive in character and provides no direct indication of how fixed-points can be calculated.

In recent path-breaking work (3), Scarf has presented an algorithm for computing approximations of fixed-points of continuous mappings of a simplex into itself, based on a combinatorial theorem that is similar in statement to Sperner's Lemma. Scarf proved his theorem by a constructive procedure that is also central to his algorithm. Thus, he has opened the possibility of efficient computation for a class of nonlinear optimization problems that can be cast as fixed-point problems.

The purpose of this paper is to explore some of the connections between Sperner's Lemma and Scarf's Theorem; these connections suggest new algorithms and, it is hoped, shed some useful light on Scarf's work. In order to introduce the investigations, it will be helpful to recall the statement of Sperner's Lemma and the passage to Brouwer's Theorem in 2-dimensions.

Consider a triangle T presented with barycentric coordinates $X = (x_0, x_1, x_2)$, where $x_o \geqq 0$, $x_1 \geqq 0$, $x_2 \geqq 0$ and $x_0 + x_1 + x_2 = 1$. By a <u>proper labeling</u> of T, we shall mean the assignment of label $\ell(X) = 0, 1,$ or 2 to each $X \epsilon T$ such that if $\ell(X) = k$ then $x_k > 0$. (For a triangle, this condition says merely that the three vertices of T are labeled 0, 1, and 2, respectively, and that a point on an edge of T carries the same label as one of the endpoints of the edge.) By a <u>subdivision</u> of T, we shall mean a decomposition of T into smaller triangles such that each edge appearing is the edge of either one or two small triangles. The mesh of a subdivision is the largest diameter of any triangle of the subdivision.

SPERNER'S LEMMA. For any subdivision of T and any proper labeling of its vertices, some small triangle of the subdivision carries a complete set of labels (0, 1, and 2) on its vertices.

The proof of the lemma (for 2-dimensions) follows easily from the fact that any small triangle that does not contain a complete set of labels has an even number of edges labeled by 0 and 1. Thus, if the lemma were false, the total number of such edges on the boundary of T would be even. However, this number is clearly odd.

For the derivation of the Brouwer Fixed-Point Theorem from Sperner's Lemma, let $f: X \rightarrow Y = f(X)$ be a continuous function defined on T into T, that is, such that $y_o \geqq 0$, $y_1 \geqq 0$, $y_2 \geqq 0$ and $y_0 + y_1 + y_2 = 1$ for all $(y_0, y_1, y_2) = f(X)$ for $X \in T$.

BROUWER FIXED-POINT THEOREM. There exists at least one $\bar{X} \in T$ such that $f(\bar{X}) = \bar{X}$.

PROOF. The function f induces a proper labeling of T by the rule: set $\ell(X) = k$ if $y_k \leqq x_k \neq 0$. If more than one index satisfies this condition, choose the smallest.

Choose a sequence of subdivisions of T such that the associated sequence of meshes tends to zero. For each such subdivision, choose a small triangle with a complete set of labels by Sperner's Lemma. Since T is a compact set, for some subsequence, the barycenters of these small triangles converge to a point $\bar{X} \in T$. Since the meshes tend to zero, the three subsequences of the vertices with labels 0, 1, and 2, respectively, also converge to $\bar{X}$. Hence, by the continuity of f, and the definition of the labeling,

$$\bar{y}_k \leqq \bar{x}_k \quad \text{for} \quad k = 0, 1, 2.$$

However

$$\Sigma \bar{y}_k = \Sigma \bar{x}_k = 1$$

and hence

$$\bar{Y} = f(\bar{X}) = \bar{X}. \qquad \text{Q. E. D.}$$

Although this proof leaves little to be desired by way of clarity or simplicity, it raises a very natural question:

In view of the fact that, for "well-behaved" continuous functions, the points of a "small enough" triangle with a complete set of labels "approximate" a fixed point, can such a triangle be found by a systematic and practical search?

Although Scarf has suggested in (3) that the answer is negative, it was his work on primitive sets that provided the clue as to how to answer the question affirmatively. In § 2, the basic combinatorial ideas underlying both the non-constructive existence proofs and the algorithms of systematic search are explained in graph theoretical terms. The classical proof of Sperner's Lemma is derived as a consequence in § 3. A proof of Sperner's Lemma by systematic search is given in § 4, answering the question posed above. A modification of Sperner's Lemma, applying to pseudo-manifolds is presented in § 5, and Scarf's combinatorial theorem is derived as a corollary. A final section describes some standard subdivisions that have been useful in the programming of the algorithms.

2. A Lemma from Graph Theory

The basic idea underlying the existence proofs and algorithms of this paper can be expressed as a very simple lemma in terms of graphs.

Let G be a (nonoriented) graph with vertices v and edges e (connecting pairs of distinct vertices). The degree of a vertex v is the number of edges incident at v.

MAIN LEMMA. Let G be a finite graph with all vertices of degree one or two. Then the number of vertices of degree one is even.

PROOF. This lemma is so obvious that a proof may seem unnecessary. However, let the number of edges be $|E|$ and the number of vertices of degree one and two be $|V_1|$ and $|V_2|$, respectively. Then, counting the incidence of edges with vertices in two ways,

$$2|E| = |V_1| + 2|V_2|.$$

Therefore, $|V_1|$ must be even. Q. E. D.

With a minor modification, this lemma has a number of useful corollaries. Let G denote a finite graph with no vertex of degree greater than two. We shall call G a Sperner graph if every vertex of degree one has been labeled a source or a sink (but not both) and every vertex of degree zero has been labeled as both a source and sink. If we let V_i denote the vertices of degree i, A_i denote the sources of degree i, and B_i denote the sinks of degree i, for i = 0, 1, then $V_0 = A_0 = B_0$ and $V_1 = A_1 \cup B_1$ with $A_1 \cap B_1 = \phi$. If A and B are the sets of sources and sinks, respectively, then $A = A_0 \cup A_1$ and $B = B_0 \cup B_1$. In the following statements, if S is a finite set then $|S|$ denotes the number of elements of S.

COROLLARY. Let G be a Sperner graph with sources A and sinks B. Then:

(a) $|A|$ and $|B|$ have the same parity.
(b) If $|A|$ is odd then $|B|$ is odd.
(c) If $|A|$ is odd then $|B| \geqq 1$.
(d) If $|A| = 1$ then $|B| \geqq 1$.

PROOF. To show (a), note that $|A| + |B| = 2|V_0| + |V_1|$ and $|V_1|$ is even by the Main Lemma. Statements (b), (c), and (d) follow directly from (a).

For existence proofs, statements (a), (b), or (c) suffice; for algorithms of systematic search, it is statement (d) of the Corollary that is crucial. It can be given a separate statement and proof which place its constructive character in evidence.

ALGORITHM. Let G be a Sperner graph with exactly one source a_0. The examination of successive adjacent vertices in the component of G starting with the vertex a_0 leads in a finite number of steps to a sink.

PROOF. If a_0 is the only vertex of the component (that is, if a_0 is of degree zero) then a_0 is both a source and a sink and we are done. Otherwise, we shall generate a finite sequence $a_0, a_1, \ldots, a_n$ of distinct vertices such that a_{k-1} and a_k are connected by an edge for $1 \leqq k \leqq n$. Since a_0 is a source and not a sink, it is of degree one and hence a_1 is uniquely defined. Suppose $a_0, a_1, \ldots, a_k$ have been chosen, where $k \geqq 1$. If a_k is of degree one then it must be a sink (since $a_k \neq a_0$, the unique source) and we are done. Otherwise, it is of degree two and there is a unique vertex $a_{k+1} \neq a_{k-1}$ which is connected to a_k by an edge. We need only show $a_{k+1} \neq a_\ell$ for $0 \leqq \ell \leqq k-2$ to add a_{k+1} to the sequence. If $a_{k+1} = a_0$ then a_0 would be connected to the distinct vertices a_1 and a_k which contradicts the assumption that a_0 is a source. If $a_{k+1} = a_\ell$ for $1 \leqq \ell \leqq k-2$ then a_ℓ would be connected to the three distinct vertices $a_{\ell-1}$, $a_{\ell+1}$, and a_k which contradicts the assumption that no vertex has degree greater than two.

Since G is finite, the construction must terminate after a finite number of steps at a vertex of degree one $a_n \neq a_0$, which is the sink that is sought. Q. E. D.

3. The Classical Proof of Sperner's Lemma

Let $X = (x_0, x_1, \ldots, x_n)$ denote a point in the $(n+1)$-dimensional real vector space R^{n+1}. If $\{X^0, X^1, \ldots, X^m\}$ is a set of m+1 points in this space that spans an m-dimensional linear manifold, then the m-simplex S^m spanned by these points is the set of all $X = \Sigma_k \lambda_k X^k$ with all $\lambda_k \geqq 0$ and $\Sigma_k \lambda_k = 1$. If $\{X^{j_0}, \ldots, X^{j_r}\} \subset \{X^o, \ldots, X^m\}$ then the r-simplex spanned by this set is called an r-face of S^m. If $X \in S^m$ with $X = \Sigma_k \lambda_k X^k$ and $\lambda_k > 0$ if and only if $k \in \{j_o, \ldots, j_r\}$ then the r-face is called the carrier of X. A simplicial subdivision of S^m is a partition of S^m into finitely many m-simplices which are such that any two simplices of the partition are either disjoint or they have a common face as their intersection.

If S^n is spanned by $\{X^o, X^1, \ldots, X^n\}$, then a simplicial subdivision may be specified by giving additional (subdivision) points $X^{n+1}, \ldots, X^N$ from S^n and providing the family $D = \{\{X^{j_0}, X^{j_1}, \ldots, X^{j_n}\}\}$ of simplices of the subdivision. It is well-known that this family has the following important combinatorial property.

EXCHANGE PROPERTY. Given a subdivision of S^n specified by D, then for any $\{X^{j_0}, X^{j_1}, \ldots, X^{j_n}\} \in D$ and $k = 0, 1, \ldots, n$ there exists a unique $X^{j(k)} \neq X^{j_k}$ such that $\{X^{j_0}, \ldots, X^{j_{k-1}}, X^{j(k)}, X^{j_{k+1}}, \ldots, X^{j_n}\} \in D$ unless all of the vertices $X^{j_0}, \ldots, X^{j_{k-1}}, X^{j_{k+1}}, \ldots, X^{j_n}$ lie in the same (n-1)-face of S^n.

This property can be stated geometrically in a way that renders it intuitively obvious. Any (n-1)-face of a simplex of the subdivision is either interior to S^n and is the face of exactly two simplices of the subdivision or on the boundary of S^n and is the face of exactly one simplex of the subdivision.

Let the n-simplex S^n, spanned by $\{X^o, X^1, \ldots, X^n\}$ be subdivided by points $X^{n+1}, \ldots, X^N$. A proper labeling of the subdivision is a function ℓ defined on $\{X^o, X^1, \ldots, X^N\}$ with values in $\{0, 1, \ldots, n\}$ and such that $\ell(X^k) = j$ implies X^j is a vertex of the carrier of X^k in S^n.

SPERNER'S LEMMA. Given any proper labeling of any subdivision of an n-simplex S^n, there exist an odd number of simplices $\{X^{j_0}, \ldots, X^{j_n}\} \in D$ with $\{\ell(X^{j_0}), \ldots, \ell(X^{j_n})\} = \{0, 1, \ldots, n\}$, that is, with a complete set of labels.

PROOF. The proof is by induction on n; the lemma is trivially true for n = 0. Construct a graph G in which each vertex corresponds to a simplex with {0, 1, ..., n-1} among its labels. An edge connects two distinct vertices if and only if the intersection of the two associated simplices has exactly the labels {0, 1, ..., n-1}. This graph clearly has no vertex of greater than two. We shall call a vertex a source if it has labels {0, 1, ..., n-1} on points in the face S^{n-1} of S^n and a sink if it has a complete set of labels {0, 1, ..., n}. Clearly, every vertex that is called both a source and a sink is of degree zero and conversely. Moreover, any vertex that is called neither a source nor a sink must have some label from {0, 1, ..., n-1} repeated and, by the Exchange Property, must be of degree two. Hence G is a Sperner graph.

By the induction hypothesis, there are an odd number of sources. Hence, by part (b) of the Corollary of § 2, there are an odd number of sinks and the proof is complete. Q.E.D.

4. A Proof of Sperner's Lemma by Systematic Search

Sperner's Lemma has generally been proved by non-constructive methods (the elegant argument of Daniel I. A. Cohen (4) is a near-exception) similar to that of § 2. However, it can be proved by a method of systematic search, dispelling the doubts expressed by Scarf on this matter in (3).

PROOF. Let S^m be the simplex spanned by $\{X^0, X^1, \ldots, X^m\}$ for m = 0, 1, ..., n. Clearly, the subdivision of S^n induces a subdivision of each S^m. We define a graph G^m associated with each S^m in which each vertex corresponds to a simplex of the subdivision of S^m with {0, 1, ..., m-1} among its labels. An edge connects two distinct vertices if and only if the intersection of the corresponding simplices has exactly the labels {0, 1, ..., m-1}. We shall assign the vertices of this graph to four disjoint classes as follows:

	Simplex has labels {0, 1, ..., m}	Simplex has some label repeated
Simplex has a face in S^{m-1} with labels {0, 1, ..., m-1}	A^m	B^m
Simplex has no face in S^{m-1} with labels {0, 1, ..., m-1}	C^m	D^m

By the Exchange Property, the only vertices that are incident to exactly two edges are those in D^m. Vertices in B^m and C^m are incident to exactly one edge; the vertices in A^m are isolated and have no edges incident to them.

We now interconnect the graphs G^m by edges. Each vertex in $A^m \cup C^m$, for m = 0, 1, ..., n-1, is connected to the unique vertex in G^{m+1} corresponding to the simplex of S^{m+1} that can be made by adding one vertex to the simplex in S^m. In this way, each vertex in $A^{m+1} \cup B^{m+1}$ is connected to the unique vertex in G^m corresponding to the face of the simplex in S^m with labels $\{0, 1, \ldots, m\}$. The extreme cases m = 0 and m = n deserve special attention. The graph G^o consists of a single vertex $\{X^o\}$ and it is in class C^o. It is connected by one edge to a vertex in G^1. Each vertex in $A^n \cup C^n$ is incident to but one edge. <u>All other vertices are of degree two.</u> Hence, if we make the vertex $\{X^o\}$ a source and all vertices in $A^n \cup C^n$ sinks, we have defined a Sperner graph. Since it has a single source, the Algorithm of § 2 applies to it. That is, if we initiate a systematic search with the vertex $\{X^o\}$ and proceed through the graph we are lead inevitably to a vertex of class A^n or C^n. By the definition of these classes, this vertex corresponds to a simplex of the subdivision with a complete set of labels. Q. E. D.

(The lemma just proved is ordinarily stated in the stronger form of § 3 that there exist an odd number of simplices with a complete set of labels. This follows obviously from part (b) of the Corollary of § 2.)

EXAMPLE. Consider the simplex S^2 spanned by X^o = (1, 0, 0), X^1 = (0, 1, 0), and X^2 = (0, 0, 1) and subdivided by points $X^j = (\frac{k_o}{4}, \frac{k_1}{4}, \frac{k_2}{4})$ where the k_i are nonnegative integers that sum to 4. The figure below shows a proper labeling of this subdivision.

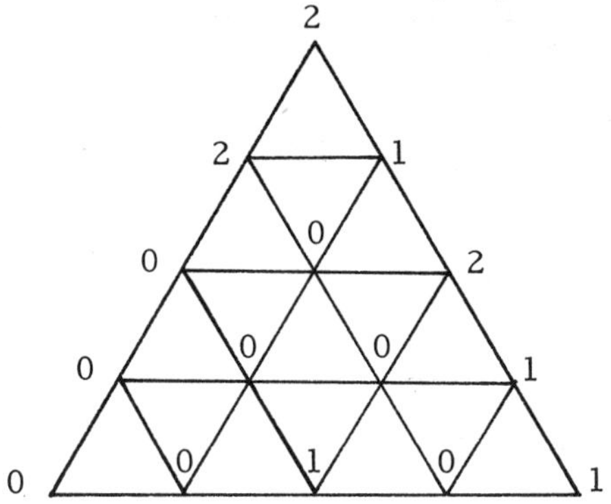

	Vertices	Edges
G^0:	$\{(1, 0, 0)\} = \gamma_{01}$	None
G^1:	$\{(1, 0, 0), (\frac{3}{4}, \frac{1}{4}, 0)\} = \beta_{11}$	$\beta_{11}\ \gamma_{11}$
	$\{(\frac{3}{4}, \frac{1}{4}, 0), (\frac{1}{2}, \frac{1}{2}, 0)\} = \gamma_{11}$	
	$\{(\frac{1}{2}, \frac{1}{2}, 0), (\frac{1}{4}, \frac{3}{4}, 0)\} = \gamma_{12}$	$\gamma_{12}\ \gamma_{13}$
	$\{(\frac{1}{4}, \frac{1}{2}, 0), (0, 1, 0)\} = \gamma_{13}$	
G^2:	$\{(\frac{3}{4}, \frac{1}{4}, 0), (\frac{1}{2}, \frac{1}{2}, 0), (\frac{1}{2}, \frac{1}{4}, \frac{1}{4})\} = \beta_{21}$	$\beta_{21}\ \delta_{21}$
	$\{(\frac{1}{2}, \frac{1}{2}, 0), (\frac{1}{2}, \frac{1}{4}, \frac{1}{4}), (\frac{1}{4}, \frac{1}{2}, \frac{1}{4})\} = \delta_{21}$	$\delta_{21}\ \beta_{22}$
	$\{(\frac{1}{2}, \frac{1}{2}, 0), (\frac{1}{4}, \frac{3}{4}, 0), (\frac{1}{4}, \frac{1}{2}, \frac{1}{4})\} = \beta_{22}$	
	$\{(\frac{1}{4}, \frac{3}{4}, 0), (0, 1, 0), (0, \frac{3}{4}, \frac{1}{4})\} = \beta_{23}$	$\beta_{23}\ \delta_{22}$
	$\{(\frac{1}{4}, \frac{3}{4}, 0), (0, \frac{3}{4}, \frac{1}{4}), (\frac{1}{4}, \frac{1}{2}, \frac{1}{4})\} = \delta_{22}$	$\delta_{22}\ \gamma_{21}$
	$\{(0, \frac{3}{4}, \frac{1}{4}), (0, \frac{1}{2}, \frac{1}{2}), (\frac{1}{4}, \frac{1}{2}, \frac{1}{4})\} = \gamma_{21}$	
	$\{(\frac{1}{4}, 0, \frac{3}{4}), (0, \frac{1}{4}, \frac{3}{4}), (\frac{1}{4}, \frac{1}{4}, \frac{1}{2})\} = \gamma_{22}$	$\gamma_{22}\ \gamma_{23}$
	$\{(0, \frac{1}{4}, \frac{3}{4}), (0, \frac{1}{2}, \frac{1}{2}), (\frac{1}{4}, \frac{1}{4}, \frac{1}{2})\} = \gamma_{23}$	

These graphs, when interconnected, yield the following Sperner graph:

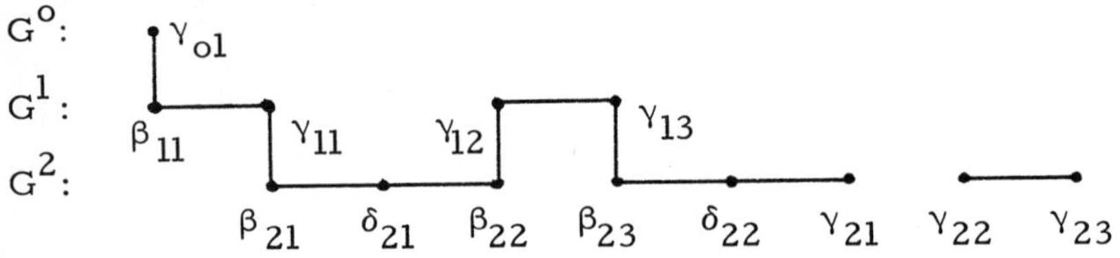

The course of the algorithm should be clear from this diagram. It starts from γ_{01} and ends at γ_{21}; there are three triangles with a complete set of labels, namely, γ_{21}, γ_{22}, and γ_{23}.

5. Sperner's Lemma on Pseudo-Manifolds

We consider the set of points $M = \{X^0, X^1, \ldots, X^N\}$ abstractly, without regard to their geometric specification. A pseudo-manifold (5) on the points M is a family D of sets, called simplices of the pseudo-manifold. Each set in D contains n+1 points from M. The family D is such that, if a set of n points is a subset of a set of D, then it is a subset of exactly two subsets of D. A proper labeling of a pseudo-manifold on M for which $\{X^0, \ldots, X^n\} \in D$ is the assignment of a label $\ell(X) \in \{0, 1, \ldots, n\}$ to each point in M such that $\ell(X^j) = j$ for $j = 0, 1, \ldots, n$.

PSEUDO-MANIFOLD LEMMA. For every proper labeling of a pseudo-manifold on $M = \{X^0, X^1, \ldots, X^N\}$ in which $\{X^0, \ldots, X^n\} \in D$, there exist a positive even number of simplices in D with a complete set of labels.

PROOF. Construct a graph G in which each vertex corresponds to a simplex in D with $\{0, 1, \ldots, n-1\}$ among its labels. Note that the assumption that $\{X^0, \ldots, X^n\} \in D$ and the definition of a proper labeling insure that there is at least one vertex. By the definition of a pseudo-manifold, there are no isolated vertices. The vertices of degree one are those corresponding to a simplex with a complete set of labels. Of these we make $\{X^0, \ldots, X^n\}$ the only source; all the rest are called sinks. The vertices of degree two are those corresponding to simplices with one label among $\{0, 1, \ldots, n-1\}$ repeated. The result then follows directly from the Main Lemma. Q. E. D.

The Pseudo-Manifold Lemma is given constructive form by noting that the component starting with the single source must end at a sink. We state this as a separate result.

PSEUDO-MANIFOLD ALGORITHM. For every proper labeling of a pseudo-manifold on $M = \{X^0, X^1, \ldots, X^N\}$ in which $\{X^0, \ldots, X^n\} \in D$, there exists a uniquely determined finite chain of simplices starting with $\{X^0, \ldots, X^n\}$ and ending at a different simplex with a complete set of labels. Every adjacent pair of simplices in the chain have exactly the labels $\{0, 1, \ldots, n-1\}$ in common.

An important special class of pseudo-manifolds is provided by those simplicial subdivisions of S^n (spanned by $X^0, X^1, \ldots, X^n$) which contain no subdivision points in the boundary of S^n. If we adjoin to D the single set $\{X^0, X^1, \ldots, X^n\}$ we have a pseudo-manifold in which $\{X^0, X^1, \ldots, X^n\} \in D$, and to which the pseudo-manifold algorithm applies. Although the algorithm applies to much more general cases (such as triangulations of a torus), this special case is closely related to Scarf's combinatorial theorem.

Two n-simplices contained in the n-dimensional hyperplane $H = \{X | \Sigma_k x_k = 1\}$ will appear in the discussion; these

$S = \{X | \text{all } x_k \leqq 1\} \cap H$ and $T = \{X | \text{ all } x_k \geqq 0\} \cap H$. As before, the points spanning S will be denoted by $X^j = (x_k^j)$, where $x_k^j = 1-n$ if $k = j$ and $x_k^j = 1$ otherwise. Following Scarf, we introduce <u>subdivision points</u> $X^{n+1}, \ldots, X^N$ chosen arbitrarily from the <u>interior</u> of T. A set of n+1 points $\{X^{j_o}, X^{j_1}, \ldots, X^{j_n}\}$ from $M = \{X^o, \ldots, X^N\}$ is called <u>primitive</u> if there is no point $X^j \in M$ such that

$$x_k^j > \min\{x_k^{j_o}, \ldots, x_k^{j_n}\} \text{ for all } k.$$

(In framing these definitions, we have used a different set of points for $X^o, X^1, \ldots, X^n$ than that employed by Scarf; our choice simplifies the statement of a number of results.)

To ensure the validity of Scarf's theorem, it is necessary to make the following assumptions which can be guaranteed by a perturbation of the subdivision points.

NONDEGENERACY ASSUMPTION. For each $k = 0, 1, \ldots, n$, the value of $\min\{x_k^{j_o}, \ldots, x_k^{j_n}\}$ is achieved by exactly one $x_k^{j_\ell}$ for every set of n+1 points $\{X^{j_o}, \ldots, X^{j_n}\}$ chosen from M.

The <u>covering simplex</u> of a set of n+1 points $\{X^{j_o}, \ldots, X^{j_n}\}$ from M is defined as

$$\{X | x_k \geqq \min\{x_k^{j_o}, \ldots, x_k^{j_n}\} \text{ for all } k\} \cap H.$$

With the Nondegeneracy Assumption, this set is a closed n-dimensional simplex contained in H. Each of its faces contains exactly one point from the given set, namely, that point for which the coordinate corresponding to that face is a minimum. A set of n+1 points is primitive if and only if no $X^j \in M$ lies in the interior of its covering simplex.

SCARF'S LEMMA. A set $\{X^{j_1}, \ldots, X^{j_n}\}$ of n points that is a subset of a primitive set is a subset of exactly two primitive sets, unless $\{X^{j_1}, \ldots, X^{j_n}\} \subset \{X^o, \ldots, X^n\}$. These n+1 exceptional sets are subsets of exactly one primitive set.

COROLLARY 1. Let D be the family of primitive sets relative to $M = \{X^o, \ldots, X^N\}$, with $\{X^o, \ldots, X^n\}$ adjoined. Then D defines a pseudo-manifold on the points M.

COROLLARY 2. For every labeling of M that assigns $\ell(X^j) = j$ for $j = 0, \ldots, n$, there exists an odd number of primitive sets with a complete set of labels.

This lemma, which is proved by Scarf in (3), essentially establishes the pseudo-manifold structure of the family of primitive sets when the "missing" simplex $\{X^0, \ldots, X^n\}$ is added. Corollary 2 is Scarf's combinatorial theorem; his algorithm is the pseudo-manifold algorithm.

The connection between the combinatorial structures that can be realized by primitive sets and those of the special class of pseudo-manifolds related to simplicial subdivisions with no subdivision points in the boundary is quite interesting. For example, if $n = 2$, the family of primitive sets determines a simplicial subdivision of S, in which the (geometric) simplices are the convex hulls of the primitive sets. For $n = 3$, there exists a simplicial subdivision with four subdivision points which cannot be realized by any family of primitive sets. These, and other related questions, will be treated in another paper on this subject.

6. Standard Subdivisions

Naturally, the efficient programming of any of the algorithms discussed above must depend on a compact description of a subdivision. A quite natural subdivision to use is that used previously for a proof of a cubical Sperner Lemma in (6). The description of a typical simplex of this subdivision and the "exchange steps" that result have been discovered independently by Terje Hansen (7) and used in an extremely effective manner for the computer programming of Scarf's algorithm.

Let $S^n = \{X | X = (x_o, x_1, \ldots, x_n) \geqq 0, \Sigma_j x_j = 1\}$. Then the standard subdivision of S^n is defined by giving a positive integer D. The vertices of the subdivision are specified by vectors $(k_o, \ldots, k_n)$ where the k_j are nonnegative integers and $\Sigma_j k_j = D$. A simplex of the subdivision may be given by a vertex P^o, where $DP^o = (k_o^o, \ldots, k_n^o)$, and a permutation $\pi = (j_1, \ldots, j_n)$ of $(1, \ldots, n)$. The vertices of the simplex are then defined recursively by

$$DP^t = (k_o^{t-1}, \ldots, k_{j_t-1}^{t-1} -1, k_{j_t}^{t-1} + 1, \ldots, k_n^{t-1})$$

for $t = 1, \ldots, n$.

If we drop one vertex of a simplex of this subdivision, then by the Exchange Property, either there is a unique new vertex that can be introduced to form a new simplex or the remaining vertices lie on the boundary. The description of the new simplex may be calculated by simple formulas given below.

When the vertex P^t is dropped from the simplex $[P^o, \pi]$:

	$(k_o^o, k_1^o, \ldots, k_n^o)$ becomes	$\pi = (j_1, \ldots, j_n)$ becomes
$t = 0$	$(k_o^o, \ldots, k_{j_1-1}^o -1, k_{j_1}^o +1, \ldots, k_n^o)$	$(j_2, \ldots, j_n, j_1)$
$0<t<n$	$(k_o^o, k_1^o, \ldots, k_n^o)$	$(j_1, \ldots, j_{t+1}, j_t, \ldots, j_n)$
$t = n$	$(k_o^o, \ldots, k_{j_n-1}^o +1, k_{j_n}^o -1, \ldots, k_n^o)$	$(j_n, j_1, \ldots, j_{n+1})$

This standard subdivision has been used in the Example of § 4; the reader may wish to test his understanding of the description of a simplex by P^o and π on the nodes of G^2. For example, the 2-simplex β_{21} is given by $P^o = (\frac{3}{4}, \frac{1}{4}, 0)$ and $\pi = (1, 2)$.

Lloyd Shapley (8), who discovered the algorithm of § 4 independently, has programmed it using an iterated barycentric subdivision. If an n-simplex is subdivided k times, at level j for $1 \leq j \leq k$, each simplex of the subdivision is identified by a string of j "words", each word being a permutation of the "letters" 0, 1, ..., n. The rules for naming these simplices and for identifying two simplices with an (n-1)-face in common are easily derived.

7. Acknowledgements

The presentation of this paper at the Conference was supported, in part, by the Office of Naval Research. The preparation of the manuscript has been supported by MATHEMATICA, Inc., Princeton, New Jersey.

REFERENCES

1. B. Knaster, K. Kuratowski, and S. Mazurkiewicz, Fund. Math. 14 (1929) 132.

2. E. Sperner, Abh. math. Sem. Hamburg 6 (1928) 265.

3. H. Scarf, SIAM J. Appl. Math. 15 (1967) 1328.

4. D. I. A. Cohen, J. Combinatorial Theory 2 (1967) 585.

5. H. Seifert and W. Threlfall, Lehrbuch der Topologie,

Berlin, Teubner, 1934.

6. H. W. Kuhn, IBM J. Res. Development 4 (1960) 518.

7. T. Hansen, "On the Approximation of a Competitive Equilibrium", Ph. D. Thesis, Yale University, 1968.

8. L. Shapley, private communication.

OPTIMAL VARIABLE ALLOCATION IN MULTIPLE WORKING POSITIONS (*)

F. Luccio
Politecnico di Milano
Milano, Italy.

1. INTRODUCTION - FORMULATION OF PROBLEM

A tipical optimal allocation problem arises when a sequence of operations is to be executed on the data of a given set, and a restricted numbers of working positions (briefly, w.p.'s) is available. All the data are contained in a general storage , and operations can be performed only on data present in the w.p.'s. Then, for each operation, the relative data must be transferred from storage to w.p.'s, and can be returned to storage after the operation is completed. Data will be referred to as variables. If there are N w.p.'s, any operation can affect 1 to N variables.

Assume that the cost of the allocation process depends only on transfers of variables from storage to w.p.'s, and vice versa. Each time a new variable is transferred into one of the w.p.'s, a previous transfer to storage of the variable already contained in that w.p. is required. Assign a cost 1 to such double transfer. We are then concerned in determining, for any given sequence of operations, the sequence of transfers yielding the minimum total cost, i.e. the optimal variable allocation in the w.p.'s. Obviously, the problem may have more than one optimal solution.

From each operation in the sequence, the group of variables to which the operation refers is extracted. The sequence of groups of variables thus obtained, called the program, gives the only information relevant to the allocation problem. A sample program

(*) This work was carried out in part while the author was visiting staff member of the AED Cooperative Program, MIT Electronic Systems Laboratory, Cambridge,Mass.-

is shown in Table 1.a, where variables are indicated by x1,...,x7. Assume that there are N = 3 w.p.'s, indicated by P1,P2,P3, initially containing x1,x2,x3. An optimal allocation, and relative costs, are shown in Table 1.b,1.c. Total cost is 6.

Table 1. a. Sample program;
b. Optimal allocation;
c. Cost.

				P1	P2	P3	
				x1	x2	x3	
1)	x4	x5		x1	x4	x5	2
2)	x6			x1	x4	x6	1
3)	x4			x1	x4	x6	0
4)	x1	x6	x7	x1	x7	x6	1
5)	x5			x5	x7	x6	1
6)	x2	x6		x5	x2	x6	1
	(a)				(b)		(c)

The allocation problem mentioned above was formerly considered in connection with optimal index register loading in computer programming (1,2), and applies straight-forward to the optimal use of any type of multiple registers (index and arithmetic registers, accumulators etc.) in computing systems. In these cases, the w.p.'s represent registers into which variables must be transferred from central memory before operating on them. However, other applications can be encountered having a similar logical structure. For istance, this same scheme can be used in real time computer organization, when different blocks of information must be transferred time by time into core memory (3).

In this paper , an algorithm is presented to obtain one optimal allocation for programs constituted of a single sequence of groups of variables, called "straight-line" programs. Then, the case of programs composed of different "branches" is discussed, and a procedure is developed to determine all the different w.p.'s in which a variable may appear at given steps of the program (in the straight-line case, such a procedure is not needed).Note that the allocation techniques proposed in the literature refer to straight-line programs only (1,2). They make use of algorithms for optimal trajectories (4), thus requiring in general a much larger enumeration than the one involved here.

2. THE OPTIMAL ALLOCATION ALGORITHM

An algorithm for optimal variable allocation in straight-line programs is now illustrated. It is based on the use of a special table of variable occurrences, called <u>link diagram</u>. For the sake of brevity, no formal proof is given here on the optimality of the proposed solutions, but a proof can be easily carried out as extension of the ones given in (2).

The simple case of programs having one single variable per step is examined firts. Refer to the example of Table 2.

Table 2. a. Program
b. Link diagram
c. Optimal allocation
d. Cost
e. Available positions.

(a)	(b)	(c) P1	(c) P2	(c) P3	(d)	(e)
	x1 x2 x3	x1	x2	x3		
1) x4	x4	x4	x2	x3	1	<u>P1</u> P3
2) x5	x5	x5	x2	x3	1	<u>P1</u> P3
3) x2	x2	x5	x2	x3	0	P3
4) x6	x6	x5	x2	x6	1	<u>P3</u>
5) x5	x5					
6) x2	x2					
. . .	. . . .					

The program is scanned step by step. Variables are displayed in the link diagram (Table 2.b) in an obvious way. A <u>link</u> (vertical line) is built to connect the variable at the present step with its previous occurrence, if any. A link is said to <u>cover</u> all the program steps falling along its extension, extremes excluded.
Whenever a step k is found, covered by N-1 links (N is the number of w.p.'s), the process

of link determination is temporarily quitted, since variable allocation for a portion of program can be carried out: k is called a stop-point. Actually, it can be proved that an optimal allocation is obtained if each variable is maintained in a w.p. along all the steps covered by its link. Then, at the stop-point k, the w.p.'s must contain the N-1 variables relative to the links covering k, and the variable occurring at step k itself. Since w.p. content at the stop-point is fixed, the optimal allocation is carried out for the portion of program preceding that step, maintaining the variables in their w.p.'s along the corresponding links.

Then, the process of link determination is resumed until a new stop-point is found, and so on. In this way, the program is subdivided into different portions, separated by the stop-points. The allocation process for each portion takes place independently of the others, starting from the w.p. content relative to the preceding stop-point.

For the program of Table 2.a, after steps 1 to 6 have been examined, the link diagram of Table 2.b is obtained. Step 4 is a stop-point, since it is covered by N-1=2 links. The optimal allocation shown in Table 2.c is then carried out for steps 1 to 4, before the link diagram determination is resumed for the remaining part of the program.

Some remarks on the above procedure are in order.

The optimal allocation for any step of the program cannot be determined until a succeeding stop-point is found. In (5) a technique is discussed to temporarily assign "symbolic" w.p.'s to the occurring variables, and to determine the correspondence between actual and symbolic w.p.'s when the stop-point is found.

In the above algorithm, some degrees of freedom are left in the w.p. assignment phase. Referring to Table 2, both w.p.'s P1 and P3 can be assigned to variable x4 at step 1. Namely, there is no link leaving the variables x1 and x3 contained in those w.p.'s. A similar condition arises at step 2. Such alternatives are listed in Table 2.e : the w.p.'s actually employed in the example are underscored. All these alternatives could have been used, giving rise to a number of optimal allocations, different from one another in the disposition of variables in the w.p.'s. This point will be further discussed in the next sections.

The optimal allocation algorithm is easily extended to the general case of programs with more than one variable occurring at given steps. Refer to Table 3.

Table 3. Link diagram, in the general case.

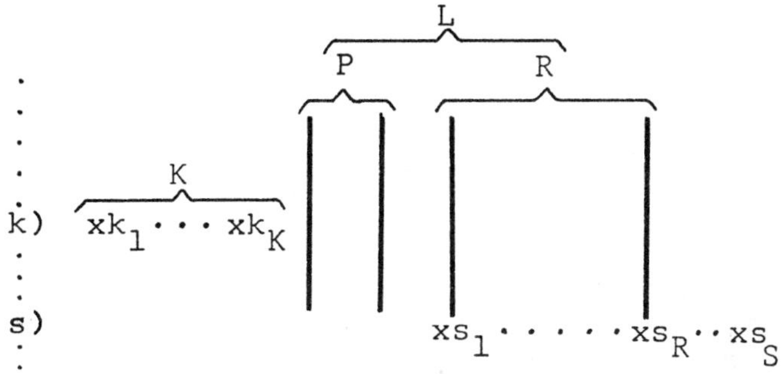

When s is met, R links are built in the link diagram, relative to the variables $xs_1, \ldots, xs_R$ of this step having a previous occurrence. The total number of links covering step k, including the P links already present in the diagram, is now L=P+R. If $L+K \geq N$ (K is the number of variables occurring at step k, N is the number of w.p.'s), then k is a stop-point. Since no more than N variables can be allocated at step k, L+K-N links covering k must be deleted from the diagram. They are chosen at will among the last R, so that only R-(L+K-N)=N-K-P links are actually built at step s. No other modification is required for the algorithm.

3. BRANCHED PROGRAMS

Programs composed of different branches, called <u>branched programs</u>, are now considered. Each branch is a straight-line sequence of groups of variables, to be allocated into the w.p.'s.

Since the structure of these programs is tipical of computer programs, a computer-type terminology can conveniently be adopted for their description. A branched program is shown in Fig. 1, where S1,S2,S3 and S4 are straight-line sequences. In this example, one <u>branching-point</u> B and one <u>merging point</u> M are present.

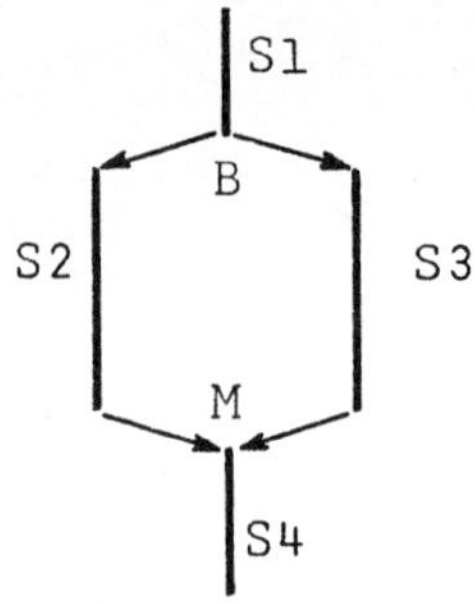


```
S1;
IF Boolean THEN S2  ELSE S3;
S4;
```

Fig. 1. Branched program composed of four straight-line sequences.

Variable allocation for a branched program can be performed by applying the algorithm for the straight-line case to each branch independently. Note, however, that this solution in only locally optimal, since to determine a global optimal allocation the occurrences of the same variable in different branches should be taken into account. This point will not be further investigated here. In (5), a more sophisticated algorithm has been proposed for a special class of branched programs.

Instead, a new problem is discussed here, in connection with programs containing merging points. Namely, not only the presence of given variables in the w.p.'s is relevant in this case, but also their disposition in the w.p.'s. In particular, w.p. contents at the end of merging sequences, called final-configurations for the sequences, are to be examined

Consider for example the program in Fig. 1. If the final configurations for S2 and S3 are identical S4 can be entered from both sequences. Otherwise, a certain number of w.p. loading operations must be inserted at the and of S2 and/or S3, to render identical such configurations. These additional operations are not needed for any variable appearing in the same w.p. in the two final configurations.

Considerable aid for the merging point problem is supplied by the technique presented in the next section, that gives, for any sequence, all the possible positions for the variables in the final configuration.

4. THE PERMUTATION TABLE TECHNIQUE

While, for a given sequence, the variables in

the final configuration are fixed by the optimal allocation algorithm, their mutual positions can be modified by taking into account the freedom degrees left by the algorithm itself. This possibility has been already pointed out in section 2, in connection with the groups of w.p.'s available at each step (Table 2.e).

A technique is now presented to determine, for a given sequence, all the possible dispositions of variables in the final configuration, due to the different choices of available w.p.'s. No formal justification for this technique will be given, but proofs can be easily carried out .

Obviously, the technique is to be applied to all the sequences merging in one point. Then, the actual goal of the merging problem, i.e. obtaining the greatest matching among the final configurations for such sequences, can easily be reached, since all the possible final configurations are known for each sequence. For brevity, this point will not be further discussed here.

The only case of sequences having one variable per step is considered. When the optimal allocation algorithm is applied to a sequence, a list of all the possible choices (permutations) of w.p.'s available at different steps is formed. Consider the example of Table 2. The list of permutations contains: a={P1,P3}; b={P1,P3}. At step 1, P1 is selected for the occurring variable x4. However, the first item, a, of the list indicates a possible permutation between P1 and P3, that would affect w.p. contents for the succeeding steps up to the final configuration. Then, the permutations in the above list can be directly applied to the w.p. contents in the final configuration, to determine all the possible dispositions of the variables in such configuration.

Without loss of generality, the above permutations will be restricted to pairs of w.p.'s. Namely, any choice among $k > 2$ w.p.'s can be substituted by the list of k-1 couples, constituted of the w.p. actually used in the allocation algorithm, and all the other w.p.'s in the choice.

The permutations for a given sequence are used to form a permutation table, whose rows and columns correspond to the N w.p.'s. In cell (P_i,P_j) of this table, i.e. the cell in row P_i, column P_j, all the possible groups of permutations are listed that can be employed to have the content of P_i in P_j, in the final configuration.

Consider for example the list of permutations

$$a = \{P1, P3\} \quad ; \quad b = \{P1, P2\} \quad ; \quad c = \{P1, P3\} .$$

The corresponding permutation table is shown in Fig. 2.c.

(a)

	P1	P2	P3
P1	$0\bar{a}$		$0a$
P2		0	
P3	$0a$		$0\bar{a}$

(b)

	P1	P2	P3
P1	$0\bar{a}\bar{b}$	$0\bar{a}b$	$0a$
P2	$0b$	$0\bar{b}$	
P3	$0a\bar{b}$	$0ab$	$0\bar{a}$

(c)

	P1	P2	P3
P1	$\bar{a}\bar{b}\bar{c}$ ac	$\bar{a}b$	$a\bar{c}$ $\bar{a}\bar{b}c$
P2	$b\bar{c}$	$\bar{b}$	bc
P3	$a\bar{b}\bar{c}$ $\bar{a}c$	ab	$\bar{a}\bar{c}$ $a\bar{b}c$

Fig. 2. Filling a permutation table.

To have the final content of P1 in P3, any of the groups listed in cell (P1,P3) can be employed. These groups are:

$$a\bar{c} \quad ; \quad \bar{a}\bar{b}c .$$

$a\bar{c}$ means that permutation a is to be employed, b is not relevant, c must not be employed. The second alternative $\bar{a}\bar{b}c$ means that only permutation c is to be employed.

The permutation table is filled using the following rules (see Fig. 2.a,b,c).

1) Start with a table containing blanks in all the cells (P_i, P_j), $i \neq j$, and 0's in cells (P_i, P_i). 0's indicate that the content of any Pi is maintained in such w.p. if no permutation is employed.

2) Examine the permutations one by one. For each permutation $p = \{P_i, P_j\}$: i) append $\bar{p}$ to all the entries in columns P_i and P_j; ii) enter all the entries of column P_i (P_j) into column P_j (P_i), same rows, changing $\bar{p}$'s to p's.

Note that 0's can be eliminated in the final table (Fig. 2.c).

To make use of the permutation table, a problem of compatibility arises among different groups. Assume that, in the above example, the contents of

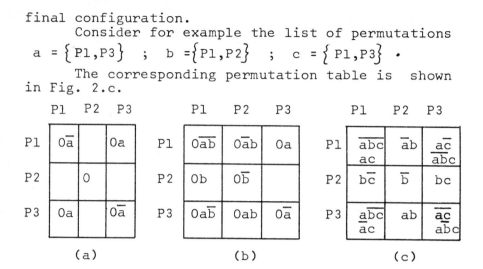

P1 and P2 are to be found in P3 and P1 respectively. Then, $a\bar{c}$ or $\overline{ab}c$, and $b\bar{c}$, must be employed. Groups $a\bar{c}$ and $b\bar{c}$ must be selected (i.e. permutations a and b will be executed, c will not), since $\overline{ab}c$ is not compatible with $b\bar{c}$, due to the opposite requirement on b. The selection of a compatible set of groups is left here to the examination of all possible cases. A systematic procedure to solve this problem, and different properties of the permutation table, will be discussed in a next paper.

5. CONCLUSION

The problem of optimal allocation of a sequence of variables (program) in a restricted number of working positions has been discussed, and an allocation algorithm has been proposed for straight-line sequences. Programs composed of different branches have then been examined. In this case, a particular problem arises in connection with merging points. To solve this problem, a technique has been developed to determine all the possible dispositions of variables in the working positions, due to permutations between couples of them.

REFERENCES

(1) L.P. Horwitz, R.M. Karp, R.E. Miller, S. Winograd, "Index Register Allocation". J. ACM 13, 1 (Jan 1966), 43-61.

(2) F. Luccio, "A Comment on Index Register Allocation". Comm. ACM 10,9 (Sept. 1967), 572-574.

(3) W.J. Karplus, "On line Computing". Mc Graw Hill, 1967.

(4) R. Bellman, S. Dreyfus, "Applied Dynamic Programming". Princeton Univ. Press, 1962.

(5) F. Luccio, "Techniques for Optimal Index Register Allocation". Istituto di Elettrotecnica ed Elettronica, Internal Report 68-5, 1968.

The function f takes its values in Euclidean n-space E_n and is assumed to be continuously differentiable with respect to x and u. The subset $U(x,t) \subset E_p$, which determines the admissible control values, is usually a connected set depending continuously on x and t. In addition to Eq. (2), the control function is required to be piecewise continuous.

The terminal time t_f may be either fixed or free. The only constraints on the state vector x occur at the terminal time t_f and are described by the inequality Eq.(3), where G is an m-dimensional vector-valued function of x and t. Problems having integral constraints or an integral objective functional of the form

$$\int_{t_o}^{t_f} \ell(x(t),u(t),t)\,dt$$

can, as is well known, be converted to problems of the type described above. As presented here, however, the procedure is not applicable to problems having state vector constraints at each $t \in [t_o, t_f]$, but the method can be modified to handle these problems as well.

The selection of a suitable computational procedure for such a problem depends essentially on the nature of the constraints (i.e., the set U and the function G). In the special case of no constraints and fixed final time, a variety of effective computational methods are available including the gradient method (1), the method of conjugate gradients (2,3), parallel tangents (4), and Newton's method (5). Most of these techniques are easily modified to account for the constraint $u(t) \in U[x,t]$, but often cannot be modified to handle the terminal constraints in any generally effective manner. In this paper it is shown that the efficiency of these routines for solving unconstrained control problems can, in conjection with duality theory, be exploited to solve constrained problems.

In Sec.II the essential elements of duality theory for mathematical programming problems upon which the proposed method is based are presented. Then in Sec.III the proposed method is described for constrained optimal control problems having fixed terminal time. The method is extended to problems with free terminal time in Secs. IV, V, and VI. Examples of the method are presented in Sec.VII.

II. BASIC PRIMAL-DUAL ALGORITHM IN FINITE DIMENSIONS

Let Γ be a convex subset of an n-dimensional vector space X, and let ψ be a real-valued convex functional on Γ. Let F be a convex mapping from Γ into Euclidean m-space E_m.

A PRIMAL-DUAL ALGORITHM FOR THE COMPUTATION OF OPTIMAL CONTROL*

David G. Luenberger
Stanford Electronics Labs, Stanford University,
Palo Alto, California

ABSTRACT

This paper describes a computational method, based on the finite-dimensional duality theorem of convex programming, for the solution of a wide class of optimal control problems. The method converts an optimal control problem having terminal constraints to a series of unconstrained problems that can be rapidly solved by standard gradient techniques. The method is applicable to problems having either fixed or free terminal time.

I. INTRODUCTION

In this paper a computational procedure is proposed for solving the following class of optimal control problems: given the dynamic system

$$\dot{x}(t) = f(x(t),u(t),t) \qquad x(t_o) = x_o \text{ fixed;} \tag{1}$$

find the control input function $u(t)$ that satisfies the constraints

$$u(t) \in U(x,t), \tag{2}$$

$$G(x(t_f),t_f) \leq \theta, \tag{3}$$

and minimizes the real-valued objective functional

$$\psi(x(t_f),t_f). \tag{4}$$

*This research was supported in part by Joint Services Contract Nonr 225(83) and in part by Contract DA-01-021-AMC-90006(Y) awarded to Stanford Research Institute.

A general convex programming problem has the form

$$\left.\begin{array}{r}\text{minimize} \quad \psi(x) \\ \text{subject to} \quad x \in \Gamma,\ G(x) \leq \theta\end{array}\right\} \qquad (5)$$

In order to avoid certain singularity difficulties, it is assumed that the origin $\theta \in E_m$ is an interior point of the set

$$\{z: G(x) \leq z \quad \text{for some} \quad x \in \Gamma\}$$

This is referred to as the regularity condition.
Definition: The dual function φ, corresponding to problem (5), is defined on the set

$$\Gamma^* = \{\lambda \in E_m: \inf_{x \in \Gamma} [\psi(x) + \lambda' G(x)] > -\infty\}$$

by the equation

$$\varphi(\lambda) = \inf_{x \in \Gamma} [\psi(x) + \lambda' G(x)]. \qquad (6)$$

The following duality theorem, which is a direct consequence of the Lagrange saddle-value theorem (6), is applicable under the assumptions stated above† and forms the basis for the primal-dual method:
Theorem: Let

$$\mu_o = \inf \{\psi(x): x \in \Gamma,\ G(x) \leq \theta\} \qquad (7)$$

be finite, then

$$\mu_o = \max_{\lambda \geq \theta} \varphi(\lambda) \qquad (8)$$

Furthermore, if λ_o is the maximizer of Eq.(8) and the infinum of Eq. (7) is achieved by x_o, then x_o minimizes $\psi(x) + \lambda_o' G(x)$.

The primal-dual method for solving Eq.(7) consists of solving, instead, the dual problem Eq.(8), which has simpler constraints. Of course, evaluation of $\varphi(\lambda)$ for any given λ itself requires the solution of a minimization problem, but one that is unconstrained.

---

† Define the set $A \subset R \times Z$ as $A = \{(r,z)$: For some $x \in \Gamma$, $G(x) \leq z,\ f(x) \leq r\}$. Then the duality theorem holds if the regularity condition is satisfied and A is convex. Convexity of A is implied by convexity of Γ, ψ and G.

In the course of the primal-dual procedure, the dual function is maximized either by a simple search technique if m is small (say $m = 1$ or 2), or more often by a gradient-based technique such as steepest ascent or conjugate gradients. Such gradient techniques for solving the dual problem are particularly attractive in view of the following observation:

__Lemma:__ Given λ_o let x_o be a minimizer of $\psi(x) + \lambda_o'G(x)$, subject to $x \in \Gamma$. Then $\lambda'G(x_o) \leq 0$ implies $\varphi(\lambda_o + \lambda) \leq \varphi(\lambda_o)$.

__Proof:__

$$\begin{aligned}\varphi(\lambda_o + \lambda) &= \inf \{f(x) + \lambda_o'G(x) + \lambda'G(x)\} \\ &\leq f(x_o) + \lambda_o'G(x_o) + \lambda'G(x_o) \\ &\leq f(x_o) + \lambda_o'G(x_o) \\ &= \varphi(\lambda_o).\end{aligned}$$

The above statement says that the vector $G(x_o)$ defines a half-space of nonascent for the function φ and is therefore a so-called subgradient of φ at λ_o. In particular, if φ has a gradient at λ_o, it is equal to $G(x_o)$.

The primal-dual method for solving the constrained problem Eq.(5) proceeds by first selecting $\lambda \geq \theta$, solving the unconstrained primal problem Eq.(6) to evaluate $\varphi(\lambda)$ and its gradient, and then changing λ, according to a gradient-based technique, to increase φ; and so forth. A single constrained problem is therefore converted to two interwoven simpler problems.

III. FIXED TERMINAL-TIME CONTROL PROBLEMS

Consider the fixed terminal-time optimal control problem

$$\left.\begin{aligned} \text{minimize} \quad & \psi(x(t_f)) \\ \text{subject to} \quad & G(x(t_f)) \leq \theta \\ & u(t) \in U(x,t) \\ & \dot{x}(t) = f(x,u,t) \end{aligned}\right\} \tag{9}$$

with $x(t_o)$ specified. Here the explicit dependence of ψ and G on t_f is suppressed since t_f is fixed. This problem can be solved by the primal-dual method by formulating the control problem in the finite-dimensional space of terminal state vectors $x(t_f)$ and considering the finite-dimensional problem of minimizing $\psi(x(t_f))$ subject to $G(x(t_f)) \leq \theta$ and $x(t_f) \in \Gamma$, where Γ is the set of end points attainable from $x(t_o)$ by application of admissible controls.

Assuming that ψ and G are convex functions and that Γ is a convex set (this assumption is examined below), application of the dual method converts the constrained control problem to the problem:

$$\max_{\substack{\lambda \geq \theta \\ \lambda \in E_m}} \left\{ \min_{x(t_f) \in \Gamma} [\psi(x(t_f)) + \lambda' G(x(t_f))] \right\}$$

The interior minimization reduces to a control problem of type Eq. (9) but without terminal constraints. This problem is therefore susceptible to any of the standard minimization routines. The exterior problem can be solved by a finite-dimensional gradient-based technique as discussed in Sec.II.

In order to guarantee the success of this approach, some assumption must be made concerning the nature of the set Γ. Obviously, it is sufficient that Γ be convex, but in most practical problems involving nonlinear differential equations this assumption is probably not justified. This assumption can, however, be replaced by a weaker, more realistic, assumption.

Suppose that the terminal state vector $x(t_f)$ is partitioned as

$$x(t_f) = \begin{bmatrix} y \\ w \end{bmatrix},$$

where $\dim y = p$ and $\dim w = n - p$. Suppose further that in the original optimal control problem both the terminal objective functional ψ and terminal constraints G can be written as explicit functions of the vector y. Thus

$$\psi(x(t_f)) = \psi(y)$$

$$G(x(t_f)) = G(y).$$

Often in large complex control problems p is considerably less than n. In rocket guidance, for instance, objectives and constraints are often expressed in terms of position variables only, without explicit reference to velocities.

Definition: The optimal control problem Eq. (9) with $\psi(x(t_f)) = \psi(y)$, $G(x(t_f)) = G(y)$ is said to satisfy the weakened convexity hypothesis if the set

$$\gamma = \left\{ y \colon x(t_f) = \begin{bmatrix} y \\ w \end{bmatrix} \text{ for some } w \text{ and some admissible control} \right\}$$

is convex.

The set γ consists of all reachable y points in the p-dimensional space. An equivalent characterization of γ is that it is the projection of the set Γ in E_n onto the space generated by the first p components of $x(t_f)$.

Convexity of γ is a weaker assumption than convexity of Γ since, for example, in the extreme case where $p = 1$, Γ need only be connected for γ to be convex.

As a general rule, for a given system, the weakened convexity assumption is more likely to be satisfied as p is reduced. Therefore, it appears that in considering various problem formulations the analyst might well strive to select ψ and G so as to minimize p.

Satisfaction of the weakened convexity assumption is, of course, sufficient to guarantee success of the primal-dual algorithm since the optimal control problem is then equivalent to

$$\begin{aligned} &\text{minimize} && \psi(y), \\ &\text{subject to} && G(y) \leq \theta \\ & && y \in \gamma \end{aligned}$$

IV. WEAKENED CONVEXITY FOR VARIABLE-TIME PROBLEMS

Now consider problems with unspecified terminal time of the form

$$\left.\begin{aligned} &\text{minimize} && \psi(x(t_f), t_f) \\ &\text{subject to} && \dot{x} = f(x,u,t), \quad x(t_o) \text{ given} \\ & && u(t) \in U(x,t) \\ & && G(x(t_f), t_f) \leq \theta. \end{aligned}\right\} \qquad (10)$$

A problem of this form having particular interest is that of hitting a target, specified by $G[x(t_f)] \leq \theta$, in minimum time; i.e., $\psi(x(t_f), t_f) = t_f$.

Since the additional variable t_f is introduced in these problems, one must consider the geometry in the space $X \times T$. In $X \times T$, let Γ be the set of all points attainable from the dynamical system by use of admissible control functions, and, in a manner similar to that if the previous section, let γ be the projection of Γ onto the subspace $Y \times T$ where Y represents the space of variables appearing explicitly in ψ and G.

Let γ_t be the set in the space Y, which is the cross-section of γ at time t. From the discussion in the previous section, γ_t can be argued to be convex in many cases, although γ itself may not be. The sets γ_t, however, are for many systems, increasing as t increases, i.e. $\gamma_{t_1} \subset \gamma_{t_2}$ for $t_1 \leq t_2$. In these cases the t-axis can be rescaled monotonically so that γ, when drawn with respect to this new variable, say t', is convex. Such a transformation from the variable t to the variable t' changes the form of the underlying differential equations and the cost functional, but it is assumed that with respect to the new variable the usual convexity requirements are satisfied.

As an example, in the problem of hitting a target in minimum time, if γ is not convex but can be made convex by a monotone increasing transformation $t' = m(t)$, then the problem can be regarded as minimization of t' and all the convexity requirements will now be satisfied. Finally, observe that it is not actually necessary to perform the transformation to t' as indicated since minimization of t' is itself equivalent to minimization of t. It is only necessary to hypothesize that an appropriate transformation exists so that the theory is justified.

For the general variable terminal-time problem, it is sufficient to require satisfaction of the following: Weakened Convexity Assumption:‡ Let Y be the subspace of X, which explicitly appears in $G(x(t_f),t_f)$ and $\psi(t_f),t_f)$. The optimal problem satisfies the weakened convexity hypothesis if there is a monotone increasing transformation of the t-axis such that the projection of the set Γ onto $Y \times T$ is convex, and the functions $\psi(y,t)$ and $G(y,t)$ are convex on $Y \times T$.

V. COMPUTATIONAL PROCEDURE FOR VARIABLE TERMINAL TIME

In this section the primal-dual algorithm is applied to variable terminal-time optimal control problems. The method is based on the following special duality theorem.

Theorem: Under the weakened convexity assumption, problem (10) is equivalent to

$$\max_{\lambda \geq \theta} \; \min_{u \in U} \; \min_{t_f} \{\psi(x(t_f),t_f) + \lambda' G(x(t_f),t_f)\}$$

Proof: The two minimizations are equivalent to minimization, over the convex set γ , of an objective function that is itself a convex function. Hence, the equation can be conceived as

$$\max_{\lambda \geq \theta} \; \min_{(y,t) \in \gamma} \{\psi(y,t) + \lambda' G(y,t)\}$$

‡ The weakened convexity assumption implies convexity of the set A in footnote †.

Now by ordinary duality theory this is equivalent to

$$\underset{(y,t)\in\Upsilon}{\text{minimize}} \quad \psi(y,t)$$

$$\text{subject to} \quad G(y,t) \leq \theta.$$

This is the desired conclusion.

The algorithm for solving such problems is now read from Eq.(11) as follows:

(1) For a given $\lambda \geq \theta$, use any standard algorithm to find $u \in U$ minimizing the objective functional

$$\min_{t_f} \{\psi(x(t_f),t_f) + \lambda' G(x(t_f),t_f)\}$$

(This is discussed in greater detail below.)

(2) Maximize with respect to λ by using any standard gradient-based routine by using the fact that the gradient is $G(x(t_f),t_f)$.

The weakened convexity assumption is sufficient to guarantee the success of this method. In practice the method has been successful for a large number of complex rocket problems where the weakened convexity assumption could not be verified. In general one would expect the method to succeed in many well-posed problems.

VI EVALUATION OF GRADIENT FOR CONTROL SUBPROBLEM

As a fundamental step in the procedure outlined in the preceding section, one must solve an optimal control problem of the form*

$$\text{Minimize} \quad \{\min_{t_f} \psi(x(t_f),t_f)\}$$

$$\text{subject to} \quad \dot{x}(t) = f(x(t),u(t),t), \qquad x(t_o) \text{ given}$$

$$u(t) \in U(x,t).$$

A number of effective algorithms are available for problems of this kind that require evaluation of the gradient of

$$J = \min_{t_f} \psi(x(t_f),t_f)$$

with respect to u. The problem can be written alternatively as

---

* Here $\psi + \lambda' G$ has, for convenience, been replaced by ψ.

$$\min_u \ \psi(x(t_f), t_f)$$

$$\text{subject to} \quad \dot{x} = f(x,u,t), \qquad x(t_o) \quad \text{given}$$

$$u(t) \in U(x,t).$$

$$t_f = \arg\min \psi(x(t),t) \tag{12}$$

Therefore, the gradient can be computed for the problem of minimizing ψ subject to the usual differential equation constraint and the additional constraint Eq.(12), which serves as a stopping condition, since it determines t_f once a control function $u(t)$ has been selected.

To first-order, the incremental change in the cost ψ due to a change δu in control and a change δt_f in the final time, is

$$\delta\psi = \int_{t_o}^{t_f} \eta'(t) \ D(t) \ \delta u(t) \ dt + \dot{\psi}\Big|_{t_f} \cdot \delta t_f \tag{13}$$

where $\dot{\eta}(t) = -F'(t) \ \eta(t), \qquad \eta(t_f) = \psi_x\Big|_{t_f}$

$$F(t) = \left[\frac{\partial f_i}{\partial x_j}\right]$$

$$D(t) = \left[\frac{\partial f_i}{\partial u_j}\right]$$

The change δt_f is determined by the stopping condition Eq. (12) but is of no direct importance at present since the total derivative of ψ with respect to t, $\dot{\psi}$, is zero at t_f, and, hence, δt_f does not enter Eq. (13). Thus, the gradient of ψ with respect to u is simply the function $\eta'(t) \ D(t)$.

In a typical application, then, one changes u by some constant multiple of this gradient and integrates the equations of motion forward until the optimal t_f is found satisfying the stopping condition Eq.(12). In case there are constraints $u \in U(x,t)$, the standard methods for selecting u on the basis of the gradient can be employed.

If it turns out that δt_f is positive during one of these iteration steps, the new step will require selecting $u(t)$ on an interval that is larger than that on which it was previously defined. It probably makes little difference how u is selected on this interval, but one possible method, having certain theoretical justification, is to select $u(t)$ so as to minimize $\psi_x f(x,u,t) + \psi_t$ subject to $u \in U(x,t)$.

This tends to reduce $\psi_x f + \psi_t$ to zero as soon as possible and hence minimizes the new t_f. In the problems solved so far, however, the control function has been extended to a larger interval when necessary by using the same value as at the last available time instant.

VII. EXAMPLES

Two examples illustrating the type of results obtained by the primal-dual method are presented in this section. Both examples consider Van der Pol's equation, which in state variable form is

$$\dot{x}_1 = x_2$$

$$\dot{x}_2 = x_1 + (1 - x_1^2)\, x_2 + u,$$

with initial conditions $x_1(0) = 1$, $x_2(0) = 0$

1. Fixed Time, Minimum Energy to a Line

In this problem one seeks to minimize

$$J = \tfrac{1}{2} \int_0^5 (x_1^2 + x_2^2 + u^2)\, dt$$

while satisfying the terminal constraint

$$-x_1(5) + x_2(5) = 1.$$

In dual form the problem becomes

$$\max_{\lambda} \min_{u} \tfrac{1}{2} \int_0^5 (x_1^2 + x_2^2 + u^2)\, dt + \lambda[-x_1(5) + x_2(5) - 1] \tag{14}$$

The derivative of the dual function is simply $H(\lambda) = -x_1(5) + x_2(5) - 1$, where $x_1(5)$ and $x_2(5)$ are taken as the terminal state variables resulting from the indicated minimization in Eq. (14). The problem was solved by finding λ to make $H(\lambda) = 0$, which corresponds to a stationary point of the dual function. The equation $H(\lambda) = 0$ was solved using regula-falsi (7) starting with $\lambda_1 = 0.0$, $\lambda_2 = 1.0$. In each case the unconstrained optimal control subproblem was solved using the method of parallel tangents. The resulting succession of trajectories is shown in Fig. 1.

2. Bounded Control, Minimum Time to a Disk

In this problem the control u is constrained to satisfy $|u(t)| \leq 1$, and the objective is to minimize time to the disk

$$x_1^2 + (x_2 - 1)^2 \leq .04.$$

In solving the problem by the primal-dual method, the objective function was taken to be $t_f^2/10$ so that at each stage of the iterative process the modified objective function was

$$t_f^2/10 + \lambda[x_1^2 + (x_2 - 1)^2 - .04]$$

for some positive scalar λ. Each of the optimal control subproblems was without terminal constraints but was subject to $|u(t)| \leq 1$, which rendered solution by a gradient-based technique somewhat slow but still feasible.

Starting with $\lambda_1 = 0.5$ and $\lambda_2 = 1.5$, a stationary point of the dual function was found by regula-falsi. Representative trajectories, optimal for various λ, are shown in Fig. 2.

REFERENCES

1. A.E. Bryson and W.F. Denham, "A Steepest-Ascent Method for Solving Optimum Programming Problems," ASME, J. of Appl.Mech., June 1962, pp. 247-257.

2. L.S. Lasdon, S.K. Mitter, and A.D. Waren, "The Conjugate Gradient Method for Optimal Control Problems", IEEE Trans. on Automatic Control, Vol.AC-12, No.2, pp.132-138 (April 1967).

3. J.F. Sinnott and D.G. Luenberger, "Solution of Optimal Control Problems by the Method of Conjugate Gradients," Preprints of 1967 Joint Automatic Control Conference, Philadelphia, pp. 566-573.

4. B.V. Shah, R.J. Buehler, and O. Kempthorne, "Some Algorithms for Minimizing a Function of Several Variables," J. Soc. Indust. Appl. Math., Vol.12, No.1, p.p. 74-91 (March 1964).

5. H.J. Kelley, R.E. Kopp, and H.G. Moyer, "A Trajectory Optimization Technique Based upon the Theory of the Second Variation," Progress in Astronautics and Aeronautics, 14, pp.559-582 (Academic Press, New York,1964).

6. Samuel Karlin, Mathematical Methods and Theory in Games, Programming, and Economics, Vol.1 (Addison-Wesley Publishing Company, Inc., Reading, Massachusetts, 1959).

7. A.Ralston, A First Course in Numerical Analysis, p.323 (McGraw-Hill, New York, 1965).

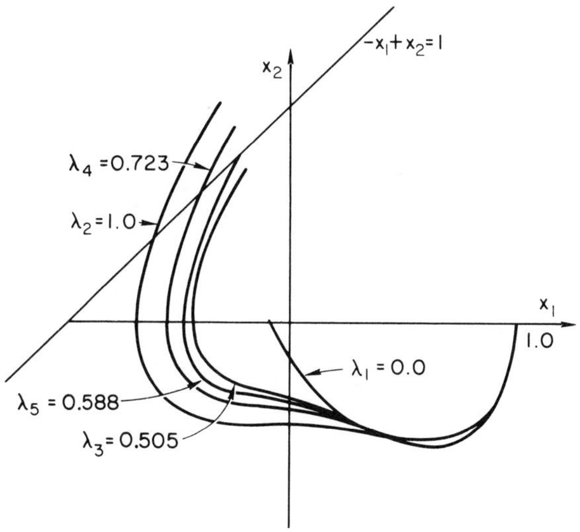

Fig. 1 Trajectories for Problem 1

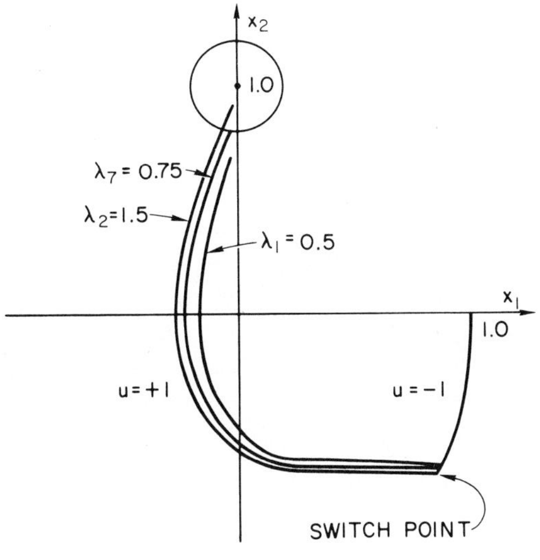

Fig. 2 Trajectories for Problem 2

OPTIMAL INPUT CODE ASSIGNMENT FOR THRESHOLD-OR SYNTHESIS

A. MARZOLLO and P. SIPALA
Istituto di Elettrotecnica, Universita' di TRIESTE (ITALY)

I. Introduction.

The problem to be considered here is the one of finding a minimal threshold-or realization of a given two-valued function g of m variables, where each variable may take any of $q>2$ values.

A preliminary step for the realization of the function g consists in assigning some binary code C to the values assumed by the input variables, in order to get, instead of g, a Boolean function f^C (it is clear that, for a given g, the corresponding function f^C depends on the chosen code C). The threshold-or realization of g is in this way reduced to that of the Boolean function f^C, as shown in Fig.1. The minimal threshold-or realization of f^C may be determined through a standard procedure (cfr.(1),ch.6); its complexity will clearly depend, for the given g, on the function f^C obtained from it, that is on the binary coding of the input variables. The essential problem consits then in the choice of this input code.

In this paper a meaningful and effective cost function for the complexity of the threshold-or realization of g is taken, and the problem is treated of the choice of the input code which corresponds to a minimum of such a cost function.

II. Statement of the problem.

Let g be a two-valued function of the m variables $y_1,\dots,y_m$, where each y_j may assume any of the distinct values $a_1,\dots,a_q$ $(q>2)$.

Let the function g be defined by giving the two disjoint sets Y_a and Y_b:

$$Y_a=\{\underline{y}: g(\underline{y})=1\} \quad ; \quad Y_b=\{\underline{y}: g(\underline{y})=0\} \qquad (1)$$

where $\underline{y}$ is the vector $(y_1,\dots,y_m)$. Notice that g needs not

to be completely specified, but may have also don't care arguments.
To obtain a threshold-or synthesis of g it is necessary to substitute it with a two-valued function f^C of binary variables (-1,1) through a binary codification of the original variables $y_1,\dots,y_m$. This is done in the following way.
Let k be the least integer such that $2^k \geq q$, and let B be the set of all k-component vectors $\underline{b}_1,\dots,\underline{b}_{2^k}$, where each component of $\underline{b}_j=(b_{j1},\dots,b_{jk})$ may be either -1 or 1. Let C be any coding function which assigns to each a_i a different element of B:

$$\underline{b}_j = C(a_i) \qquad (2)$$

The binary vectors $\underline{b}_j$ may be interpreted as the vertices of the k-dimensional unit hypercube. A code C means then an assignment of each of the values $a_1,\dots,a_q$ to a different vertex of this hypercube according to (2).
Through any coding (2) the given function g is reduced to a Boolean function f^C:

$$f^C(z_{11},\dots,z_{1k},\dots\dots,z_{m1},\dots,z_{mk}) = g(y_1,\dots,y_m) \qquad (3)$$

where

$$(z_{i1},\dots,z_{ik}) = C(y_i) \qquad (i=1,\dots,m) \qquad (4)$$

and each z_{ir} is either -1 or 1.
From the sets Y_a and Y_b defining g according to (1) and from the relation (4) it is clear how to obtain the two disjoint sets Z_a^C and Z_b^C defining f^C:

$$Z_a^C = \{\underline{z}: f^C(\underline{z}) = 1\} \quad ; \quad Z_b^C = \{\underline{z}: f^C(\underline{z}) = 0\} \qquad (5)$$

$$\underline{z} = (z_{11},\dots,z_{1k},\dots\dots,z_{m1},\dots,z_{mk})$$

It is usual to consider the sets Z_a^C and Z_b^C defining f^C through (5) as sets of vertices of an $(m \times k)$-dimensional unit hypercube. From a geometrical point of view, a threshold-or synthesis of f^C consists in finding a piecewise linear hypersurface S separating Z_a^C and Z_b^C .Let $H_1,\dots,H_r$ be the r hyperplanes defining S; then to each one of them there corresponds one threshold element of the network realizing f^C(cfr.Fig.1).
For any Boolean function a method exists to obtain an optimal threshold-or realization of it, i.e. one consisting of a minimal number of threshold elements (cfr.(1),ch.6). The number of elements of which the optimal realization of f^C consists will clearly depend, for a given g, only on the code C, and will therefore be denoted by $r^*(C)$.

As mentioned in the introduction, the problem to be treated here is the one of finding an optimal code $\bar{C}$, i.e. a code such that, for the given g, $r^*(C)$ is minimal for $C = \bar{C}$.

III. Choice of the cost function.

It is quite difficult to given an explicit expression for the function $r^*(C)$, which is the actual cost function associated with the realization of g through a coding C of the input variables $y_1,\ldots,y_m$. Indeed, $r^*(C)$ is obtained from C first by transforming the given function g into f^C according to (3) and then by applying to f^C a complex algorithm which gives its minimal threshold-or realization. For these reasons, the cost function $r^*(C)$ will here be substituted with a different cost function J(C). Such a function has to meet the requirements of being both easily expressible in terms of C and of being closely related to $r^*(C)$.
It is proposed here to adopt, as J(C), a function proportional to the distance between the centers of mass of the sets Z_a^C and Z_b^C defining f^C as in (5).
Recall that Z_a^C and Z_b^C are two disjoint sets of vertices of an $(m \times k)$-dimensional hypercube. To any C there corresponds a particular unique placement of the elements of the sets Z_a^C and Z_b^C on vertices of the hypercube. It is intuitive that the farther sets Z_a^C and Z_b^C are pulled apart by changing C, the easier it will be to separate them, i.e. to find a smaller number of hyperplanes forming a piecewise linear separation hypersurface S. An effective way to achieve this aim is certainly to maximize, within the given constraints, the distance of the center of mass $\underline{p}(C)$ of Z_a^C and of the center of mass $\underline{q}(C)$ of Z_b^C .
It is possible to find an expression for the components of $\underline{p}(C)$ and $\underline{q}(C)$ in the following way.
Observe first that, if $q < 2^k$, dummy values $a_{q+1},\ldots,a_{2^k}$ may be introduced so that the correspondence C maps $A=a_1,\ldots,a_{2^k}$ onto $B=\underline{b}_1,\ldots,\underline{b}_{2^k}$. Correspondence C may then be represented by a matrix $X = \|x_{ij}\| (i,j=1,\ldots,2^k)$, where

$x_{ij} = 1$ if vector $\underline{b}_j$ corresponds to a_i, i.e. $\underline{b}_j$ is used as code for a_i;

$x_{ij} = 0$ if not.

Clearly, to have a one-to-one correspondence, the following constraints must be taken into account

$$\sum_{j=1}^{2^k} x_{ij} = 1 \qquad (i = 1,\dots,2^k)$$
$$\sum_{i=1}^{2^k} x_{ij} = 1 \qquad (j = 1,\dots,2^k) \tag{6}$$

Introduce now the matrix $\Phi = \| \varphi_{rs} \|$ $(r=1,\dots,m;\ s=1,\dots,2^k)$, where φ_{rs} is the number of vectors $\underline{y} \in Y_a$ (cfr.(1)) having their r-th component y_r equal to a_s, and similarly the matrix $\Psi = \| \psi_{rs} \|$ $(r=1,\dots,m;\ s=1,\dots,2^k)$, where ψ_{rs} is the number of vectors $\underline{y} \in Y_b$ with $y_r = a_s$.
Notice that, since the dummy values $a_{q+1},\dots,a_{2k}$ were introduced only for convenience and are never assumed by the input variables $y_1,\dots,y_m$, it follows that $\varphi_{rs} = \psi_{rs} = 0$ for $s > q$ and any $r = 1,\dots,m$.
Let n_a be the number of vectors $\underline{y}$ in Y_a and n_b the number of vectors $\underline{y}$ in Y_b. The components $p_{11},\dots,p_{1k},\dots,p_{m1},\dots,p_{mk}$ of $\underline{p}(C)$ and $q_{11},\dots,q_{1k},\dots\dots,q_{m1},\dots,q_{mk}$ of $\underline{q}(C)$ are then

$$p_{rt}(C) = (1/n_a) \sum_{s=1}^{2^k} \varphi_{rs} \sum_{j=1}^{2^k} x_{sj} b_{jt}$$
$$q_{rt}(C) = (1/n_b) \sum_{s=1}^{2^k} {}_{rs} \sum_{j=1}^{2^k} x_{sj} b_{jt} \tag{7}$$

for $r = 1,\dots,m$ and $t = 1,\dots,k$.
The distance $d(C)$ between $p(C)$ and $q(C)$ is

$$d(C) = \left\{ \sum_{r=1}^{m} \sum_{t=1}^{k} \left[p_{rt}(C) - q_{rt}(C) \right]^2 \right\}^{(1/2} \tag{8}$$

According to the previous considerations, as cost function $J(C)$ will be assumed the following

$$J(C) = - n_a^2\, n_b^2\, d^2(C) \tag{9}$$

which obviously takes its minima where and only where the distance $d(C)$ is maximal.

IV. Method of minimization.

It will now be shown that the problem of minimizing J(C) may be reduced to a quadratic assignment problem. This last problem has been originally formulated in economics for the choice of placements of interrelated economic activities within a given set of possible locations, such that the overall transportation cost is minimized.

The following manipulations are intended to give to J(C) the form of the cost function of the quadratic assignment problem, in the special form of Koopmans and Beckmann (2).

From Eqs. (7), (8), (9) one gets

$$J(C) = -n_a^2 n_b^2 \sum_{1}^{m}{}_r \sum_{1}^{k}{}_t \left(p_{rt} - q_{rt}\right)^2 =$$

$$= -\sum_{1}^{m}{}_r \sum_{1}^{k}{}_t \left(n_a n_b p_{rt} - n_a n_b q_{rt}\right)^2 =$$

$$= -\sum_{1}^{m}{}_r \sum_{1}^{k}{}_t \left[\sum_{1}^{2^k}{}_s \left(n_b \varphi_{rs} - n_a \psi_{rs}\right) \sum_{1}^{2^k}{}_j x_{sj} b_{jt}\right]^2 =$$

$$= -\sum_{1}^{m}{}_r \sum_{1}^{k}{}_t \left[\sum_{1}^{2^k}{}_s \sum_{1}^{2^k}{}_u \left(n_b \varphi_{rs} - n_a \psi_{rs}\right)\left(n_b \varphi_{ru} - n_a \psi_{ru}\right) \sum_{1}^{2^k}{}_j \sum_{1}^{2^k}{}_v b_{jt} b_{vt} x_{sj} x_{uv}\right]$$

$$= -\sum_{1}^{2^k}{}_{sujv} \left[\sum_{1}^{m}{}_r \left(n_b \varphi_{rs} - n_a \psi_{rs}\right)\left(n_b \varphi_{ru} - n_a \psi_{ru}\right)\right]\left[\sum_{1}^{k}{}_t b_{jt} b_{vt}\right] x_{sj} x_{uv}$$

Defining now α_{su}, β_{jv} $(s,u,j,v,=1,\dots,2^k)$ as follows

$$\alpha_{su} = \sum_{1}^{m}{}_r \left(n_b \varphi_{rs} - n_a \psi_{rs}\right)\left(n_b \varphi_{ru} - n_a \psi_{ru}\right)$$

$$\beta_{jv} = -\sum_{1}^{k}{}_t b_{jt} b_{vt} \qquad (10)$$

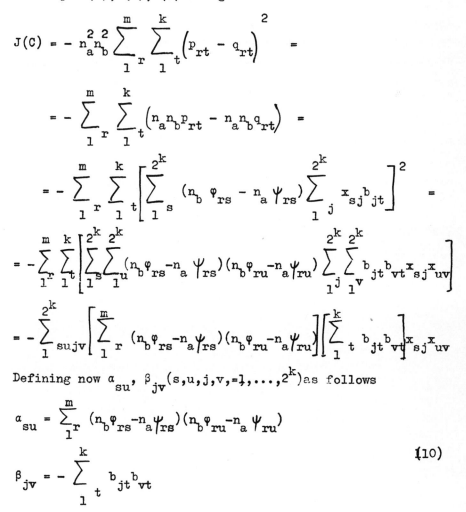

J(C) may be written in the following way

$$J(C) = \sum_{1\ sujv}^{2^k} \alpha_{su}\beta_{jv}x_{sj}x_{uv} \tag{11}$$

The determination of a matrix $X = \|x_{ij}\|$ corresponding to a minimum of a cost function of the form (11) with constraints (6) and

$$x_{ij} = 0 \text{ or } 1 \qquad (i,j = 1,\dots,2^k) \tag{12}$$

is the so called Koopmans-Beckmann quadratic assignment problem.

In the particular case examined here, coefficients α_{su} and β_{jv} enjoy the following further properties

$$\alpha_{su} = \alpha_{us} \qquad ; \qquad \beta_{jv} = \beta_{vj} \tag{13}$$

as it is immediate to see from their definition (10).

Furthermore, notice that

$$\beta_{jj} = - \sum_{1\ t}^{k} b_{jt}^2 = - k \tag{14}$$

since each b_{jt} may be only -1 or 1, and that from Eqs.(6), (12) for every s $x_{sj}x_{sv} = 0$ if $j \neq v$, and for every j $x_{sj}x_{uj} = 0$ if $s \neq u$.

Therefore one gets

$$J(C) = \sum_{1\ sujv}^{2^k} \alpha_{su}\ \beta_{jv}\ x_{sj}\ x_{uv} = \tag{15}$$

$$= \sum_{s\neq u} {}_{su} \sum_{j\neq v} {}_{jv} \alpha_{su}\beta_{jv}x_{sj}x_{uv} + \sum_s \sum_{j\neq v} {}_{jv} \alpha_{ss}\beta_{jv}x_{sj}x_{sv} +$$

$$+ \sum_{s\neq u} {}_{su} \sum_j \alpha_{su}\beta_{jj}x_{sj}x_{uj} + \sum_s \sum_j \alpha_{ss}\beta_{jj}x_{sj}^2 =$$

$$= \sum_{s\neq u} {}_{su} \sum_{j\neq v} {}_{jv} \alpha_{su}\beta_{jv}x_{sj}x_{uv} - k \sum_s \alpha_{ss} =$$

$$= \sum_{\substack{su \\ s \neq u}} \sum_{\substack{jv \\ j \neq v}} \alpha_{su} \beta_{jv} x_{sj} x_{uv} + H$$

where H is a constant term.

Properties (13) and the particular form (15) for J(C) are suitable to be exploited for the construction of effective computational algorithms for the solution of the quadratic assignment problem. Indeed, they have been used for instance by Steinberg (3) and Gaschutz and Ahrens (4), who gave a procedure for the determination of suboptimal solutions. Also optimal algorithms exist (see Gilmore (5), Lawler (6)), but they are computationally feasible only for problems of relatively small dimensions. Indeed, the length of computation necessary for the solution of a quadratic assignment problem increases very rapidly with the dimension N of the matrix X, as it is obvious if one observes that the number of possible code assignments is the number $N = 2^k!$ of the permutation matrices X. However, there are important peculiarities of the present code assignment problem which allow significant further reductions of the computational effort. Indeed the search for an optimal or suboptimal code assignment does not need to be made among all $2^k!$ possible assignments. To see this recall that the code assignment has been interpreted as the placement of each of the values $a_1 \ldots a_{2^k}$ on the vertices $\underline{b}_1 \ldots \underline{b}_{2^k}$ of the k-dimensional unit hypercube. Once a placement has been made, any other placement which preserves the relative distance among the locations of the a_j's on the hypercube is equivalent to it in the sense that it leaves the value of J(C) in (15) unchanged. This is clear if one observes that coefficients β_{jv} in (15 are by (10) and (14)

$$\beta_{jv} = - \sum_{1}^{k} {}_t \, b_{jt} \, b_{vt} = \frac{1}{2} (\delta^2_{jv} - 2k)$$

where δ^2_{jv} is the squared distance between vertices $\underline{b}_j$ and $\underline{b}_v$. The number of placements equivalent to any given one is the number $k! \, 2^k$ of isometries of the k-dimensional unit hypercube. As a result, the 2^k possible code assignments may be grouped into

$$\frac{2^k!}{k! \, 2^k} = \frac{(2^k - 1)!}{k!}$$

classes and the search may be limited only among $\frac{(2^k-1)!}{k!}$ elements, each representing a different class.

V. Example.

The following example is intended to given an illustration of the assignment of an input code in a simple case, and to clarify the above procedure and notations.
Let g be a two-valued function of $m=2$ variables y_1, y_2, each of them being allowed to take any of $q=4$ values a_1, a_2, a_3, a_4.
Let g be defined by the following sets

$$Y_a = \{(a_1,a_1),(a_1,a_2),(a_1,a_3),(a_1,a_4),(a_2,a_4)\\ (a_3,a_4),(a_4,a_1),(a_4,a_2),(a_4,a_3),(a_4,a_4)\} \qquad (n_a = 10)$$

$$Y_b = \{(a_2,a_1),(a_2,a_2),(a_2,a_3)\\ (a_3,a_1),(a_3,a_2),(a_3,a_3)\} \qquad (n_b = 6)$$

In this case $k=2$, vectors $\underline{b}_1,\ldots,\underline{b}_{2^k}$ are $\underline{b}_1=(-1,-1)$; $\underline{b}_2=(-1,1)$; $\underline{b}_3=(1,-1)$; $\underline{b}_4=(1,1)$, and matrices $\alpha = \|\alpha_{rs}\|$ and $\beta = \|\beta_{jv}\|$ are

$$\alpha = \begin{Vmatrix} 640 & -512 & -512 & 384 \\ -512 & 640 & 640 & -768 \\ -512 & 640 & 640 & -768 \\ 384 & -768 & -768 & 1152 \end{Vmatrix} \qquad \beta = \begin{Vmatrix} -2 & 0 & 0 & 2 \\ 0 & -2 & 2 & 0 \\ 0 & 2 & -2 & 0 \\ 2 & 0 & 0 & -2 \end{Vmatrix}$$

A code C_1 may be defined as follows
$C_1(a_1)=\underline{b}_1$; $C_1(a_2)=\underline{b}_2$; $C_1(a_3)=\underline{b}_3$; $C_1(a_4)=\underline{b}_4$.
With this choice of the code, the transformed Boolean function $f^{C_1}(z_{11},z_{12},z_{21},z_{22})$ is defined by the sets $Z_a^{C_1}$ and $Z_b^{C_1}$ as follows:

$$f^{C_1}(\underline{z}) = 1$$

for $\underline{z} \in Z_a^{C_1} = \{(-1,-1,-1,-1),(-1,-1,-1,1),(-1,-1,1,-1),\\ (-1,-1,1,1),(-1,1,1,1),(1,-1,1,1),(1,1,-,-1),\\ (1,1,-1,1),(1,1,1,-1),(1,1,1,1)\}$

$$f^{C_1}(\underline{z}) = 0$$

for $\underline{z} \in Z_b^{C_1} = \{(-1,1,-1,-1),(-1,1,-1,1),(-1,1,1,-1),\\ (1,-1,-1,-1),(1,-1,-1,1),(1,-1,1,-1)\}$.

The value of the function $J(C) = n_a^2 n_b^2 d^2(C)$ is in the case $J(C_1) = -2048$.
The optimal threshold-or realization of $f^{C_1}(\underline{z})$ is shown in Fig.2 and requires two threshold elements in the first level (see (1),p.125).
A code $\bar{C}$ which minimizes $J(C)$ is the following

$\bar{C}(a_1)=\underline{b}_2;\bar{C}(a_2)=\underline{b}_1;\bar{C}(a_3)=\underline{b}_3;\ \bar{C}(a_4)=\underline{b}_4,$
i.e. the optimal x_{ij} from the matrix

$$\bar{X} = \begin{Vmatrix} 0 & 1 & 0 & 0 \\ 1 & 0 & 0 & 0 \\ 0 & 0 & 1 & 0 \\ 0 & 0 & 0 & 1 \end{Vmatrix}$$

The cost function $J(C)$ takes its minimal value $J(\bar{C})= -11264$. In this case sets $Z_a^{\bar{C}}$ and $Z_b^{\bar{C}}$ are

$$Z_a^{\bar{C}} =\{(-1,1,-1,1),(-1,1,-1,-1),(-1,1,1,-1),(-1,1,1,1),(-1,-1,1,1),(1,-1,1,1),(1,1,-1,1),(1,1,-1,-1),(1,1,1,-1),(1,1,1,1)\}$$

$$Z_b^{\bar{C}} =\{(-1,-1,-1,1),(-1,-1,-1,-1),(-1,-1,1,-1),(1,-1,-1,1),(1,-1,-1,-1),(1,-1,1,-1)\}.$$

The optimal threshold-or realization of $f^{\bar{C}}(\underline{z})$ requires only one threshold element (cfr.(1),Table 5.2) and is shown in Fig.3.

VI. Conclusions.

The problem of the choice of a code for the input variables of a two-valued function g of non-binary variables, in order to obtain an optimal threshold-or synthesis, has been reduced to a quadratic assignment problem of a special form. Existing algorithms for the solution of this problem have been considered, and possible improvements, particularly suitable for the special case under consideration, have been suggested.

Acknowledgement.

The authors wish to thank Prof. A. Lepschy for his encouragement and useful suggestions during the writing of this paper.

References.

(1) M.L. Dertouzos: " Threshold logic: a synthesis approach" M.I.T. Research Monograph No.32.M.I.T. Press, Cambridge, Mass., 1965

(2) T.C. Koopmans, M. Beckmann: " Quadratic Assignment Problems Algorithms and the location of indivisible facilities" Econometrica vol.25,pp.52-76, 1957

(3) L. Steinberg: " The Backboard wiring problem: a placement algorithm" S.I.A.M. Review vol.3 No.1, pp. 37-50,

January 1961

(4) G.K. Gaschütz, J.H. Ahrens: " Suboptimal algorithms for the quadratic assignment problem" Naval Research Logistic Quarterly vol.13 No.1, pp. 49-62, March 1968

(5) P.C. Gilmore: " Optimal and suboptimal algorithms for the quadratic assignment problem" S.I.A.M. Journal vol.10 No. 2, pp. 305-313, June 1962

(6) E.L.Lawler: " The Quadratic Assignment Problem" Management Science vol. 9 No.4, pp. 586-599, July 1963

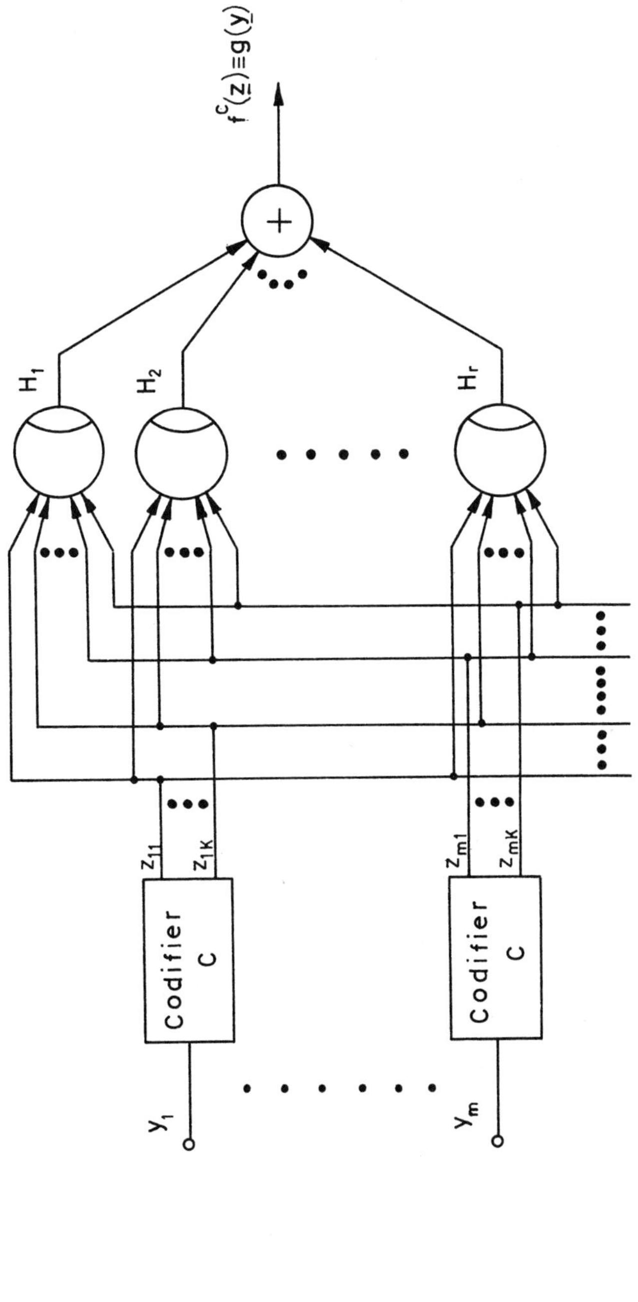

Figure 1 - Threshold-or realization of $f^C(\underline{z}) = g(\underline{y})$

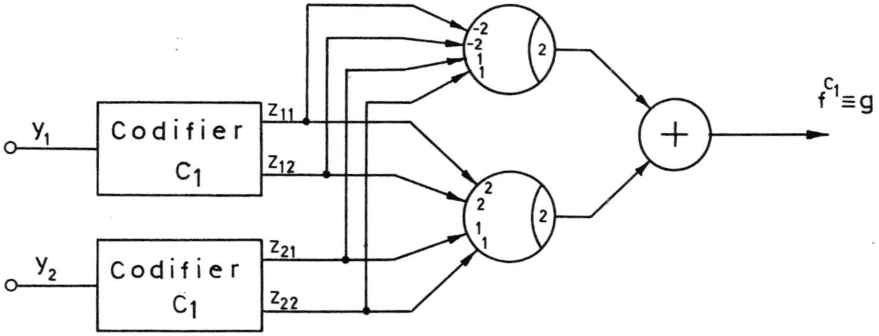

Figure 2 - Optimal threshold-or realization of $f^{C_1}(\underline{z})$

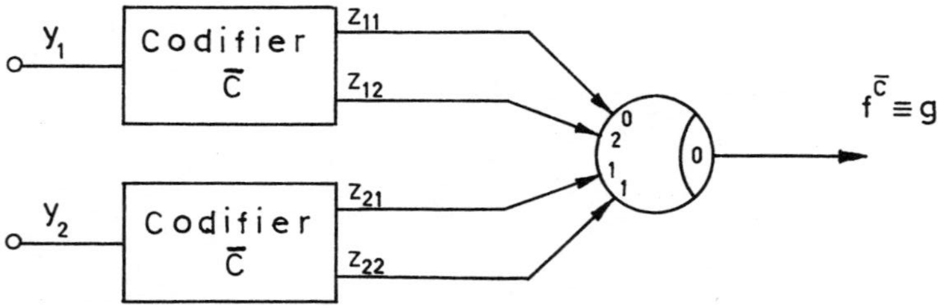

Figure 3 - Optimal threshold-or realization of $f^{\bar{C}}(\underline{z})$

FILE COMPRESSION USING HUFFMAN CODING

W. D. Maurer
Department of Electrical Engineering and Computer Science
University of California
Berkeley, California

This paper describes the application of well-known techniques of minimum redundancy coding to a problem of growing importance in computer systems.

1. The File Compression Problem

The problem with which we shall be concerned arises in all time-sharing systems, but the solution is applicable to more general systems, including multiprogrammed and simple batch-processing systems, in which tape, disk, drum, or even card files are used. It is probably most useful in a time-sharing environment, because in such an environment the cost of keeping files is quite high. In a commercial time-sharing system, all data which would in a batch-processing system be kept on cards -- such as source programs, object programs, test data, and actual data -- is kept on disk and charged for by the month; typical rates are between 25¢ and $2.00 per thousand characters per month. When this is compared with the negligible cost of storing a deck of cards, it is seen that any method that can be found to reduce the size of disk files, while still retaining the information which they contain in a retrievable manner, will be well worth the effort. Even in a batch-processing system, however, it is often advisable to reduce the size of card or tape files.

We may view the file compression problem in the abstract by considering a file as a sequence of n bits. Given a file f, we wish to apply to it an invertible transformation T which will reduce the number of bits n. It is clear that no transformation T will reduce n for all possible sequences f of n bits; however, in practice, we are never concerned with all such sequences, but only with a certain subclass of sequences, each of which possesses a certain redundancy property. By considering this property we derive, corresponding to the given subclass, an approperiate transformation T. Other factors that enter into our choice of T are the amounts of time and memory space taken up by the algorithm which performs T, and by the algorithm which performs the inverse of T.

Frequently the cost (in terms of computer time) of performing the transformation T and its inverse can be effectively reduced to zero. For example, an algorithm which reads the file f may be input-output limited; that is, it may take more time to read f than it takes to process f. In this case, the algorithm may be modified to read the transformed file Tf rather than f, and, at the same time, perform the inverse of T; it is quite possible that the resulting algorithm will still be input-output limited and therefore that no extra computer time will be taken. Similarly, if an input-output limited algorithm writes f, it may be altered to transform f and write Tf instead.

Most file compression which has been performed up to now is of a trivial nature and not worth a separate mention in print. For the compression of symbolic files, a very commonly used method is the elimination of blanks (for FORTRAN source files) or the replacement of a string of blanks by a single blank or by a special character followed by a count of the number of blanks. The use of relocatable binary files may be considered as allied to file compression, although in this case the transformation T is not strictly invertible. The SQUOZE feature of the SOS system for the IBM 709 is an excellent example of quite complex file compression based on numerous technical details of a symbolic program. One might also mention the so-called "exception method" in commercial data processing, which attempts to reduce the number of times that identical data is entered into a system; this amounts to compression of input files. Still another example of file compression is the "I-language" for the IBM 1401 (unpublished), which allowed print files produced by the IBM 7090 to be produced on tape in a compressed manner; this tape would then be read by the 1401, expanded, and printed.

The file compression algorithms which we consider in this paper are mathematical in nature. They are universal in the sense that they may be applied to any collection of files and do not depend on special-case analysis of properties of the particular class of files under consideration. There is, of course, no guarantee that compression actually compresses -- that is, the length of the transformed file is not always less than the length of the original file. In practice, however, it is found that the amount of redundancy in a file increases with the length of the file, and hence each transformation T will actually compress almost all files under consideration which are longer than some threshold value.

The algorithms themselves have been coded by a graduate student, Vikas M. Sahasrabudhe. Work on this algorithm was started under National Science Foundation Grant JO-00043, and is continuing under the auspices of the Institute of Library Research at the University of California (Berkeley).

2. Message Compression and Huffman Coding

The problem of file compression is closely related to the problem of message compression. This is a historically earlier problem which was considered by Huffman in his pioneering paper (1). Whenever a digital message is transmitted over a channel, there may be reasons to reduce the size of the message, particularly if the transmission rate is slow. The abstract message compression problem is the same as the abstract file compression problem. Our approach is to use Huffman's methods, but to cast them in the form of a computer program.

In Huffman's work, it is assumed that the message is composed of a sequence of n characters, and that the characters are further coded as sequences of bits. The use of the word "character" in this context, however, is unduly restrictive, as Huffman's solution applies equally well to any other two-level coding scheme. An English text, for example, may be thought of as composed of English words, each of which is coded as a sequence of bits. An ALGOL program may be considered as containing certain special words such as begin, end, if, for, step, until, procedure, and so on, together with other words and special characters, which may then be coded as sequences of bits. (In fact, the Polish-string ALGOL interpretive routines such as BC-ALGOL effectively perform a transformation of this type on the source program in the first pass.) We will assume only that there is a set S of symbols, and that the message to be compressed consists of a sequence of these symbols. Huffman's solution consists entirely of devising a way of assigning binary codes to symbols which takes into account the frequency of occurrence of the symbols. A symbol which occurs more frequently should be encoded in such a way as to take fewer bits. At the same time, the coding scheme should be consistent, in that no code for a symbol should be an initial segment of any other such code, in order that the message may be unambiguously decoded. We illustrate Huffman's method with a simple message:

THE NEST IS HERE IN THE TREE

Considered as a string of characters in the usual sense, including blank characters, there are eight distinct characters: T, H, E, N, S, I, R, and the blank. Eight characters may be given integer codes from 0 to 7, each of which takes three bits. If the given message is encoded in this way, it will take a total of 84 bits, since there are 28 characters in the message. The Huffman code for this message, however, does not assign a three-bit code to each character. Instead, it assigns two-bit codes to E and the blank, three-bit codes to T and H, and four-bit codes to N, S, I, and R. Using this code, a message consisting of one instance of each of the eight characters would be encoded in 26 bits, as against 24 bits for the simple universal three-bit code. Nevertheless, the actual message THE NEST IS HERE IN THE TREE is encoded in 79 bits, rather than 84, if the Huffman code is used. This is due to the fact that the letters N, S, I, and R, to which four-bit codes were assigned, occur only twice each, while the blank occurs six times and the character E occurs seven times.

The actual method of assigning codes is as follows:

(1) Write each symbol to be coded in a horizontal line, and under each symbol its corresponding frequency. (In Huffman's work, the frequencies were often expressed as probabilities of occurrence, i. e., as real numbers between 0 and 1; however, an equivalent and simpler formulation may be made in this case by giving the actual count, for each character, of the number of times it occurs.) Thus in this case we have:

E	blank	T	H	N	S	I	R
7	6	4	3	2	2	2	2

(2) Build a coding tree underneath these symbols, which are considered as the leaves of the tree. The coding tree is built up by an iteration on the nodes of the tree. During this process, certain nodes are referred to as <u>current</u>. Initially, the current nodes are the leaves; the process terminates when the number of current nodes has been reduced to one, namely, the trunk of the tree. The process to be iterated is as follows:

(a) Consider the two smallest current nodes. (Every node will have a number associated with it. One node is smaller than another if its associated number is smaller. If there are several nodes which are smallest and equal, an arbitrary choice may be made.)

(b) Remove these two nodes from the collection of current nodes.

(c) Form a new node under these two nodes, with pointers to the two nodes in question. The number associated with the new node is the sum of the numbers associated with the original two nodes. The new node is added to the collection of current nodes.

(The tree-building process is shown in Figure 1 for the message THE NEST IS HERE IN THE TREE.)

(3) Mark the two pointers emerging from each node created by the tree-building process as the 0 and 1 pointers (in an arbitrary way).

(4) The code of each symbol is now found by starting at the trunk of the tree and reading off the zeroes and ones in order, through the tree up to the given symbol. (Any symbol may, of course, be reached from the trunk in one and only one way.)

The codes assigned to the eight characters of the message in Figure 1 are as follows:

E	--	00
Blank	--	01
T	--	100
H	--	101
N	--	1100
S	--	1101
I	--	1110
R	--	1111

It may be observed that the conditions previously mentioned have here been satisfied. The code is internally consistent; no character code is an initial segment of any other character code. This Huffman code is, of course, only one of several possibilities, because of the arbitrary choices made in selecting the smallest current node and in assigning pointers as zero or one.

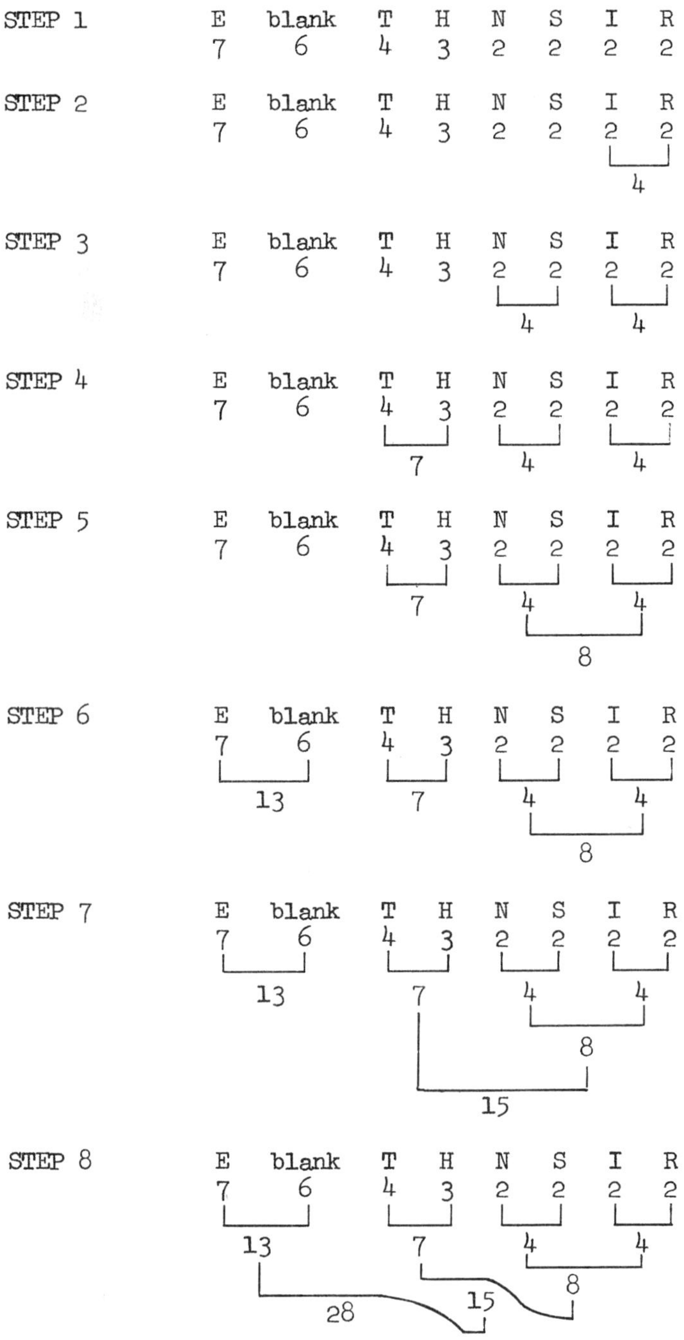

Figure 1. Huffman Coding Example

These Huffman codes are actually minimum redundancy codes, in the following sense: We may ask, of all possible methods of assigning binary codes to the symbols in a message in an internally consistent manner, which methods, when applied to the message, will produce a transformed message of smallest length. The answer is that any of the Huffman codes (relative to the arbitrary choices) will always produce a transformed message of smallest length.

3. Huffman Coding Algorithms

In encoding a file, we must first ask whether the file itself is to be taken as the sample from which the tree process mentioned above proceeds, or whether it is to be taken as part of a larger schema.

In the first case, there must be included, together with the encoded message, a description of the code. This may consist of the characters in order, each one followed by its code. Or the codes may be given first, followed by the corresponding characters. It is to be noted that, if all the codes are given together, this collection of codes may be compressed by simply noting the difference between each code and the preceding code. (It is clear that if all the codes are the same length, for example, the list of codes, as given, is completely redundant.) However, in any case, such a description of the code adds to the size of the coded message. We have found that for sample (character) messages of about 200 characters, there is often no significant reduction in the total size of the message when this transformation is performed; sometimes, there is no reduction at all.

Two ways may be found out of this difficulty. The first is to apply Huffman coding only to large messages, where the problem is not so apparent. The second is to consider each message, or file, as being of a certain type, and producing a single, global code for this type. For example, a code could be produced which is based on the frequency of letters in the English language. In this case, there will be included with the coded file a field giving the name of a library file which contains this global code. Whenever the coded file is read, this library file may be referenced to provide the decoding.

The processing of trees by a computer program is a subject which has received increasing attention in recent years; an excellent introduction to the subject is given in (2). In order to make the presentation as simple as possible, we shall build our trees as parallel items. To each of the nodes of the tree to be constructed, the computer will assign a sequence number, which has no purpose other than to identify the given node. Three arrays, count, left, and right, will be given; the node with sequence number k is then described completely by count(k), left(k), and right(k), as follows: The value of count(k) is the number associated with this node (not the sequence number k, but the number as given in Figure 1); the values of left(k) and right(k) are the sequence numbers of the two nodes to which this node points. If left(k) is zero, then this node is a leaf; in this case, right(k) denotes the corresponding symbol (in some way).

The current nodes are contained on a list, which we shall implement as a fourth array called current which is parallel to the others. The value of current(k) has a meaning only if the node with sequence number k is current. If this holds, then current(k) is the sequence number of the node which is next on the list of current nodes, following k. If the node k is the last node on this list, then current(k) is zero. The list is sorted; that is, the nodes are in ascending order by their associated (not sequence) numbers. This sorting is performed in order to have immediately available the smallest two nodes, as specified in the procedure above.

A variable called start gives the sequence number of the start of the list of current nodes. The iterative process of building the tree may now be implemented as follows:

(1) Set x equal to start; x is the sequence number of the smallest node.

(2) Set y equal to current(x); y is the sequence number of the next smallest node.

(3) Set start equal to current(y). This removes from the list of current nodes the two smallest nodes, x and y.

(4) Determine the sequence number of the new node. For this purpose, a counter called sequence may be kept. Initially, sequence is set to zero. At this stage, sequence is increased by 1.

(5) Set count(sequence) equal to the sum of count(x) and count(y); set left(sequence) equal to x, and set right(sequence) equal to y.

(6) The item whose sequence number is sequence must now be inserted on the list of current nodes in its proper order.

This is a well-known algorithm which is described, for example, in (3), pp. 96-97. For completeness, we give it here, with special reference to the parallel array situation we have set up. To start, we set a variable v to start.

(7) Compare count(sequence) with count(v). If count(v) is smaller, go to step 8; otherwise, go to step 10.

(8) We have not yet found the place on the list at which the new node is to be inserted. Therefore, move down the list by setting v equal to current(v).

(9) If v is now equal to zero, the new item is to be inserted at the end of the list. In this case, we may go to step 10. Otherwise, return to step 7.

(10) The new item is to be inserted at this point. We set current(sequence) equal to v, to indicate that v is the next node after the new node. We must also set current(u) equal to sequence, where u is the node preceding v on the list. This part of the algorithm will not be made explicit; but what we must do is to keep track, not only of v, but of u, at all times. In particular, in step 8, we must set u equal to v (that is, the previous value of v) before re-setting v.

This iterative process, then, will be continued until there is only one node left on the list. This condition may be sensed at step 2, where an attempt is made to get the second smallest element. At this point, y will be equal to zero, and a test for this condition may be made.

The above description is meant to be an example of the techniques which we have used. It does not describe them completely; in fact, other steps will be intermixed with the given steps, and our parallel arrays will actually be replaced by a more compact item structure. From a logical point of view, however, the steps given above are followed.

The actual algorithms were written in the FORTRAN language. They could, however, have been written in ALGOL or LISP, or in assembly language ("machine language"). The sample texts which were encoded were English texts. As the symbols, both the characters and the English words were taken; a word was defined as the collection of characters between two blanks. When words are taken as the elementary symbols, a longer text is necessary in order for this coding method to produce an actual reduction in length. However, for very long English texts, the word method provides a greater length reduction.

4. Extensions

In the algorithms discussed so far, it has been assumed that no encodable symbol is an initial segment of any other encodable symbol. It is true that one English word may be an initial segment of another, but the encodable symbols in this case consist of a collection of symbols terminated by a blank. Work is now proceeding on the removal of this restriction. For example, if characters are taken as the symbols, it might be economical to encode certain very common combinations of two characters (such as "qu") or three characters (such as "the") separately, rather than as combinations of two or three codes. This, however, introduces an additional difficulty into the encoding process (although not into the decoding process); for there is now more than one way of encoding a given message. The algorithm must attempt to decide, out of several possible ways of encoding, which will give the best code. This work is now proceeding under the Institute of Library Research, for the encoding of the very large files found in library work.

REFERENCES

1. Huffman, D. A., A method for the construction of minimum redundancy codes, Proc. IRE, September 1952, pp. 1098-1101.

2. Knuth, D. A., The art of computer programming, Vol. 1: Fundamental Algorithms, Addison-Wesley, 1968.

3. Maurer, W. D., Programming, Holden-Day, 1968.

OPTIMAL CONTROL COMPUTATIONS FOR NUCLEAR REACTORS*

By R. R. Mohler, S. F. Moon and H. J. Price†
University of New Mexico
Department of Electrical Engineering
Albuquerque, New Mexico

1. Introduction

The purpose of this paper is to analyze the optimal control of nuclear reactors. In particular, computations are made for time-optimal control of the classical mono-energetic kinetics with magnitude and rate constraints on neutron multiplication or reactivity (1) and for optimal control of a nuclear rocket reactor with numerous state constraints (2).

Minimal-propellant start of a nuclear rocket engine is most significant since a saving in propellant consumption can yield a compounded increase in payload by a saving in tankage. Due to its nonlinear nature and high dimensionality only a few simple constraints such as magnitude constraints on reactivity, propellant flow rate and reactor power have been included in previous work (3). By means of a quasilinear programming algorithm, the analysis presented here considers more complicated constraints which are present in practical systems. First however, an analysis of the time-optimal neutron kinetics allows a more basic understanding of optimal reactor control.

2. Time-Optimal Neutron Kinetics.

Time-optimal reactor control processes can be of distinct advantage for space-power applications, for military applications and the fuel-optimal rocket start (studied in the next section). Here the neutron kinetics are approximated by

$$\begin{aligned} \dot{x}_1 &= (v - a)x_1 + \lambda x_2 \\ \dot{x}_2 &= ax_1 - \lambda x_2 \end{aligned} \qquad (1)$$

where $x_1 > 0$ is neutron density, $x_2 > 0$ is average precursor

---

*Work sponsored by NSF Grant GK-1173.
†R. R. Mohler is presently with University of California, Engineering College, Los Angeles, California (1968-69).
H. J. Price is presently with Kaman Aircraft Co., Col. Spgs., Col.

density, v is the ratio of reactivity to mean generation time of neutrons, a is portion of neutrons from precursors divided by the mean generation time of neutrons and λ is average precursor decay constant.

The time-optimal v(t) that transfers the state from some initial equilibrium state $x(t_0) = x_0$ to some terminal equilibrium state $x(t_1) = x_1$ or to some terminal line $x_1(t_1) = x_{11}$ in two-dimensional state space is analyzed here. To be practical, it is further stipulated that the desired terminal condition is maintained for $t \geq t_1$, and that $|v| \leq \alpha$ and $|\dot{v}| \leq \eta$. Though the negative constraints may be less than the positive constraints in practice, symmetrical values are assumed for convenience. Here, α is a constant normally less than a, and η is a constant which depends on the application. Though a similar problem with the first constraint was solved in (4), the physical problem is complicated by the rate constraint. Nevertheless, with $x_3 = v$ and $\dot{x}_3 = u$, a straight-forward application of the maximum principle and its extensions for state constraints (5) yields

$$\begin{aligned} u &= \eta \operatorname{sgn} p_3 \text{ for } g(x) < 0 \\ u &= 0 \text{ for } g(x) = 0 \end{aligned} \tag{2}$$

where $g(x) = x_3^2 - \alpha^2$ and x is the state vector.

Since $u \equiv 0$ for $g(x) = 0$, the switching function, $p_3(t)$, is described by the usual adjoint system:

$$\begin{aligned} \dot{p}_1 &= (a - x_3)p_1 - ap_2 \\ \dot{p}_2 &= \lambda(p_2 - p_1), \\ \dot{p}_3 &= -x_1 p_1 \end{aligned} \tag{3}$$

for all t on (t_0, t_1) except at those values of t when trajectories enter a state constraint surface. Obviously the problem does not have a normal singular solution because $p_3(t) = 0$ requires that $p_1(t) = p_2(t) = 0$ from Eq. (3). If x(t) enters the state constraint boundary, $g(x) = 0$, at $t = t_a$, the corner condition shows a jump discontinuity in $p_3(t_a)$.

Analytic solution of Eqs. (1) and (3) is quite difficult, but the following argument yields the maximum number of control switchings (i.e., zeros of $p_3(t)$). For convenience it is assumed that $x_{11} > x_{10}$ and $t_0 = 0$.

Since Eq. (1) shows that $x_3(t)$ must take positive values to increase $x_1(t)$ from an initial equilibrium state, it might be guessed that an optimal control consists of $x_3(t) = \eta t$ on $(0, t_a)$, $x_3(t) = \alpha$ on $[t_a, t_b]$ and $x_3(t) = \alpha - \eta(t - t_b)$ on (t_b, t_1). The following argument, however, shows that the equilibrium set, $X_e = \{x: x_2 = (a/\lambda)x_1, x_3 = 0\}$, cannot be reached in finite time t_1 with $x_3(t) \geq 0$. For with time reversed, it is apparent from (1) that only these states $A = \{x: \dot{x}_2 < 0\}$ can be reached with $x_3(t) \geq 0$. Consequently, some negative reactivity ($x_3(t) < 0$) is required, and $p_3(t)$ must have more than two zeros on $(0, t_1)$ if $x_3(t) = \alpha$ on the non-zero interval $[t_a, t_b]$.

Since $x_3(t_1-) < 0$ and $u(t_1-) = \eta$, $p_3(t_1-) > 0$ from Eq. (2). Then, with

$$H(x,p,u) = p\cdot f = p_1[(x_3 - a)x_1 + \lambda x_2] + p_2[ax_1 - \lambda x_2] + p_3 u$$

non-negative, $\dot{x}_1(0) = \dot{x}_2(0) = 0$ and $x_{11} > x_{10}$ it is obvious that $p_3(0) \geq 0$.

Then, since $p_3(t)$ must have at least three zeros if $x_3(t) = \alpha$ on $[t_a, t_b]$, $\dot{p}_3(t_a) < 0$ with $p_3(t_a) = 0$ and $\dot{p}_3(t_d) > 0$ with $p_3(t_d) = 0$, where t_d is the last zero of $p_3(t)$ on $(0, t_1)$. Since $x_1(t)$ is positive for all t, $p_1(t_a) > 0$ and $p_1(t_d) < 0$ from Eq. (3). But it is shown in Appendix A that $p_1(t)$ has at most one zero. Hence $p_1(t_f) = 0$ where $t_a < t_f < t_d$. From (3) it is apparent that $p_3(t) = p_{30} - \int_0^t p_1 x_1 d\sigma$ can have at most two zeros, but since $p_3(t)$ can have two jump discontinuities at the state constraint-boundaries, $p_3(t)$ can have four zeros at most as shown on Fig. 1.

Since $|x_1 p_1| = |\dot{p}_3|$ is normally much larger near the terminal time than for $t < t_b$ (see Eqs. (1) and (3)). $t_1 - t_c$ is much smaller than t_b. In practice, the negative reactivity portion normally can be neglected since the resulting terminal error is smaller than the instrumentation error.

Obviously, the first switching occurs at $t_a = \alpha/\eta$, and the second at $t_b \simeq t_1 - \alpha/\eta$, but t_1 is not easily determined in closed form. For a particular problem, however, the time-optimal strategy is easily computed as shown by the examples.

Examples

Neglecting the negative reactivity, which results in an error of less than 0.4 per cent for this model, several sub-optimal trajectories are presented in Fig. 2. For these graphs $a = 65$ sec^{-1}, $\lambda = 0.4$ sec^{-1}, $\alpha = 58.5$ sec^{-1}, $\eta = 65$ sec^{-2}, and Runge-Kutta integration was utilized to obtain the data with an IBM 360.

For example, if $x_{11}/x_{10} = 2$ there is one switching at $t_a = t_1/2 = 0.825$ sec from Fig. 2. And, if $x_{11}/x_{10} = 10$, $t_a = \alpha/\eta \doteq 0.9$ sec, $t_1 = 2.34$ sec and $t_b = 1.44$ sec.

Neutron Level Control

The previous control of equilibrium end states is pertinent for some practical problems such as calibration during a reactor experiment for which time is at a premium. More

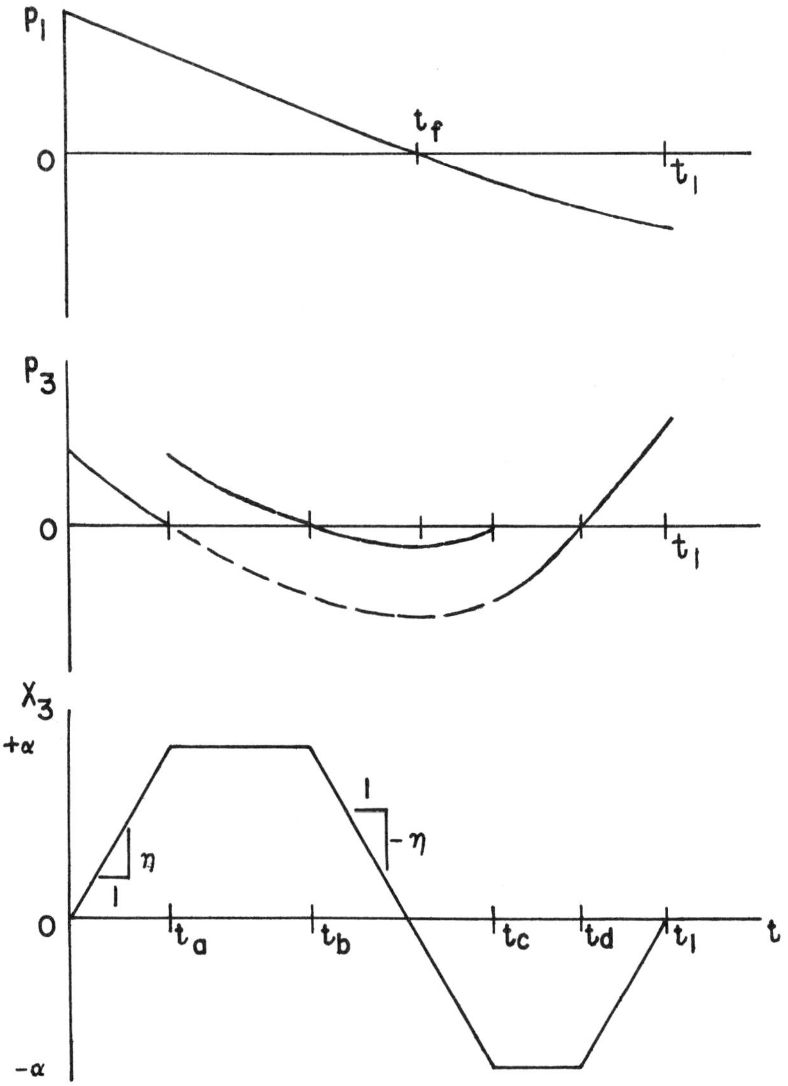

Fig. 1. Form of Time-Optimal Reactivity and Switching Function.

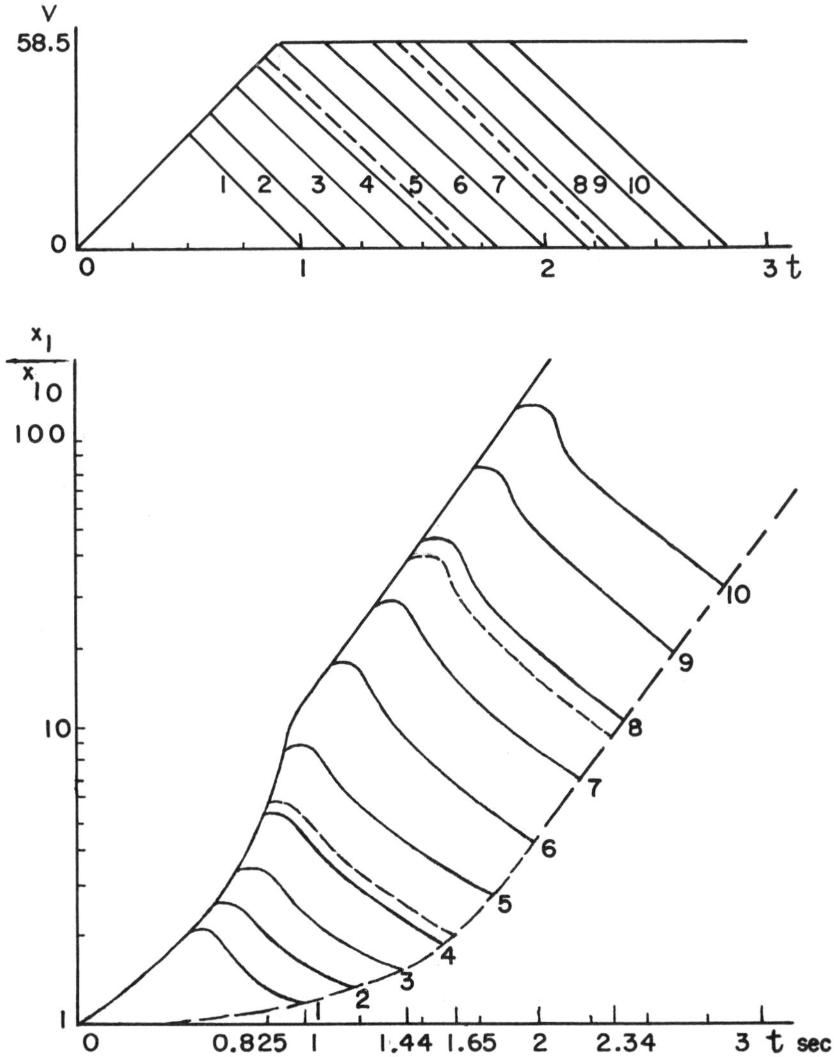

Fig. 2. Optimal Reactivities and Corresponding Neutron Levels

generally, however, the precursor level is of little interest, and it may be desired to control the kinetics from some initial equilibrium state x_0 to some $x_1(t_1) = x_{11} > x_{10}$ in such a manner that $x_1(t) \leq x_{11}$, $|x_3(t)| \leq \alpha$, $|u| \leq \eta$ for all t, and $\dot{x}_1(t) = 0$ for $t \geq t_1$.

For this problem $p_3(t_1) = 0$, and hence $p_3(t)$ can have only one zero on $(0, t_1)$. With a jump in $p_3(t)$ at $t = t_a$, $p_3(t)$ cannot have more than two zeros, or the time-optimal reactivity variation is a truncated trapezoid on $(0, t_1)$ where the terminal time t_1 is considerably less than for the previous problem. Time-optimality of this process is also obvious from the previous analysis and the principle of optimality.

From Eq. (1) and $\dot{x}_1 = 0$ the required terminal control is

$$v = x_3 = \dot{x}_2/x_{11}$$

for $t \geq t_1$, and it can be shown from Eq. (1) that $x_3(t)$ is continuous at $t = t_1$ with

$$x_3(t_1) = a - \frac{\lambda x_2(t_1)}{x_{11}}.$$

Also, from Eq. (1) it is apparent that the required terminal control is admissible if $\eta \geq a\lambda$. Then for $t \geq t_1$

$$x_1(t) = x_{11},$$

$$x_2(t) = (x_{21} - \frac{a}{\lambda} x_{11}) \exp [\lambda(t_1 - t)] + \frac{a}{\lambda} x_{11}$$

and

$$x_3(t) = (a - \frac{\lambda}{x_{11}} x_{21}) \exp [\lambda(t_1 - t)]$$

where $x_{21} = x_2(t_1)$. Again, the example time-optimal starts may be utilized with t_1 equal to the first time that $x_1(t) = x_{11}$ and with $\dot{x}_1(t) = 0$ for $t > t_1$.

It should be noted that the terminal trajectory is not stable; i.e., a small error such as results from the estimation measurement of $x_2(t)$ results in a divergence of $x_1(t)$ from x_{11}. This can be seen from a perturbation analysis. In practice this difficulty may be overcome by means of a suboptimal feedback controller of the classical type or by means of a dither (multiple bang-bang) controller — both of which are described in (6).

Multiple Precursors

A single-precursor model can be formulated to approximate accurately the short-time dynamics of the actual system. Also, it can be shown in a manner similar to that presented for the single precursor model that a nondegenerate singular solution does not exist for any multi-precursor neutron kinetics. In light of added precursors (increased dimensionality), however, the maximum number of control switchings might be questioned. But the following analysis shows that an added precursor group does not change the maximum number of switchings.

For the two-precursor group time-optimal control problem, the state and costate equations are given by

$$\begin{aligned} \dot{x}_1 &= (x_4 - a)x_1 + \lambda_2 x_2 + \lambda_3 x_3, \\ \dot{x}_2 &= a_2 x_1 - \lambda_2 x_2, \\ \dot{x}_3 &= a_3 x_1 - \lambda_3 x_3, \\ \dot{x}_4 &= u, \end{aligned} \tag{4}$$

$$\begin{aligned} \dot{p}_1 &= (a - x_4)p_1 - a_2 p_2 - a_3 p_3 \\ \dot{p}_2 &= \lambda_2 (p_2 - p_1), \\ \dot{p}_3 &= \lambda_3 (p_3 - p_1), \\ \dot{p}_4 &= -x_1 p_1, \end{aligned} \tag{5}$$

where $a = a_2 + a_3$, $|x_4| \leq \alpha$ and $|u| \leq \eta$.

Then if $x_{11} > x_{10}$, it is readily shown from the state equation (4) and the previous problem, that

$$u(t_1-) = \dot{x}_4(t_1-) > 0, \text{ and } x_4(t_1) = 0 . \tag{6}$$

From (6) and $u = \eta \operatorname{sgn}(p_4)$,

$$u(t_1-) = \eta \text{ , and } p_4(t_1-) > 0.$$

It was shown in the previous problem that

$$p_4(0) > 0, \text{ if } x_{11} > x_{10}.$$

Now, let t_a and t_d be the time of the first and the last zeros of $p_4(t)$ respectively as defined before. It is obvious from Eq. (5) that $\dot{p}_4(t_a) < 0$, $p_1(t_a) > 0$, $\dot{p}_4(t_d) > 0$, $p_1(t_d) < 0$.

Since $p_1(t)$ is continuous and cannot have more than two zeros on $[0, t_1]$ (see Appendix B), $p_1(t)$ has exactly one zero on $[t_a, t_d]$. Also, since t_a and t_d are so defined that $p_4(t)$ has no zeros on $(0, t_a)$ or on $(t_d, t_1]$, all the zeros of $p_4(t)$ must be on $[t_a, t_d]$. But $\dot{p}_4(t) = -x_1 p_1$ has exactly one zero on $[t_a, t_d]$ and $p_4(t_a) = p_4(t_d) = 0$. Therefore $p_4(t)$ can have at most two zeros on $[t_a, t_d]$, and since $p_4(t)$ can have **two jumps at the state-constraint boundary**, $|x_4(t)| = \alpha$, the maximum number of zeros of $p_4(t)$ is four.

For the neutron level control problem with two precursor groups, a similar argument also shows that the maximum number of switchings is the same as the single precursor group neutronic problem. Though unstable in practice, the required **terminal** control is $x_4 = (\dot{x}_2 + \dot{x}_3)/x_{11}$ for two precursor groups.

3. Power Reactor Control

A simple model (3) to approximate the dynamics of a power reactor with a gaseous coolant and a predominantly convective direct-cycle heat exchanger is represented by **Eqs.** (1), **and**,

$$\dot{x}_3 = x_1/c - bw\, x_3, \tag{7}$$

where now x_3 is average core temperature, b is a heat-transfer constant and c is core mass heat capacity. Also, x_1 and x_2 are expressed in units of heat power. Due to pump constraints and reactor thermal limitations, coolant weight flow rate is constrained by $w_1 \leq w \leq w_m$. For power reactors, reactivity is a nonlinear function of x and sometimes it can be expressed as a sum of control reactivity, core temperature reactivity and coolant density reactivity, but the safety constraint is on v and $\dot{v}$ as for the previous problem.

For the nuclear rocket reactor, it is desired to start-up the system from some equilibrium state x_0 to a terminal set such that $x_1(t_1) = x_{11}$, $x_3(t_1) = x_{31}$ and so that coolant (hydrogen propellant) consumption is minimized. Added to the above constraints on reactivity and coolant flow rate, there **are** necessary physical limitations in the form of $0 \leq x_1 \leq Q_m$, $0 \leq x_2$, $0 \leq x_3 \leq T_m$ and $|\dot{x}_3| \leq T_r$.

Due to computational difficulties with the maximum principle for numerous state/control constraints and the presence of divergent optimal response, which hinders solution by gradient techniques, a quasilinear programming algorithm is developed to solve the problem (7). This algorithm is based on an iterative sequence of linear-programming problems with each iterate formed from a linearization of the equations about the linear programming solution at the previous iterate.

By linear programming, state constraints are just as manageable as control constraints and the linear approximation at each iterate can be limited to a compact set. Any standard numerical integration procedure may be used to obtain the necessary algebraic equations. For example, if $\dot{x} = f(x, u)$ and t_1 is free, the linear approximation may take the form

$$x_{i+1} - x_i = \frac{\Delta t^*}{2} [f(x_i^*, u_i^*) + f(x_{i+1}^*, u_{i+1}^*)] + [\frac{\partial f}{\partial x_i}\Big|_* (x_i - x_i^*)$$
$$+ \frac{\partial f}{\partial x_{i+1}}\Big|_* (x_{i+1} - x_{i+1}^*)] + \frac{\Delta t}{2}[\frac{\partial f}{\partial u_i}\Big|_* (u_i - u_i^*)$$
$$+ \frac{\partial f}{\partial u_{i+1}}\Big|_* (u_{i+1} - u_{i+1}^*)]$$
$$+ \frac{1}{2} [f(x_i^*, u_i^*) + f(x_{i+1}^*, u_{i+1}^*)] (\Delta t - \Delta t^*),$$

where * refers to the linear-programming solution at the previous iterate. Similarly the performance index can be algebraicly approximated. In this manner, an example solution is given on Fig. 3. Despite rapid convergence of the linear-programming algorithm, optimality of the solution cannot be guaranteed, but it is at least plausible from physical arguments. To start the computation, a maximum-effort control of the type analyzed in the previous section is utilized. From Fig. 3 the solution consists of a maximum -effort increase of reactivity $v(t)$ with power $x_1(t)$ increasing in minimum time until core temperature $x_3(t)$ attains its maximum allowable rate of increase. Then $\dot{v}(t)$ varies to maintain the $\dot{x}_3 = T_R =$ 2880° R/sec. From Eq. (7) and Fig. 3 it is observed that $x_1(t)$ is nearly constant at small flow rate w. The oscillation exhibited on Fig. 3 is due to the error from the difference-equation approximation and the trajectory instability which was discussed in the previous section in regards to the terminal control. Just prior to the terminal time t_1, with $x_{31} = T(t_1) = 4500°$ R, $\dot{v}(t) = \eta$ again so that power increases in minimal time to its terminal value (x_{11} = 20 mw). Meanwhile, $w(t)$ increases to maintain $\dot{x}_3 = 2880°$ R/sec until the terminal time at which $w = x_{11}/(bcx_{31})$ to maintain constant temperature according to Eq. (7). Then for $t \geq t_1$ the theoretic terminal control is $w(t) = x_{11}/(bcx_{31})$ and $v(t) = \dot{x}_2(t)/x_{11}$. In practice this terminal control can be replaced by a simple closed-loop control, and it is even possible to closely approximate the optimal process with conventional closed-loop control (6).

Though the use of linear programming was suggested early for optimal control problems, it has not been widely adopted. Availability of "canned" linear programming routines, such as the Mathematical Programming System for the IBM 360 used here, makes the method most feasible (9). While con-

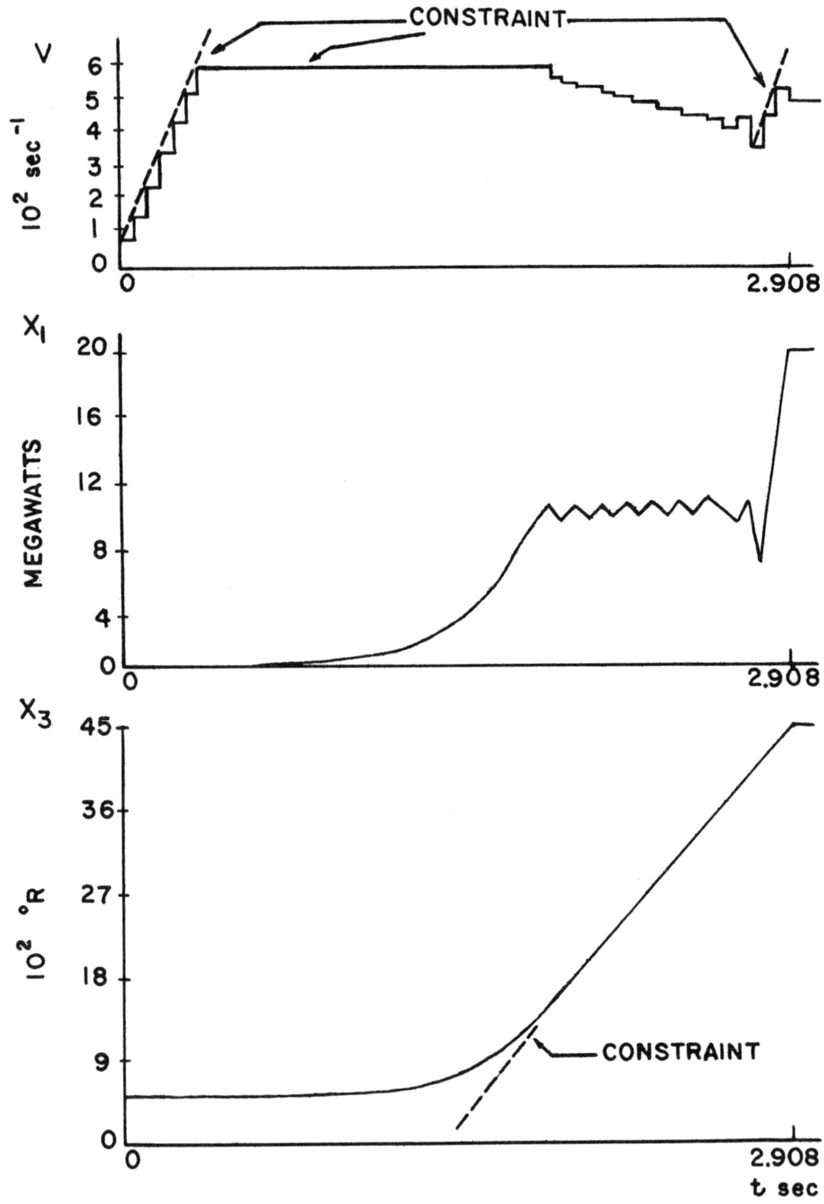

Fig. 3 Fuel Optimal Nuclear Rocket Start with $w = w_1 = 2$ lb/sec until final increment where $w = 30.17$ lb/sec. $\alpha = 600$ sec^{-1}, $\eta = 1500$ sec^{-2}, $x_{31} = T_m = 4500°$R and $T_r = 2880°$ R/sec.

vergence of solutions cannot be assured, it occurs for the reactor problem, and convergence has been established for a class of problems (10).

4. Conclusions

The time-optimal control of reactor neutronics is one of maximum allowable effort with a small triangular or trapezoidal pulse of neutron multiplication required at the terminal end to bring the state to equilibrium. This pulse is required by the presence of delayed precursor neutrons, but usually it can be neglected in practice. If only neutron density is controlled, the terminal neutron density must be constant while precursor density is not at equilibrium.

Though the model considered here is a simplification of the actual system to conserve computer time, the computations indicate that linear programming can be utilized effectively to compute optimal control processes for practical reactor systems and other systems for which the optimization process is complicated by numerous state constraints.

Appendix A

Zeros of $p_1(t)$ for Single-Precursor Model

From Eq. (3), $\dot{p}_1 < 0$ if $p_2 > 0$ and $p_1 \leq 0$; similarly $\dot{p}_1 > 0$ if $p_2 < 0$ and $p_1 \geq 0$. Also, $\dot{p}_2 = 0$ if $p_1 = p_2$; $\dot{p}_2 > 0$ if $p_2 > p_1$; and $\dot{p}_2 < 0$ if $p_2 < p_1$. Hence, if $p_1(t) \not\equiv 0$ it can only have one zero since trajectories entering the set $P_{II} = \{p: p_1 < 0, p_2 > 0\}$ cannot leave it. Similarly trajectories entering the set $P_{IV} = \{p: p_1 > 0, p_2 < 0\}$ cannot leave it. Hence, a continuous $p_1(t)$ cannot have more than one zero if $p_1(t) \not\equiv 0$.

Appendix B

Zeros of $p_1(t)$ for Two-Precursor Model

In this appendix it is shown that $p_1(t)$ for the two-precursor group neutron kinetics (see Eqs. (4) and (5)) cannot have more than two zeros.

Define:

$$g(p) = -(a_2 p_2 + a_3 p_3),$$

$$G^+ = \{p: g(p) \geq 0\},$$

$$G^- = \{p: g(p) \leq 0\},$$

$$G^\circ = G^+ \cap G^-,$$

$$F_i^+ = \{p: p_i \geq 0\},$$
$$F_i^- = \{p: p_i \leq 0\},$$
$$\overset{\circ}{F}_i = F_i^+ \cap F_i^-, \quad (i = 1, 2, 3, 4),$$
$$N = \frac{\partial g(p)}{\partial p} = (0, -a_2, -a_3, 0).$$

Assume $\lambda_2 > \lambda_3$ without loss of generality. Then consider

$$\begin{aligned} N \cdot \dot{p} &= -a_2\dot{p}_2 - a_3\dot{p}_3 \\ &= Cp_1 + D(p) \end{aligned}$$

where

$$C \equiv (a_2\lambda_2 + a_3\lambda_3) > 0, \text{ and}$$
$$D(p) \equiv -(a_2\lambda_2 p_2 + a_3\lambda_3 p_3).$$

Since $\lambda_2 > \lambda_3 > 0$, $\lambda_2 = \lambda_3 + \lambda' > 0$, with $\lambda' > 0$, then

$$\begin{aligned} D(p) &= -[a_2(\lambda_3 + \lambda')p_2 + a_3\lambda_3 p_3] \\ &= -\lambda_3(a_2p_2 + a_3p_3) - a_2\lambda' p_2 \qquad (9) \\ &= \lambda_3\, g(p) - a_2\lambda' p_2. \end{aligned}$$

Let t_α be the first zero of $p_1(t)$ on (t_0, t_1). If $p(t_\alpha) \in G^+ \cap F_2^- \cap F_1^\circ$ (or $p(t_\alpha) \in G^- \cap F_2^+ \cap F_1^\circ$), then $p_1(t) > 0$ (or $p_1(t) < 0$) for all t on $(t_\alpha, t_1]$ since in $G^+ \cap F_2^- \cap F_1^+$, $\dot{p}_1 > 0$, $\dot{p}_2 < 0$, $N \cdot \dot{p} > 0$ (or in $G^- \cap F_2^+ \cap F_1^-$, $\dot{p}_1 < 0$, $\dot{p}_2 > 0$, $N \cdot \dot{p} < 0$). If $p(t_\alpha) \in G^+ \cap F_2^+ \cap F_1^\circ$ (or $p(t_\alpha) \in G^- \cap F_2^- \cap F_1^\circ$), then p(t) either remains in the region $G^+ \cap F_2^+ \cap F_1^+$ [or $G^- \cap F_2^- \cap F_1^-$] or moves into the region $G^+ \cap F_2^- \cap F_1^+$ (or $G^- \cap F_2^+ \cap F_1^-$) or into the region $G^- \cap F_2^+ \cap F_1^+$ (or $G^+ \cap F_2^- \cap F_1^-$) as shown by the costate velocity vector $\dot{p}$ pointing inward (see Eqs. (5), (8), (9)).

Suppose p(t) remains in $G^+ \cap F_2^+ \cap F_1^+$ or moves into $G^+ \cap F_2^- \cap F_1^+$, then $p_1(t) > 0$ for all $t > t_\alpha$, and $p_1(t)$ has no zero for $t > t_\alpha$. Suppose p(t) moves into the region $G^- \cap F_2^+ \cap F_1^+$, then $\dot{p}_1(t) \gtreqless 0$, and $p_1(t)$ can have another zero. Let $p(t_\beta)$ be the second zero, and it is easily seen that $p(t_\beta)$ lies in $G^- \cap F_2^+ \cap F_1^\circ$. But, it was previously shown that if $p(t_\beta) \in G^- \cap F_2^+ \cap F_1^\circ$, then $p_1(t) < 0$ for all $t > t_\beta$. Hence, $p_1(t)$ can have at most two zeros.

References

1. M. Ash, Nuclear Reactor Kinetics, McGraw-Hill, New York, 1965, p. 16.
2. R. R. Mohler and J. E. Perry, Jr., "Nuclear Rocket Engine Control," Nucleonics, 19, No. 4 (1961), pp. 80-84.
3. R. R. Mohler, "Optimal Nuclear Rocket Engine Control," Neutron Dynamics and Control, AEC Symposium Series 7 (1966), pp. 137-163.
4. R. R. Mohler, "Optimal Control of Nuclear Reactor Systems, ANS Transactions, 7 (1964), pp. 58-59.
5. L. S. Pontryagin, et al., The Mathematical Theory of Optimal Processes, Interscience, New York, 1962, pp. 257-316.
6. R. R. Mohler, "Optimal Control of Nuclear Reactor Processes," Los Alamos Scientific Laboratory, LA-3257-MS (1965). Also see Optimal Nuclear Reactor Control (with C. N. Shen), forthcoming, Academic Press, New York.
7. R. R. Mohler and H. J. Price, "Optimal Nuclear Reactor Control," Engr. Res. Report EE142, University of New Mexico (1967).
8. L. A. Zadeh and B. H. Whalen, "On Optimal Control and Linear Programming," IRE Trans. Auto. Control, AC-7, (1962), pp. 45-46.
9. "Mathematical Programming System /360 (360A-CO-14X) Linear Programming User's Manual, International Business Machines, New York, (1966).
11. J. B. Rosen, "Iterative Solution of Nonlinear Optimal Control Problems," J. SIAM Control, 4 (1966), pp. 223-224.

ON SOME PROBLEMS IN OPTIMUM SYSTEMS SYNTHESIS THEORY

N. N. Moiseev
Computing Center, USSR Academy of Sciences
Moscow, USSR

During the last few years optimization methods have been applied with increasing efficiency to problems of technology and economics. There arise new problems, and some well-known problems may be discussed from new points of view. Research workers (specialists in numerical methods) now pay more and more attention to problems of synthesis and to construction of computing methods in synthesis theory. This paper deals with some questions in this theory.

It contains a survey of numerical methods and discussion of some problems which arise in synthesis theory.

At present there exist different understandings of this term. That is why I start my paper by considering simple examples, which may clarify the contents of problems considered.

1. Preliminary Notes. One particular problem in technology and economics is the computation of so called programmed movements. If we think, for example, about launching a rocket into an orbit around the earth, we have a problem of programmed movement which is simply a problem of optimum control theory. Here the objective is usually amount of fuel required for launching of given load into orbit or amount of useful load while amount of fuel is given. In economics computation of optimum program is a problem of construction of a plan which has to supply, for example, by the end of a certain period of time a maximum output of production (resource is given). It is also a problem of optimum control.

A great deal of assumptions are usually introduced when one wants to solve a problem of optimum program computation: initial state of controllable system and acting forces are supposed to be known and determinate; it is assumed that theoretically predicted control is realized absolutely exactly, etc. And besides, the dynamic system evolution scheme itself is over-simplified. For example, when one computes the optimum trajectory of a rocket the latter is always supposed to be a material point. That is why a controllable system never moves along the optimum path. To reach the desired objective one must construct some additional control system which utilizes information on differences of real movement from the programmed one and takes into account the action of stochastic forces. This problem is usually called in technology the problem of control system synthesis. Using achievements of optimization methods one can formulate problems of synthesis as variational ones. For instance, in the first example we can formulate a problem in the following way: how can we construct a control system which has to supply maximum accuracy of launching the rocket into given orbit? In the second example the control system has to maximize production output. However, as we shall see later this problem is of different type.

The examples considered are rather typical examples for two main classes of problems in theory of control system synthesis. Now we are going to concentrate our attention on these problems.

The statement of the synthesis problem is usually based on some assumptions. The main assumption is a hypothesis on linearization. Suppose that the system of equations used to determine the programmed movement is as follows

$$\dot{x} = X(x, u) \tag{1}$$

where x is a phase vector and u is a programmed control.

Let the complete system of equations be in the form

$$\dot{y} = Y(y, u, v, f) \tag{2}$$

where v is a correcting control and f is a stochastic force vector.

Now the sense of this hypothesis is: we assume that the magnitude of $\| y-x \|$ is small. This assumption allows us by introducing vector $z = y-x$ to linearize the system (2) near z (remember that vector x is a known solution of system (1)).

For linearization hypothesis to have sense one must assume that $\|f\|$ is small and initial conditions for systems (1) and (2) are close to each other. However, these assumptions are not sufficient, first, because the order of system (2) is usually higher than the order of system (1) and, second, because the function x(t) (in the neighborhood of which linearization takes place) is not a particular solution of system (2).

That is why in general it is impossible to use linearization, and one must investigate every concrete problem.

2. Statement of the Synthesis Problem. Now when considering synthesis problems we shall only deal with dynamical processes which can be described by the following equations:

$$\dot{z} = A(t)z + v + f(t) . \qquad (3)$$

Here v is the control vector, f(t) is a stochastic process, for which the statistical description is known. We shall find vector v by minimizing a functional of type

$$J(v) = E\Phi(z(T)) = \overline{\Phi(z(T))}$$

We shall deal with quadratic functionals in those problems where the control variable has to supply accuracy of realization of program:

$$J(v) = \overline{(z(T), Rz(T))} . \qquad (4)$$

Here R is a given matrix.

In problems of economics there are most useful linear functionals of the following type:

$$J(v) = \overline{(c, z(T))} . \qquad (4')$$

We shall not fix initial condition z(0). We shall treat it as a stochastic quantity; its mathematical expectation is equal to zero.

There is no sense in the problems considered to search for a control as a function of time v = v(t) to be chosen in advance (as we do it in optimum control theory).

Indeed let denote by Γ Green's operator for the

homogeneous part of system (3). Then we have

$$z(T) = \Gamma v + \Gamma f .$$

Hence,

$$\overline{z^2} = (\Gamma v)^2 + \overline{(\Gamma f)^2}$$

It follows from this relation that in order to minimize $\overline{z^2}$ it is necessary to put v equal to zero (which means that control is absent). That is why in the synthesis problems one should think about control as a function of phase coordinates

$$v = v(z, t) .$$

One of the pecularities of the synthesis problem is: even knowing function v(z) we do not have (except by Monte Carlo method) any standard method for calculation of functional (4). This calculation is very easy only in the case when function v(z) is a linear one.

There exist various modifications of this problem.

a) We must consider control v not as a function of coordinates but as function of stochastic quantity $\xi(t)$, which we observe, ξ and z being connected by some relationship, which in the simplest case has the following form:

$$\xi = z + h \qquad (5)$$

where h(t) is some stochastic process.

b) Stochastic processes f and h can be completely determined, for example, by their correlation functions or by canonical decompositions, but in some cases we know only some characteristics of these processes (or we know nothing).

c) Programmed trajectory (hence, matrix A) can be given, which means that we give our autopilot a certain program. But there can be another case, when we design the autopilot for some set of programs, etc.

Various modifications of this problem demand different numerical methods for solving. I am not able to describe all the possible situations in this report, so I restrict myself to some problems in the theory of synthesis where I pay attention only to simple examples.

3. Application of Dynamical Programming Methods.

The differential equation which describes dynamical

process

$$\dot{z} = Az + w + F(t)$$

we replace by the following difference one

$$z_{k+1} = \Phi_k z_k + v_k + f_k$$

where the form of Φ_k, v_k, f_k depends on the method of difference approximation. For instance, in the simplest case

$$\Phi_k = I + \tau A(t_k)$$

$$v_k = \tau w(t_k); \quad f_k = \tau F(t_k) .$$

As a result of this approach we obtain the optimization problem for some multistage process. It is natural first to use the dynamic programming method. That was done by many authors and there exist a great deal of references on the subject. Here we point out the following two results.

1) The case where the quality criterion of the control system is a quadratic functional

$$J = (z(T), Rz(T)) .$$

Suppose that no restriction is imposed on the control. In this case the control is a linear function of coordinates

$$v_k = B_k z_k$$

where the matrix B_k could be obtained by a recursion method. It is easy to generalize this result in the case, where not all the coordinates are observable and controllable or the error of coordinate measurement is a known stochastic process. This theorem ceases to be valid if there exist control constraints or phase restrictions. In these cases the standard dynamic programming approach ceases to be efficient.

2) The case where the quality criterion of the control system is a linear functional

$$J = (c, z(T))$$

c being a given vector.

In this case the problem has sense only if a restriction is imposed on the control. Let this restriction be in the form:

$$v_k \in G_k$$

where G_k are some closed sets.
The following result is easily obtained by the dynamic programming method:

Optimum control does not depend on phase coordinates or on the structure of the stochastic process. It could be found as a solution of the following problem of mathematical programming

$$\min_{v_i \in G_i} (c, \Phi_{N-1} \Phi_{N-2} \cdots \Phi_{i+1} v_i) \qquad i=0,1,2,\ldots N-1$$

We can give the following economic interpretation to this result. Suppose that evolution of the economic body is described by the linear difference equation

$$\Delta x = Ax + u$$

and that the objective is a linear function.

Programmed control being known we then pass to the synthesis problem. Solution of this problem will coincide with the programmed control. It means that such a system does not require any correction control. Correction control is only necessary if there are some constraints.

4. Problems of Linear Synthesis.

Dynamic programming methods allow us to solve some important synthesis problems. However, amidst these problems an important class of optimization problems (standard error optimization problem while there exist constraints on control) is absent. Now we pass to the consideration of these problems. The possibility of obtaining efficient solutions is reached at the expense of narrowing the permissible control class.

We shall search for a control in the form

$$v = B(t)\, z \qquad (7)$$

where the matrix $B(t)$ must be determined from the minimum-functional condition (4) subject to constraints of following type:

$$B_{ij} \in G_{ij}$$

It is supposed that stochastic process $f(t)$ is completely

given.

This problem can be reduced to one particular problem in the theory of optimum control for which it is possible to propose some efficient numerical methods.

Let us introduce vector p_i satisfying the adjoint equation

$$\dot{p}_i = -(A + B)^* p_i \qquad i=1,2,\ldots$$

Then

$$\frac{d}{dt}(z, p_i) = (f, p_i) .$$

Let

$$p_i^{(j)}(T) = \delta_i^j . \tag{9}$$

Then we have

$$z^{(j)}(T) = (z(0), p_j(0)) + \int_0^T (f, p_j)\, dt . \tag{10}$$

The expression (10) allows us to construct in explicit form an expression for functional (4) in the form of a double integral.

Now by introducing vector y ($y^{(k+i)} = p_k^i$, dimension n^2), which satisfies the equation

$$\dot{y} = Dy \tag{11}$$

where

$$D = \left\| \begin{array}{ccc} -(A+B)^* & & \\ & -(A+B)^* & \\ & & \ddots \\ & & & -(A+B)^* \end{array} \right\|$$

we arrive at the following problem of optimum control: To find control B(t) subject to differential constraints (11), which minimizes the functional

$$J = (y(0), K_o y(0)) + \int_0^T \int_0^T (y(t),\ K(t,\tau)\, y(\tau))\, dt\, d\tau . \tag{12}$$

Boundary conditions for vector y and correlation matrices K_0 and $K(t, \tau)$ can be easily determined by using (9) and (10).

In the case where z is a scalar and a functional J has the form $(R = I)$

$$J = \overline{z^2(T)} \tag{13}$$

we shall have

$$K_0 = \overline{z^2(0)} \qquad K(t, \tau) = \overline{F(t)\, F(\tau)} \tag{14}$$

It is easy to formulate the maximum principle for the problem of optimum control with the functional (12), containing a double integral. However, it is very difficult to apply this principle for obtaining the solution of the problem since the equations for Lagrange multipliers turn out to be integro-differential.

For the problem considered one can use the gradient method. Let us explain that for the particular problem (13)-(14). Let $\widetilde{B}(t)$ be some permissible matrix, δB being variation of control. We put

$$y = \tilde{y} + \delta y$$

where $\tilde{y}$ satisfies the equation

$$\dot{\tilde{y}} = -(A+B)^* \tilde{y}$$

and the condition (a): $\tilde{y}(T) = 1$. δy satisfies to the equation

$$\delta \dot{y} = -(A+\widetilde{B})\delta y - \delta B^* \tilde{y} \tag{15}$$

and is equal to zero when $t = T$. Let us calculate a variation of the functional (15)

$$\delta J = \alpha \delta y(0) + \int_0^T \delta y(t)\, \varphi(t)\, dt \tag{16}$$

where

$$\alpha = 2K_0 .$$

Let us calculate further

$$\min_{\substack{\delta B \\ \widetilde{B} + \delta B \in G_B}} \delta J \tag{17}$$

subject to condition (15). Since the constraint on δy is imposed only when $t = 7$, we can reduce the problem (17) by using the maximum principle to two CAUCHY problems.

Let $B = \widetilde{B} + K\,\delta B$, $J = J(k)$. Then we find

$$\min_{k\in[0,1]} J(k) .$$

For the applications it is important to consider the case where F(t) is a stationary Markov process. In this case by Doob's Theorem the components of the correlation matrix $K(t, \tau)$ have the form

$$\sigma_{ij}^2 \exp\{-K_{ij}\,|t-\tau|\}$$

and the doub.ie integral in (12) is reduced to a one dimensional integral. Let us explain the corresponding problem using the particular case of a first order system where the functional has the form (13)

$$\int_0^T\int_0^T y(t)y(\tau)K(t,\tau)dt\,d\tau = \sigma^2\int_0^T\int_0^T y(\tau)y(t)\,e^{-k|t-\tau|}dt\,d\tau =$$

$$= \sigma^2\int_0^T y(t)\exp\{-kt\}\int_0^t y(\tau)\exp\{k\tau\}\,d\tau\,dt .$$

By introducing new variable

$$\dot{z} = e^{kt}\,y(t)$$

we arrive at the problem of finding function B(t), which minimizes functional

$$J = K_0 y^2(0) + \sigma^2\int_0^T e^{-kt}\,y(t)\,z(t)\,dt \tag{18}$$

subject to constraints

$$\begin{aligned} \dot{z} &= e^{kt}\,y\ ; & z(0) &= 0 \\ \dot{y} &= -(A+B)^*\,y\ ; & y(T) &= 1 \end{aligned} \tag{19}$$

Transversality conditions for impulses (Lagrange multipliers) will be

$$p_y(0) = 0; \qquad p_z(T) = 0 \tag{20}$$

while $\dot{p}_z = \sigma^2 e^{-kt} y$. These circumstances allow us to develop an efficient method of successive approximations:

We take a permissible control $B_0(t)$ and obtain then $y_0(t)$ as the solution of Cauchy problem (19) and $p_{z0}(t)$ as the solution of Cauchy problem (20). As a result, we find

$$p_{z0}(0) \qquad \text{and} \qquad y_0(0) \ .$$

This allows us to integrate then all the p-system from 0 until T. At the same time we find a new control from the maximum of Hamilton function condition.

NOTE 1. Methods described can be applied to the case where not all the coordinates are available to measure, i.e., where

$$v = B\xi, \qquad \xi = Lz' + h(t) \tag{21}$$

z' being the projection of vector z in a subset of less dimension, $h(t)$ being a stochastic process; the dimension of vector ξ is not more than the dimension of vector z.

NOTE 2. These methods can be applied also for studying systems where not all the coordinates are controllable. Dimension of matrix B is not more in general than $n \times n$, where n is the dimension of vector x, while part of its elements could be by condition equal to zero.

NOTE 3. Method described cannot be directly used for problems with phase constraints.

5. Synthesis Problems for Control Systems Under Uncertainty Conditions.

We considered in previous sections two classes of synthesis problems. The possibility of the reduction of technologic problems to the problems considered is based on certain hypotheses on information. For instance, for everything mentioned above to have sense it is necessary to assume that we know programmed trajectory (i.e., matrix A) and correlation functions of stochastic processes. In many technologic problems these conditions both do not take place. For example, suppose that we create an autopilot (i.e., we design a system of feedback control) for control of rockets which are launching on various orbits. Autopilot must supply necessary correction of different programs. We often know very badly the structure of stochastic perturbations and, hence, correlation functions.

So in many real problems we meet with an uncertainty while formulating a problem. Nevertheless, we must make decision, i.e., create a feedback system.

There exist several conceptions of decision-making under uncertainty conditions. One of them is an ideology of adaptation. The second one is a conception of guaranteed strategy design. In this paper we shall talk only about guaranteed strategies and consider two examples.

We shall start studying this question from the consideration of an auxiliary problem.

a) Test estimate problem. Suppose that the designer has to choose parameters of the autopilot for the control of some set of trajectories G_γ. Usually an engineer behaves in the following way. He calls one of the trajectories $\tilde{\gamma}$ a test one. Hence he fixes a known matrix $A = A(t)$ in the equation describing the process:

$$\dot{z} = A(t)\, z + v + f \ .$$

After that he solves control v synthesis problem. Suppose that he searches for a control in the form

$$v = Bz$$

and uses our method. Let us denote the obtained solution by $\tilde{B}$ and $\tilde{y}$. A certain matrix A corresponds to every trajectory of G_γ set. These matrices form a set G_A. Let us calculate ΔJ^*

$$\Delta J^* = \max_{A \in G_A} \{ J(A, \tilde{B}) - J(\tilde{A}, \tilde{B}) \} \ . \tag{21}$$

The magnitude of ΔJ^* characterizes the quality of test.

A solution of problem (21) can be considerably simplified if we put $A = \tilde{A} + \delta A$, $\|\delta A\|$ being small, and linearize the problem. Let $y = \tilde{y} + \delta y$ where δy is a solution of the following Cauchy problem

$$\delta \dot{y} = -(A+B)^{*} \delta y - \delta A^{*} \tilde{y}$$
$$\delta y(T) = D \tag{22}$$

Then δJ is determined by formula of type (16):

$$\delta J = (\delta y, \tilde{K}_{o} \delta y)_{t=0} + \int_{0}^{T} \delta y(t) \varphi(t) \, dt \tag{23}$$

while $\tilde{K}_o$ and $\varphi(t)$ are easily calculated.

So the problem of finding $\delta J^{*} = \min \delta J$ is a linear problem of optimum control and it is reduced to the solution of two Cauchy problems.

b) Guaranteed test design problem. Let us consider a problem of the choice of guaranteed control $B \in G_B$.

We shall call control B(t) a guaranteed one if it minimizes a functional

$$\max J(A, B) = J_{1}(B) .$$

So the guaranteed strategy design problem is reduced to the determination of J^{*}

$$J^{*} = \min_{B \in G_B} \max_{A \in G_A} J(A, B) . \tag{24}$$

The functional J_1 is not differentiable over B and the problem of determination of J^{*} is sufficiently difficult and in general case it is impossible to propose standard methods for its solving. On the other hand this problem becomes almost trivial if one assumes that the sets G_B and G_A are sufficiently narrow. In this case two efficient algorithms are available.

f_1: Replacement of the problem (24) by the linear one. Let $\tilde{A}$, $\tilde{B}$ and $\tilde{y}$ be variables corresponding to the test trajectory. Let

$$A = \tilde{A} + \delta A, \quad B = \tilde{B} + \delta B, \quad y = \tilde{y} + \delta y, \quad \delta y = \delta y_1 + \delta y_2,$$

and linearize the problem in regard to variations. Then we have

$$\delta J = \delta J_{\alpha} (\delta J_1) + \delta J_{\beta} (\delta y_2)$$

where

$$\delta J_\alpha = (\delta y_1, K_o \tilde{y}) + \int_0^T \delta y_1(t)\,\varphi(t)\,dt$$

$$\delta J_\beta = (\delta y_2, K_o \tilde{y}) + \int_0^T \delta y_2(t)\,\varphi(t)\,dt$$

and δy_i satisfy to the following Cauchy problems

$$\delta \dot{y}_1 = -(\tilde{A}+\tilde{B})^* \delta y_1 - \delta A^* \tilde{y}, \qquad \delta y_1(T) = 0$$

$$\delta \dot{y}_2 = -(\tilde{A}+\tilde{B})\, \delta y_2 - \delta B^* \tilde{y}, \qquad \delta y_2(T) = 0 .$$

We replace

$$J(A, B) = \tilde{J}(\tilde{A}, \tilde{B}) + \delta J .$$

Then the problem (24) is replaced by

$$\begin{aligned} J^* &= \tilde{J} + \min_{\delta B} \max_{\delta A} \delta J = \\ &= \tilde{J} + \min_{\delta B} \delta J_\beta + \max_{\delta A} \delta J_\alpha \end{aligned} \tag{25}$$

We took into account here that $\tilde{B} + \delta B \in G_B$, $\tilde{A} + \delta A \in G_A$. The problem (25) is reduced now to two linear problems of optimum control with free terminal point and, hence, is reduced to a Cauchy problem.

f_2: Successive approximations method. We take test trajectory A_o and find then B_o as a result of solving of the problem:

$$J_o = \min_{B \in G_B} J(A_o, B) .$$

Then we shall find

$$J_1 = \max_{A \in G_A} J(A, B_o) \qquad \text{etc.}$$

This algorithm is similar to Brown-Robinson algorithm in matrix game theory.

c) Guaranteed strategy in the case of stationary Markov processes. Suppose we know that a perturbation or observation error is a stationary Markov process. In this case correlation matrix elements have the form

$$\sigma_{ij}^2 \exp\{-K_{ij}|t-\tau|\} .$$

For sake of simplicity let us put all the K_{ij} equal to each other, i.e.

$$K(t,\tau) = \exp\{-K|t-\tau|\}Q$$

where Q is constant matrix. Suppose we know only that correlation coefficient K:

$$K_o - \delta \leq K \leq K_o + \delta$$

where δ is known positive number. We can write functional J in the form

$$J(K,B) = (y(0), K_o y(0)) + \int_0^T\int_0^T e^{-K|t-\tau|}(y(t), Qy(\tau))\,dt\,d\tau$$

and guaranteed strategy design problem is reduced to the calculation of J^*

$$J^* = \min_{B\in G_B} \max_{K\in[K_o-\delta, K_o+\delta]} J(K,B). \quad (26)$$

If δ is small, the functional J(K, B) can be linearized. Let $K = K_o + \delta K$ we find

$$\delta J = (y(0), K_o y(0)) - \delta K \int_0^T\int_0^T |t-\tau|\, e^{-K_o|t-\tau|}(y(t), Q(y(\tau))dtd\tau \quad (27)$$

We replace then problem (26) by the following one

$$\delta J^* = \min_{B\in G_B} \max_{\delta K\in[-\delta, +\delta]} \delta J(\delta K, B) .$$

Let us define two functions B^- and B^+ as solutions of following problems

$$\delta J_-^* = \min_{B\in G_B} \delta J(-\delta, B)$$

$$\delta J_+^* = \min_{B\in G_B} \delta J(\delta, B) .$$

It is easy to show by using the fact that δJ is a linear function of δK that guaranteed strategy will be one of two functions B_+ and B_- which correspond to the least of the numbers δJ_-^* or δJ_+^*.

We considered two synthesis problems where we are forced to make a decision under uncertainty conditions. There are many similar problems in synthesis theory. I think that the proposed method of the analysis of these problems using theory of games ideas will be of some practical value if efficient computing methods of this theory are designed.

6. Division Problem. We started this paper from the assertion that the technologic problem of the optimum control system design is usually solved in two stages. The first one is a stage of the programmed trajectory determination. The second one is a stage of control synthesis; this control should fulfill the program. A solution of the first problem is trivial for the traditional problems of automatic control theory. In many cases it is simply a given movement: given quantity of revolutions of the rotor, given stationary regime of the plane flight and, at last, given form of trajectory of the plane during its landing. In these cases no "division problems" arise. However, during the past decades there have arisen many problems where the problems of programmed movement computation have become of some independent interest: there is, for instance, the choice of the orbit apparatus launching trajectory subject to a minimum energy condition. However, following tradition engineers continue to consider these two problems separately.

What is the content of the division problem? We shall try to show that with the example of orbit apparatus.

An engineer who designs a rocket and a control system tends to two aims. First, he must minimize fuel for launching apparatus on the given orbit and, second he must maximize accuracy of launching (minimum of variance). So by using the main and correction controls he must minimize two functionals: J_1 (dimensionless energy of launching) and J_2 (dimensionless variance of the trajectory elements at the engine-off moment). An engineer does not know how to minimize both functionals. So he behaves in the following way: first, by using simplified equations he finds the minimum of J_1, second, he takes the obtained trajectory and constructs a synthesis using the minimum condition. What is the sense of this procedure? Does this procedure always give a satisfactory solution of his problem? Really, each of the functionals J_1 and J_2 depends on both controls, the main u and correction v, and a priori it is not obvious that the procedure described leads to values of J_1 and J_2 which satisfy the engineer completely.

We shall use for analysis of this situation operation research theory ideas. In fact, we meet here the case of uncertainty. If one of the functionals (for example J_1) would be restricted, then no problem will exist. Instead of that we should have a rather complicated problem of optimum synthesis, constraints being on energy.

As a rule, we do not know in what degree functional J_1 increase could be compensated by decrease of functional J_2. That is why we must admit for clarifying of this question the existence of uncertainty, in this case, uncertainty of our intentions. Now we must formulate a new functional. It could be done by different methods. It is convenient for further study to introduce the functional

$$J = c_1 J_1(u, v) + c_2 J_2(u, v) \tag{28}$$

where c_1 and c_2 are some normalized numbers (for instance, $c_1 + c_2 = 1$). We can design guaranteed strategy (u^*, v^*) for finding a control with functional (28). There will be strategies which realize J^*:

$$J^* = \min_{u,v} \max_{c_1, c_2} J(c_1, c_2, u, v) \tag{29}$$

Suppose now that:

a) Functional J is an analytical one over u and v, and correction control has the form: $v = Bz$

b) There exists a small parameter ε such that

$$J_1 = J_1(u, \varepsilon v) \ .$$

NOTE. In the example with the rocket the small parameter means that the ratio of correction control energy to the main engine energy is small.

c) Let us denote by G_γ a set of permissible programs. Let $\tilde{\gamma} \in G_\gamma$ be some test program and $\tilde{u}$ be its control realizing $\tilde{\gamma}$. Let now

$$\min_{v} \max_{\tilde{u}+\delta u} \left\{ J_2(\tilde{u}+\delta u, v) - J_2(\tilde{u}, v) \right\} = 0(\varepsilon)$$

If conditions (a), (b), (c) are fulfilled, we have

$$J^* = \min_{u,v} \max_{c_1, c_2} \left\{ c_1 J_1(u, 0) + c_2 J_2(\tilde{u}, v) \right\} + 0(\varepsilon)$$

Hence under perturbation theory restrictions (i.e., with accuracy of order $0(\varepsilon)$) guaranteed strategies u^* and v^* coincide with strategies which we find from conditions

$$J_1^* = \min_{u} J_1(u, 0) \; ; \qquad J_2^* = \min_{v} J_2(\tilde{u}, v)$$

and do not depend on the choice of constants c_1 and c_2.

The theorem formulated gives sufficient conditions for solutions of divided problems (in a sense of both norms J_1 and J_2) to be close to guaranteed strategies.

Conclusion

We considered briefly some particular questions in the optimum systems synthesis theory. Each of these questions could be the subject of special studies which have profound sense for applications. However, the central point in optimum systems synthesis theory is obviously efficient design of correction control subject to constraints on power of control actions and phase coordinates. These controls will be nonlinear functions of the system phase coordinates.

OPTIMALITY CONSIDERATIONS IN PICTURE PROCESSING

R. Narasimhan
Tata Institute of Fundamental Research
Colaba, Bombay 5.

1. Introduction

1.1. In processing pictures with the help of computers the problem that has received the maximum attention in the last ten years or so is the "recognition problem". Under the generic name of "pattern recognition", this aspect of picture processing has been developed into a flourishing problem-area for research in statistics and decision theory. Several optimality considerations have been worked out as being specifically relevant to pattern recognition.

The principal concern of this paper is to look at all this work critically, and discuss the tenability of the fundamental assumptions implicit in this general approach to pattern recognition. We have argued on several occasions (for references, see (7)*) that pattern recognition is only one aspect of picture processing and that the primary aim in picture processing should be the design of formalisms using which picture tokens belonging to a class of pictures could be described.

There are two aspects to picture description: (1) it could be a generative description such that using this description, an acceptable version of the picture token could be generated, or (2) it could be an interpretative description of a given picture token belonging to a specified class. Pattern recognition techniques, to be generally applicable to this larger context, must clearly be based on interpretative descriptions. Except in the case of very simple classes of pictures and very rudimentary adaptive situations, picture recognition cannot be reduced to answering, 'yes', 'no', or 'don't know', to a given input picture. We shall develop this argument, in some detail, in the first part of this paper.

*A good part of the contents of this paper is to be found in (7). This latter paper, which is more tutorial in nature, contains considerably more information on picture languages, their structuring and usage. It also contains a reasonably extensive list of references to work done in the area of syntax-based analysis of pictures.

1.2. If one accepts that picture processing must ultimately be concerned with generating descriptions of pictures, and that, to this purpose, appropriate descriptive schemata for classes of pictures must be constructed, then the research problems for study in this area take on new aspects. Preoccupations with decision theory, with partitioning of property spaces, and with measuring properties, must give place to study of questions of the following sort: What are admissible structures for descriptive schemata for pictures?; For a given class of pictures, how does one construct a particular description schema?; Given a description schema for a picture class and a picture token belonging to this class, how does one apply the schema to generate a specific description of the token?

Our second concern in this paper is to investigate whether optimality considerations play a natural role in answering any of these questions, and if so, what kinds of optimality considerations these have to be. We shall see later on that there is some overlap between problems that have been studied in the decision-theoretic approach to pattern recognition and those now raised by the descriptive approach to picture processing. The second part of this paper is concerned with this and related aspects in some detail.

2. Inadequacies of the Classificatory Approach

2.1. The classificatory approach to pattern recognition typically formulates the basic problem of recognition as follows: Given a finite set of picture prototypes and a token of one of these prototypes, the task is to assign the token to the correct prototype. In his excellent review article, Kovalevsky (3) says: "A number of investigators hold the opinion now that the most general and fruitful statement of the recognition problem should be statistical". And he goes on to state the generalized problem of recognition as a statistical decision problem as follows:

"It is necessary to recognize a set of situations, k, by coming to various decisions, d. Decisions are selected depending on observed results, v, of an experiment conditioned by a situation. This dependence is characterized by the conditional probability distribution, $p(v \mid k)$. Quality of reached decisions is evaluated by a magnitude of loss, $L(k, d)$, which is specified for each situation, k, and each decision, d. It is necessary to find such a rule, $d(v)$, for reaching decisions based on observations, v, which results in minimal mathematical expectation of losses".

The set of situations, k, are the tokens. The

decision, d, are the prototypes. v are the set of property measurements made on the given tokens.

Such a statement of the recognition problem, as a problem in minimal error decision-making, naturally suggests several optimality considerations for study in arriving at viable recognition systems. As Kovalevsky states: "Using statistical theory, it was possible to formulate correctly and to solve a number of practical tasks, such as the evaluation of efficiency of recognition methods, evaluation of usefulness of features, selection of parameters of a recognition system. One of the most fruitful is the concept of sufficiency of descriptions".

2.2. Almost all the studies Kovalevsky reviews have been concerned with recognition of discrete symbols: alphabets, letters, numerals, etc. For these classes of pictures, this way of formulating the problem in terms of prototypes and images seems very relevant. In fact, adaptive systems, constructed on the basis of these decision-theoretic optimality considerations, have functioned reasonably well in recognizing alphanumeric characters. Can one, then, conclude on the basis of all these studies that this approach to pattern recognition is adequate and sound in general?

This question, clearly, can only be answered in the larger context of what these research studies aim to achieve. What is the scope of recognition problems that this decision-theoretic methodology is expected to cope with? What is the relevance of concepts like "learning" and "adaptation" as developed within this methodology to "learning" as applied to general problem-solving contexts? To quote Kovalevsky once again, he delimits the scope of these studies as follows: "The great variety of problems relating to reading devices, speech recognition, automatic control, medical and technical diagnosis, etc., are considered as pattern recognition... . The possibility of designing an adaptive recognition system without a detailed study of the situations to be recognized, and the associated prospect of constructing a brain model are very attractive. That is why the initial success of this comparatively young science arouses great expectations and inspires enthusiasts".

The question, then, is to see whether the decision-theoretic approach to pattern recognition can, in practice, be extended meaningfully to situations other than recognition of alphanumeric characters; in particular, can it be extended to situations such as reading devices, speech recognition, medical diagnosis, etc.? Secondly, the question is to consider whether viable brain models can be constructed based on decision-theoretic pattern recognition models to function meaningfully in general problem-solving contexts. A careful analysis of the recognition models based on the unstructured classificatory approach would show that the answers to both these questions must be in the negative.

2.3. Notice that the argument here is not that classification, per se, is not a viable methodology for recognition. Clearly, it is viable, and, in fact, for particular classes of pictures, this methodology could be adequate and successful as we have already seen. The contention, rather, is that this methodology, in general, cannot be sufficient. There are classes of situations - classes of pictures - where structure plays a determining role. Such situations can be handled only by defining appropriate relationships between classes. Recognition, in such cases, must depend essentially on articulating these relationships.

As an example of such a class of situations, consider the problem of scene analysis, or "recognition" of scenes. A scene, typically, is a picture token which contains a multiplicity of objects spatially distributed in some organized way. Photographs of terrains, faces, cloud covers, etc., biomedical slides, bubblechamber pictures, circuit diagrams, architectural drawings, cartoon pictures, textual illustrations, mathematical formulae, and a variety of other graphic data are instances of scenes. One might be interested in analysing these pictures to answer any of the following kinds of questions: Does a specified object occur in the scene?; Does a particular configuration of objects occur in the scene?; Does a specified object have a specified attribute value?; What is a complete description of the scene? The recognition aspect involved in answering each of these questions is different, and none of these can be really meaningfully handled within the prototype-image framework. Nor does answering these questions involve making decisions in the usual decision-theoretic sense.*

2.4. Next, consider general problem-solving, and learning and adaptation in this context. Figure 1 illustrates a

---

*Kovalevsky, in his review, is aware of difficulties of this kind and says: "Any nontrivial problem in which descriptions to be considered are fairly diverse has an extraordinarily great number of different possible decision rules. Therefore, for choosing one of them, the learning process should last so long that it could not be accomplished during a reasonable time even by means of the fastest computer".

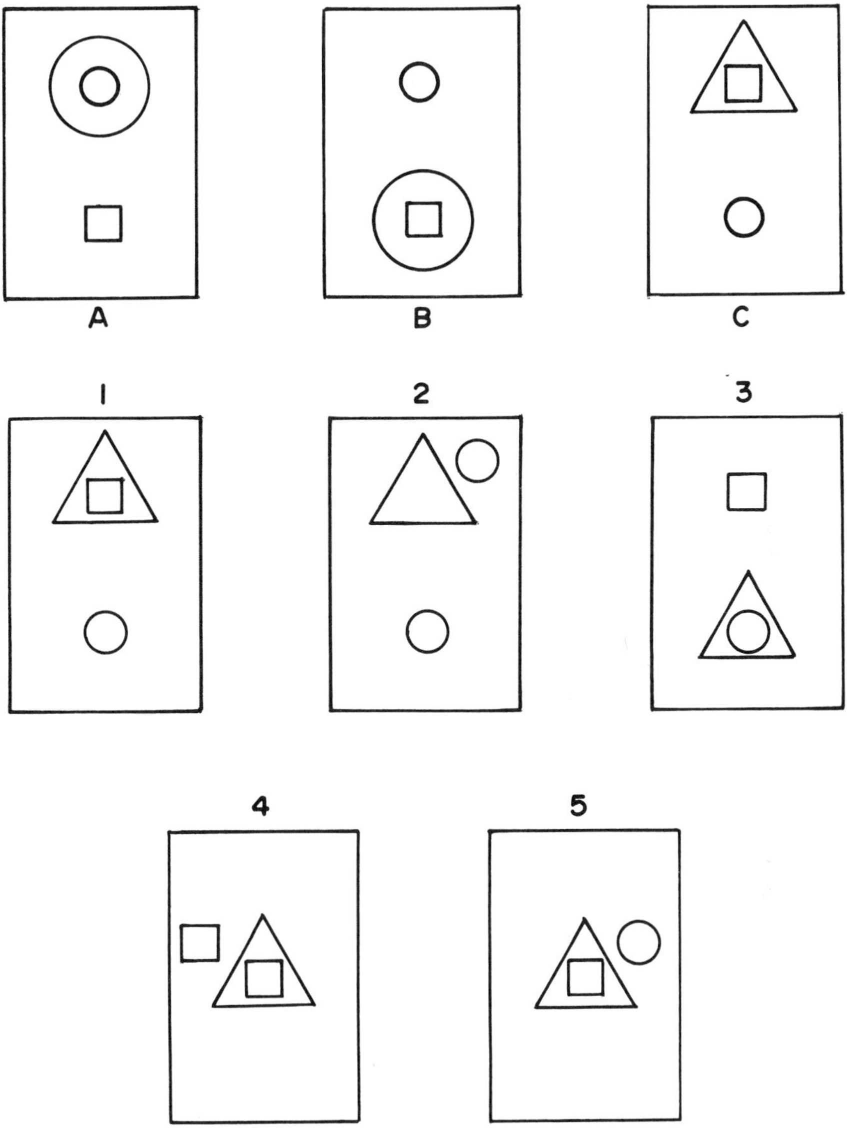

Figure 1: Figure A is to Figure B as Figure C is to which of the Figures 1,2,3,4,5 ? See Reference [2].

typical problem that can be solved by Evans' program for the solution of a class of geometry-analogy intelligence-test questions (2). Clearly, a recognition framework based on simple classification would be quite inadequate to cope with this class of intelligence-test questions. Atleast, the following aspects of the input situation have to be articulated before a solution could be successfully attempted: What are the objects in the picture?; What are their properties?; What is the spatial relationship between these objects?; Which objects are similar?; Which relationships are similar?

A powerful tool in problem-solving, in general, is the ability to compare different models or theories or pictures, on the basis of their structural analogies. Hence, a pattern analyzer, to be adaptive, must be pre-eminently a structure analyzing mechanism. Classifications must be hierarchical. And associations between classes, to be really useful, have to be vertical between the various levels, and not merely horizontal between the elements of a single level.

Notice that this latter point applies not only to scene analysis but equally well to discrete symbol recognition such as recognition of alphanumeric characters. Consider an artificial intelligence (a learning automaton) that functions in a problem-solving context. Assume that it has been exposed to a sequence of tokens of English alphabets. It is now called upon to internalize aspects of these tokens so as to be able to respond to the following kinds of questions: In what sense are an A and an R similar?; Are B and P similar in the same sense as E and F?; Is this picture more like an A or an R?; etc. In the absence of any structural information about the tokens, the artificial intelligence would find it hard, if not impossible, to cope with any of these questions. And it seems plausible that solving problems involving pattern discrimination demand the capability to cope with questions of atleast this order of complexity.

This would seem to imply that it is essential, except in very rudimentary contexts, to deal with a single alphanumeric character as if it were a scene composed of structured entities (i.e., objects) rather than as if it were an atomic entity by itself. Clearly, this is all the more true if one has to cope with textual matter, i.e., spatially distributed strings of symbols belonging to some alphabet. Hence, for even seemingly very simple classes of patterns, recognition based on the unstructured classificatory approach would seem to have severe limitations.

3. Descriptive Schemata for Classes of Pictures*

3.1. From our analysis in the previous section, we are led to conclude that what is of central relevance to picture processing and picture recognition is not so much classification as description. And, as we saw earlier, a description could be either generative and lead to the generation of some version of a picture, or it could be interpretative and lead to some action being taken on the interpretation. In either case, the need is for descriptions that could be articulated. The great advantage in being able to articulate descriptions is, ofcourse, that we can further process these articulated descriptions. For example, we could compare them, contrast them, or transform them in specified ways. Quite clearly, this is a problem in language design.

We need a description language - a specification language for generative descriptions and an interpretation language for interpretative descriptions - in which particular descriptions could be articulated. It is natural to refer to such languages which allow us to describe classes of pictures as picture languages. The principal problems, then, are to study what are plausible structures for picture languages, given a class of pictures how to construct a picture language to describe the class, and, given a picture language how to use it in specific contexts. It should be also of some importance to know what connection, if any, there is between picture recognition by classification and recognition through a description of a picture. We shall consider some of these questions, briefly, in this section.

3.2. Considering descriptive schemata in the context of scene analysis, it would follow from our earlier arguments, that an adequate schema must assign structure to a scene in terms of the occurrences of specific objects and their spatial dispositions; it must assign structure to an object in terms of subparts and their compositions; assign structure to subparts in terms of more primitive entities and their compositions; and so on. Further, the descriptive schema must assign attribute lists to objects and their subparts and compute values for them. Thus, given a picture, one would be able to generate descriptions of the following sort: that in the given picture, objects with such and such properties occur in such and such configurations. An object, itself, would be described as being composed in a specified manner of such and such subparts

*This entire section is almost verbatim borrowed from Section 3 of (7).

with specified properties.

More elaborately, a description schema could contain not only composition rules but also transformation rules. In such a case, additional descriptions of the following kind could be generated of given pictures: This object is a transform of that object in such and such a manner; This subpart of this object and that subpart of that object are transformationally related in such and such a manner; etc.

We shall develop now a meta-formalism for specificational languages for classes of pictures in a somewhat greater detail to exhibit how some of the above ideas can be formalized.

3.3. We shall be concerned, primarily, with classes of picture tokens of finite spatial extent in two-dimensions. The cardinality of the class could, nevertheless, be infinite, as we shall see presently. A specification language, G, for a class of picture tokens is a finite system of rules in terms of which specific tokens of the class can be generated.

G consists of five components: a set of <u>primitives</u>, P, a set of <u>attributes</u>, A, a set of <u>relations</u>, R, a set of <u>composition rules</u>, C, and a set of <u>transformations</u>, T; i.e., $G = G(P, A, R, C, T)$.

P consists of a set of primitive actions the performance of which generates primitive picture fragments. We shall refer to these as picture atoms (or, <u>atoms</u>) and identify them by the same names as their associated primitives. Each primitive (and, hence, the respective atom) has associated with it a set of attributes (i.e., specificational parameters), A, which can assume values from well-defined ranges. Fixing the values of all (or some) of the attributes of a primitive, results in an <u>assignment</u> (or a <u>partial assignment</u>) to the primitive. A primitive with an assignment (or a partial assignment) generates an atom with attribute values completely (or partially) determined.

P and A together, thus, allow us to generate atoms with assigned properties (i.e., with specified attribute values). We now require a machinery in G that could allow us to put together atoms with specific properties to form larger picture fragments. We call this procedure <u>composition</u> and the rules which allow us to compose picture fragments in this manner, <u>composition rules</u>. Composition rules are specified making use of the set of relationships, R. Each relation is an m-ary predicate defined over the attribute values of the constituents of a picture fragment.

Let p_1, p_2 be atoms with assigned properties. Let r be a binary relation defined over some subset of the attribute values of p_1 and p_2. Then,

$$r\ (p_1,\ p_2)$$

defines a picture fragment whose constituents are the atoms p_1 and p_2 and whose assigned properties satisfy the relation, r. Let us call this fragment f. Then,

$$f \longleftarrow r\ (p_1,\ p_2)$$

is a composition rule which specifies that f is composed of p_1 and p_2 in such a manner that their attribute values satisfy the relationship, r. To be able to repeat this process of composition, the rule, as given above, must actually be extended to include a specification of an assignment (of properties) to the fragment resulting from the application of that rule. That is, the original rule must actually be written as follows:

$$f\ (\quad) \longleftarrow r\ (p_1\ (\quad),\ p_2\ (\quad))$$

where the parentheses ( ) exhibit the explicit property assignment on both sides of the arrow. We can now generalize the schema for a composition rule as follows:

$$f_3\ (\quad) \longleftarrow r\ (f_1\ (\quad),\ f_2\ (\quad))$$

where the f_i are picture fragments, but, in particular cases, f_1 and f_2 could either or both be atoms.

So far we have not restricted, in any way, the range of values any given attribute may assume. In particular, we have not excluded the possibility that some or all of the attributes assume infinitely many distinct values. In such a case, it is clear that the cardinality of the token classes can be infinite even though the cardinality of C, the set of composition rules, is finite, and the tokens themselves are finite in spatial extent.

If, however, we also specify that the tokens have a finite <u>resolution</u> in all their attributes, i.e., the set of attributes is finite, and each attribute has a finite range, then the cardinality of the class of tokens becomes strictly finite. It must be emphasized that practically all real-life applications of picture generation and interpretation belong to this restricted variety. But this does not trivialize the problem. In fact, a fundamental assumption in our approach as presented here is that the finiteness of the token classes has little intrinsic relevance to the picture analysis and description problem.

The last component of G that remains to be discussed is the set of transformations, T. Two types of transformations are to be distinguished:

(1) Transformations that alter the properties of a given picture fragment without spatial change: coloring, texturing, shadowing, etc. are transformations of this type.

(2) Transformations that delete components of a fragment, or introduce spatial changes in part or whole of the fragment: deletion, translation, rotation, projection, mirror inversion, contraction, dilatation, distortion, etc., are transformations of this type.

It should be evident from our description of G given above, that it is essentially a programming language. In defining G formally, notational conventions would have to be introduced so that the primitives with attribute assignments, relationships and transformations could be explicitly represented and uniformly interpreted into action sequences that result in the creation and manipulation of picture fragments. Such a notational scheme would include a formal description of a program or procedure in G. We shall not discuss these technical details here.*

3.4. Although we shall not deal with interpretational aspects of picture languages in any detail here, it may be of some interest to consider, briefly, the connection between the descriptive approach to recognition and the decision-theoretic one we discussed earlier.

The pattern recognition problem, as it is usually posed, consists in assigning a given picture token to one of a finite number of categories. Notice that this problem is well-posed only when applied to picture classes generated through a finite set of schemata. In this case, one can identify each schema with a given picture category and the recognition problem can be stated as follows: Given two tokens decide whether they have been generated by two different schemata, or by the same schema although possibly with different assignments to its constituent atoms.

A uniform approach to this recognition problem is through a comparison of the generative specifications of the two tokens. An algorithm that delivers a generative specification of a given token is called a <u>parsing algorithm</u>. Even if a specification language for a given picture class is available, constructing efficient parsing

---

*A specification language for handprinted FORTRAN characters may be found fully worked out in (<u>7</u>).

algorithms, in general, need not be straightforward.

Clearly, a recognition procedure need not necessarily make use of a parsing algorithm. It may be possible to set up a battery of tests which determine whether a picture token has this or that attribute, and/or what the value of this or that attribute is. Based on the outcome of these tests, a decision procedure might be set up to assign the token to one of the predetermined categories. This is the decision-theoretic approach based on computing property lists that we have already seen.

The properties in property lists and the attribute sets of the atoms need not be the same. They may overlap completely, partially, or not at all. This can be seen most easily as follows: Given a specification language, G, let us enlarge it by appending to it a set, G*, of computable functions and predicates defined over the picture fragments of G. These added functions and predicates could otherwise be arbitrary.

Given a token or a picture fragment at some stage of a generation process, and a particular function or predicate, g*, from G* defined over the former, the value obtained by evaluating g* using the given token or fragment as the argument is called an <u>aspect of the situation</u> at that stage of the generative process. Without loss in generality we can assume that G* includes functions that compute attribute values of atoms and fragments and predicates that evaluate relationships between them, whenever these are computable.

Let us refer to an aspect of a situation as an <u>inferred property</u> of a token or a picture fragment if it does not consist of attribute values from A and relationship values from R.

A recognition procedure for a class of pictures could conceivably be set up, in special cases, through the use of property lists involving inferred properties alone. In such a scheme, the underlying specification language clearly plays no direct role in recognition. A recognition device, thus, need not know how to generate a picture in order to be able to recognize it.

However, as we discussed earlier, such an approach has severe intrinsic limitations. While it may work for discrete symbol recognition, it may not be generalizable to scene analysis. As we have already pointed out, in problem-solving situations relationships between properties of picture fragments like similarity, equivalence, etc., should play a crucial role. These relationships are most naturally defined in terms of generative schemata.

4. Optimality Considerations

4.1. The approach to picture processing through the use of picture languages suggests two avenues for further explorations and research. The first is concerned with the pragmatics of language usage. Typical questions for study are: How does one construct picture processing systems that could use efficiently given picture languages?; How does one embed picture languages in discourse languages?; How does one construct picture processing systems that could function efficiently in interactive mode with a human operator using both picture and discourse languages? Some preliminary discussions of these questions may be found in (7). We shall not discuss this aspect of research further here.

The second area of study is concerned with learning or acquisition of picture languages appropriate to given classes of pictures. It is clear that problems concerned with learning phenomena are intrinsically much more difficult both to formulate and to solve, than problems concerned with finding solution procedures for well-stated problems. Constructing a performance model that can find solutions efficiently for given problems, is a more straightforward design problem to handle conceptually, than constructing a performance model that is required to formulate problems for itself. Actually, no one has even seriously delimited a framework with any degree of coherence to study this latter class of performance models.

What needs to be studied, informally stated, is the structuring of a meta-framework, M, which, on exposure to classes of situations, $\{S_i\}$, could construct for itself suitable object languages, $\{L_i\}$, appropriate for describing specific situations belonging to these classes. In the context of dealing with pictorial data, the classes of situations would be classes of pictures, and the object languages would be picture languages. By "exposure" is meant, ofcourse, interactive exposure with an operator (human) so that teaching/training possibilities are not excluded. Thus, in structuring M, this interactive aspect, within which observation, exploration, etc., play a determining role, should be explicitly taken into account. That is, M should function as a behavioural system that can observe, explore, formulate "notions" about the situations it is exposed to and, thus, acquire a structured knowledge of the world it interacts with and use this knowledge in manipulating the world.

4.2. It is clear that our current expertise in designing artificial intelligence systems is totally inadequate to tackle this problem. But in this paper, our particular concern is with the relevance of optimality considerations in the study of the general picture articulation problem. From our discussion above, this can be restated in two different ways as follows: In learning to construct picture languages appropriate to given classes of pictures, do optimality considerations play any natural part?; Can the picture language acquisition problem be reduced to a problem in optimization of some parameters?

It is not clear that the language acquisition problem in its entirety, can be reduced to a problem in optimization. In fact, what little we know of language structures and language behaviour would seem to indicate strongly that the acquisition problem cannot be wholly formulated as an optimization problem. Still, it might be wondered a priori whether some aspects of the problem could, nevertheless, be studied meaningfully within the optimization framework.

An aspect that immediately suggests itself for consideration in this context is the choice of primitives for a picture language applicable to a given class of pictures. Restricted versions of this problem are statable even within the classificatory approach to pattern recognition and have been studied by several workers in this area. A very readable early treatment may be found, for example, in (1). The picture class here is a finite set of fixed patterns (i.e., with fixed attribute assignments). Each pattern is considered to be a set-theoretic union of a smaller set of fixed features (i.e., primitives with fixed attribute assignments). Learning algorithms for a two-layer perceptron are worked out to articulate the minimal set of features which make up the given set of patterns.

A much more elaborate approach to this problem of "optimum feature extraction" may be found in (10). A considerable amount of work in this aspect of pattern analysis has been done by Soviet workers.

A careful consideration of all this work would show, however, that the "feature extraction" problem, as studied by these workers, is not quite equivalent to the design of an 'optimal' set of primitives for a given class of pictures. For, in the way we have formalized a picture language, primitives have associated with them admissible attributes. And relationships defined over sets of these attribute values determine the composition rules that define "patterns" globally. Thus, feature extraction techniques based on clustering and other distance measures defined over subsets of picture points are not adequate to articulate primitives as we have defined them. It is not clear that discovery procedures for picture languages (or for any language, for that matter) can be meaningfully formulated within the decision-theoretic framework at all.

4.3. A distinctly different problem that is likely to be amenable to optimization studies within the framework of descriptive schemata is noise cleaning or preprocessing of noisy pictures. It is well known by now that homogeneous Boolean and thresholding operations can be used with great success to clean up noisy pictures (5). Specialized algorithms have been developed by various workers in this area; (for a good summary, see Rosenfeld's recent survey (8)). However, what has still not been systematically explored is the increase in efficiency that is likely to result from basing noise cleaning techniques on known syntactic properties of the picture classes under consideration.

Some preliminary work along these lines was done some years ago at the University of Illinois using digitized bubblechamber pictures (4). Noise cleaning algorithms were designed making explicit use of the fact that bubblechamber pictures consist of tracks with a predominant north-south orientation and that the type of noise most often encountered tends to cut up these tracks into disjoint segments. The strategy used was to assign direction labels to these dismembered track segments and try to "grow" them in the north-south direction to enable a north-end and a south-end to meet. Special precautions had to be taken, ofcourse, to ensure that spurious bridges were not grown by this process.

Labelling techniques can be very effectively used in preprocessing pictures if methods could be devised to ensure that the labels assigned mirror in some way the underlying generative syntax of the pictures. Further examples testifying to the truth of this statement may be found in (6) and (9) where the classes of pictures considered are quite different from bubblechamber pictures.

The general problem of preprocessing may be stated as follows: How to devise efficient noise cleaning algorithms given a class of picture tokens belonging to a known specification language and corrupted by noise whose classificatory properties are also known?; What kinds of optimality considerations are likely to be relevant to solve this problem in general?; Would these still be decision-theoretic as this term is understood at present?

5. Summary

We have considered in this paper, in some detail, inherent inadequacies in the classificatory approach to the pattern recognition problem. As opposed to this, the merits of a descriptive approach making use of syntax-based descriptive schemata for classes of pictures were argued. We described, in some technical detail, a meta-formalism for specification languages for picture classes. The relationship between the syntax-based descriptive and the unstructured classificatory approaches to recognition were analyzed. Finally, we investigated plausible ways in which optimality considerations could play a role in picture processing within the descriptive framework. We came to the conclusion that the most promising aspect of picture processing, where optimization techniques were likely to make a meaningful contribution, is in preprocessing or noise-cleaning of picture tokens. Much work remains to be done in this area yet.

Acknowledgments

The efficient assistance of Miss F.J. Kotwal and Mr. V.S. Patil in the preparation of the typescript is gratefully acknowledged.

References

1. H.D. Block et al.: Determination and Detection of Features in Patterns; in J.T. Tou and R.H. Wilcox (Eds.): Computer and Information Sciences, Spartan Books, Inc., (1964), 75 - 110.
2. T.G. Evans: A Program for the Solution of a Class of Geometry Analogy Intelligence-test Questions; Ph.D. Thesis, Dept. Math., M.I.T., Cambridge, (May 1963).
3. V.A. Kovalevsky: Present and Future of Pattern Recognition Theory; Proceedings of IFIP Congress 65, Vol. I, Spartan Books, Inc., (1965), 37 - 43.
4. R. Narasimhan and J.P. Fornango: A Preprocessing Routine for Digitized Bubblechamber Pictures; DCL, Univ. Illinois, File No. 558, (July 1963).
5. R. Narasimhan: Labeling Schemata and Syntactic Descriptions of Pictures; Information and Control, 7, (1964), 151 - 179.
6. R. Narasimhan and J.P. Fornango: Some Further Experiments in the Parallel Processing of Pictures; Trans. IEEE, EC-13, (1964), 748 - 750.
7. R. Narasimhan: On the Description, Generation and Recognition of Classes of Pictures; Lecture Notes for the NATO Summer School on Automatic Interpretation and Classification of Images, Pisa, Aug. 26-Sep. 7, 1968.

8. A. Rosenfeld: Picture Processing by Computers; Comp. Sc. Centre, Univ. Maryland, Tech. Rept. 68-Nonr-5144(00), (June 1968).
9. T. Sakai et al.: Line Extraction and Pattern Detection in a Photograph; Dept. Elec. Engg., Kyoto Univ., Kyoto, (June 1968).
10. J.T. Tou and R.P. Heydorn: Some Approaches to Optimum Feature Extraction; in J.T. Tou (Ed.): Computer and Information Sciences, II, Academic Press, (1967), 57 - 89.

NUMERICAL SOLUTION OF A DISTRIBUTED IDENTIFICATION PROBLEM VIA A DIRECT METHOD

G.A. Phillipson*, S.K. Mitter**

* Shell Development Company, Geophysics Department, Houston, Texas

** Case Western Reserve University, Systems Research Center, Cleveland, Ohio

A. Introduction. We consider the state identification problem for systems whose state evolution process is described by a linear parabolic Partial Differential Equation, wherein all parameters are known.* The results derived are also applicable to systems whose state evolution process is described by linear, second order, hyperbolic partial differential equations (1).

The method of approach is a variational one and, under suitable hypothesis, the results obtained have a certain "stochastic respectability." In abstract, the problem is formulated as follows:

Given:

(1) A state evolution process S

(2) Input measurements I which are inexact--that is, there are measurement errors, and

(3) Output measurements O which are incomplete and/or inexact, the former qualification being a consequence of a certain physical realizability condition.

Problem

Recover an estimate of the "true state of nature of the process S, on the basis of I,O and the state evolution process associated with S, which is optimal in some sense. This problem is equivalent to determining optimal estimates of

(a) The initial condition with which the state evolution process began, and

(b) The environmental interaction or inputs.

Denoting this vector of optimal estimates by $\underline{u}$ and an arbitrary estimate by $\underline{v}$, the criterion of optimality chosen is

*An extension is proposed for distributed parameter estimation.

that of "least squares", that is,

$$J(\underline{u}) = \inf_{\underline{v} \in V} J(\underline{v}) \qquad (1)$$

where $J(\underline{v})$ is an appropriate quadratic error functional incorporating the measurements I and O, and V is the space of admissible estimates.

The identification problem as phrased is therefore a variational one, that of minimizing a quadratic functional. Characterization of extremals to the quadratic functional is achieved via the method of variational inequalities, due to Lions and Stampaccia (2). We employ a direct numerical method which uses the aforementioned characterization to generate conjugate directions of search on the quadratic functional, which lead, in the limit, to the sought for extremals. We remark that the numerical technique (considered in the sequel) is applicable to a braoder class of problems than those arising in the context of identification. In particular, we recognize an immediate application to problems in distributed optimal control.

Remark

The foregoing implies that we solve a smoothing problem, and thus the solution is made in an "off-line" sense. The filtering problem for the class of systems introduced here has been presented elsewhere (1),(3).

B. Mathematical Statement of the Problem

Notation:

Let Ω be a simply connected open set in R^r. Points of Ω are denoted by $x = (x_1,\ldots,x_r)$. The boundary of Ω is denoted by Γ which is assumed to be regular. Let t denote time. Define the sets

$$\Sigma = \Gamma x(0,T]$$

$$Q = \Gamma x(0,T] .$$

Let $L^2(\Omega)$, $L^2(\Sigma)$ denote square integrable functions (equivalence classes) and define $V = L^2(\Sigma) x L^2(\Omega)$. Evidently $L^2(\Sigma)$, $L^2(\Omega)$ and V are Hilbert spaces under the usual inner product and norm.

State Evolution Process:

$$\frac{\partial y}{\partial t}(x,t;\underline{u})+A[y(x,t;\underline{u})] = f(x,t) \qquad x,t \in Q \qquad (1)$$

$$y(s,t) = u_1(s,t) \qquad s,t \in \Sigma \qquad (2)$$

$$y(x,o) = u_2(x) \qquad x \in \Omega \qquad (3)$$

where the hypothesis on $f(x,t)$, $u_1(s,t)$ and $u_2(x)$ is: $f(\cdot,\cdot) \in L^2(Q)$, $u_1(\cdot,\cdot) \in L^2(\Sigma)$ and $u_2(\cdot) \in L^2(\Omega)$. In addition, $A[\cdot]$ is an elliptic partial differential operator:

$$A[\psi] = - \sum_{i,j=1}^{r} \frac{\partial}{\partial x_i} [a_{ij}(x) \frac{\partial}{\partial x_j} \psi(x,t)] + a_0(x) \psi(x,t)$$

with $a_{ij}(x)$, $a_0(x)$ bounded, measurable and

$$\sum_{i,j=1}^{r} a_{ij}(x) \xi_i \xi_j \geq \alpha(\xi_1^2 + \ldots + \xi_r^2) , \alpha > 0$$

$$a_0(x) > \alpha$$

for almost every x Ω.

Quadratic (cost) Functional:

Define

$$\underline{v} = [v_1(s,t) \vdots v_2(x)]^T \quad ; \quad \underline{v} \varepsilon V$$

$$\underline{u}^* = [u_1^*(s,t) \vdots u_2^*(x)]^T \quad ; \quad \underline{u}^* \varepsilon V$$

$$\underline{z} = \underline{u}^* + \underline{K}^T \underline{N}(t) \quad ; \quad \underline{z} \varepsilon V$$

$$z(x,t) = y(x,t;\underline{u}^*)+K_0 N_0(t) \quad ; \quad z(\cdot,\cdot) \varepsilon L^2(Q)$$

In the above the K's are constants and $\underline{N}(t)$ and $N_0(t)$ are error processes in appropriate Hilbert spaces.

Remark

$\underline{u}^*$ is a vector of the true initial and boundary conditions for the system S. $\underline{z}$ and z(x,t) are the input (I) and output (O) measurements, respectively. The measurement z(x,t) given is physically unrealistic but is taken for simplicity. Parallel results have been obtained for the discrete measurement case, that is,

$$z(x,t) = \sum_{i=1}^{\nu} y(x^i,t;\underline{u}^*) + K_0 N_0(t)$$

and will be reported.

The quadratic functional $J(\underline{v})$ is given by:

$$J(\underline{v}) = ||y(x,t;\underline{v})-z(x,t)||^2_{L^2(Q)}+||\underline{v} - \underline{z}||^2_V \tag{4}$$

If we define

$$a(\underline{v},\underline{v}) = ||y(x,t;\underline{v})-y(x,t;\underline{o})\|^2_{L^2(Q)}+||\underline{v}||^2_V \tag{5}$$

$$\ell(\underline{v}) = -\{(y(x,t;\underline{v})-y(x,t;\underline{o}),y(x,t;\underline{o})-z(x,t))_{L^2(Q)} - (\underline{v},z)_V\} \tag{6}$$

$$c = ||y(x,t;\underline{o})-z(x,t)||^2_{L^2(Q)}+||\underline{z}||^2_V \tag{7}$$

Then (4) is equivalent to:

$$J(\underline{v}) = a(\underline{v},\underline{v}) - 2\ell(\underline{v}) + c \tag{8}$$

We have the following:

Proposition 1

$a(\underline{v},\underline{w})$ is a coercive, continuous, bilinear form on V. $\ell(v)$ is a continuous linear form on V.

Using the results of (2), it is possible to give the following characterization of the optimal estimate $\underline{u}$, stated as a theorem.

Theorem 1

There exists one and only one $\underline{u} \varepsilon V$ such that $J(\underline{u}) = \underset{v \varepsilon V}{\text{Inf}} J(\underline{v})$ and it is characterized by

$$a(\underline{u},\underline{v}) = \ell(\underline{v}) \quad \text{for all} \quad v \varepsilon V \tag{9}$$

Remark

(9) is the (formal) differential of the functional J evaluated at $\underline{u}$, denoted here by $\delta J(\underline{u})$. In terms of the gradient $\underline{G}(\underline{u})$,

$$\delta J(\underline{u}) = (\underline{G}(\underline{u}),\underline{v})_V$$

An equation for $\underline{G}(\underline{u})$ is given in the following Proposition:

Proposition 2

$\underline{G}(\underline{u})$ is given by

$$\underline{G}(\underline{u}) = \begin{matrix} -\frac{\partial p}{\partial \nu_{A^*}}(s,t)+u_1(s,t)-z_1(s,t) \\ p(x,o)+u_2(x) - z_2(x) \end{matrix} \tag{10}$$

where $p(\cdot,t) \varepsilon H_0^1(\Omega)$ (the first Sobolev space) and is the unique solution of

$$\begin{aligned} &-\frac{\partial p}{\partial t}(x,t;\underline{u})+A^*[p(x,t;\underline{u})]=y(x,t;\underline{u})-z(x,t) \\ &p(s,t) = 0 \\ &p(T) = 0 \end{aligned} \tag{11}$$

Remark

It is convenient to define the gradient $G(\underline{u})$ in terms of Eqs. (10) and (11). For, if we put equations (5) and (6) into Eq. (9), we obtain

$$\begin{aligned} &\int_Q[y(x,t;\underline{u})-z(x,t)][y(x,t;\underline{v})-y(x,t;\underline{o})]dxdt \\ &+\int_\Sigma[u_1(s,t)-z_1(s,t)]v_1(s,t)dsdt \\ &+\int_\Omega[u_2(x)-z_2(x)]v_2(x)dx = 0 \end{aligned} \tag{12}$$

While (12) characterizes the optimum choice of $\underline{u}$, the numerical selection of $\underline{u}$ is obscure. Noting that the variable adjoint to $y(x,t;\underline{u})$ evolves according to (11), and that the R.H.S. of the evolution equation for $p(x,t;u)$ appears in (12), we substitute where appropriate and obtain

$$\begin{aligned} &\int_\Sigma[-\frac{\partial p}{\partial \nu_{A^*}}(s,t)+u_1(s,t)-z_1(s,t)]v_1(s,t)dsdt \\ &+ \quad [p(x,o)+u_2(x)-z_2(x)]v_2(x)dx=0 \end{aligned} \tag{13}$$

Comparing (13) with the definition of $\delta J(\underline{u})$, we immediately extract $\underline{G}(\underline{u})$ given by (10). The choice of $\underline{u}$ is now conceptually clear, since

$$\underline{G}(\underline{u}) = 0 \tag{14}$$

is equivalent to Eq. (9). We attend now to an algorithm which accomplishes (14) by successive approximation.

C. The Programming Algorithm

The determination of $\underline{u}$ which satisfies (9) (and which solves the identification problem) is made by generating a minimizing sequence $\{\underline{u}^i\}$ which converges (weakly) to $\underline{u} \in V$. This sequence is generated by employing conjugate directions of search $\{\underline{s}^i\}$ on the functional $J(\underline{v})$, (4), (5). The algorithm for generating $\{s^i\}$ and $\{\underline{u}^i\}$ together with the convergence property are now considered.

Algorithm:

(1) Select $\underline{u}^0 \in V$ (Initial guess)

(2) Evaluate $G(\underline{u}^0)$. If $G(\underline{u}^0) \neq 0$, then for the (i+1)st iteration, (i = 0,1,2...) proceed as follows:

(3) $\underline{u}^{i+1} = \underline{u}^i + \alpha^i \underline{s}^i$

$$\underline{s}^0 = - \underline{G}(\underline{u}^0)$$

$$\underline{s}^{i+1} = - \underline{G}(\underline{u}^{i+1}) + \beta^i \underline{s}^i$$

$$\beta^i = \frac{(\underline{G}(\underline{u}^{i+1}),G(\underline{u}^{i+1}))_V}{((\underline{G}(\underline{u}^i),\underline{G}(\underline{u}^i))_V}$$

In addition, α^i is chosen so that

$$J(\underline{u}^i + \alpha^i \underline{s}^i) = \operatorname*{Inf}_{\gamma^i \varepsilon R^1} J(\underline{u}^i + \gamma^i \underline{s}^i)$$

It is possible to obtain an explicit expression for α^i:

$$\alpha^i = \frac{(\underline{G}(\underline{u}^i),G(\underline{u}^i))_V}{a(\underline{s}^i,\underline{s}^i)}$$

Theorem 2

The sequence $\{\underline{u}^i\}$ converges weakly to a unique $\underline{u} \in V$ and that limit $\underline{u}$ has the property that

$$J(\underline{u}) = \operatorname*{Inf}_{\underline{v} \varepsilon V} J(\underline{v})$$

We remark that the computation of $\underline{G}(\underline{u}^i)$ involves the sequential solution of (1) forwards in time (starting from $u_2^i(x)$ and evolving under the influence of $u_1^i(s,t)$) and then the solution of (11) backwards in time to recover $p(\cdot,\cdot;u^i)$ and hence $\underline{G}(\underline{u}^i)$. These solution "directions" are numerically stable. Thus to obtain $\underline{G}(\underline{u}^i)$, it is necessary to solve the PDE^s given by (1), (2),(3), and (11). We approximate these solutions by the method of Galerkin, in the manner suggested by Lions (6). The Galerkin approximations $y_m(x,t;\underline{u})$ and $p_m(x,t;\underline{u})$ are given by

$$y_m(x,t;u)=\sum_{i=1}^{m} y_i(t)w_i(x); \quad \{w_i(\cdot)\}_{i=1,2..} \quad \text{a basis in } L^2(\Omega)$$

$$p_m(x,t;\underline{u}) = \sum_{i=1}^{m} p_i(t)w_i(x)$$

where $y_i(t)$ and $p_i(t)$ satisfy the following ordinary differential equations.

$$\frac{dy_i}{dt}(t;\underline{u})+\lambda_i y_i(t;\underline{u})=f_i(t)-u_{1i}(t); \quad y_i(0)=u_{2i} \quad t \in (0,T)$$

$$-\frac{dp_i}{dt}(t;\underline{u})+\lambda_i p_i(t;\underline{u})=y_i(t;\underline{u})-z_i(t); \quad p_i(T) = 0 \quad t \in [0,T)$$

the λ_i are the eigenvalues of the following Sturm Lionville equation:

$$A[w(x)] - \lambda w(x) = 0 \qquad x \in \Omega$$
$$w(0) = 0$$
$$w(1) = 0$$

and

$$f_i(t) = (f,w_i)_{L^2(\Omega)}$$
$$z_i(t) = (z,w_i)_{L^2(\Omega)}$$
$$u_{1i}(t) = (z_1,\frac{\partial w_i}{\partial \nu_{A*}})_{L^2(\Gamma)}$$
$$u_{2i} = (z_2,w_i)_{L^2(\Omega)}$$

Remark

The choice of the basis functions $\{w_i(x)\}_{i=1,2..}$ is a question of significant importance. Experience with those reported here indicate poor approximation of $y(\cdot,\cdot;\underline{u})$ and $p(\cdot,\cdot;\underline{u})$ unless m is large. However, because of the decoupling afforded they are convenient. For, we found that for small m.

$$G_m(\underline{u}) \rightarrow 0$$

where $G_m(\underline{u})$ is computed according to Eq. (15). (Note that $\underline{u}$ is not approximated but the definition of the gradient is). There are other selections for $\{w_i\}$ possible, perhaps the most appealing of which are the splines of interpolation (1).

It should be emphasized that $\underline{G_m}(\underline{u^i})$ determined from the Galerkin approximation is an approximation to $\underline{G}(\underline{u^i})$, given by

$$G_m(\underline{u}^i) = \begin{matrix} -\sum_{j=1}^{m} p_j(t)\frac{\partial w_j(s)}{\partial \nu_{A*}} + u_1^i(s,t)-z_1(s,t) \\ \sum_{j=1}^{m} p_j(0)\, w_j(x) + u_2^i(x) - z_2(x) \end{matrix} \qquad (15)$$

The question of convergence of $\underline{G_m} \rightarrow \underline{G}$ will be reported in a later paper (7). Experience with non trivial examples indicate a striking convergence of the overall algorithm. In particular, numerical results have been obtained for the following system:

$$\frac{\partial y(x,t)}{\partial t} - \frac{\partial^2 y(x,t)}{\partial x^2} = 212.0 \qquad 0 < x < 1 \quad ; \quad 0 \leq t \leq T$$
$$y(s,t) = u_1(s,t) \qquad s = 0,\ 1 \quad ; \quad 0 < t \leq T$$
$$y(x,o) = u_2(x) \qquad 0 < x < 1 \quad ; \quad t = 0$$

Input Measurements

$$z_1(0,t) = u_1^*(0,t) + k_1\ N_1(t) \qquad t \in (0,1]$$
$$z_1(1,t) = u_1^*(1,t) + k_2\ N_2(t) \qquad t \in (0,1]$$
$$z_2(x) = u_2^*(x) + k_3 \qquad x \in (0,1).$$

where u* is the true state of nature and is defined by:

$$u_1^*(0,t) = 70 + 10 \sin 2\pi t$$
$$u_1^*(1,t) = 54.5$$
$$u_2^*(x) = 70\ e^{-0.25x}$$

and $N_1(t)$, $N_2(t)$ are random telegraph signals with amplitude ± 1.0. k_1 and k_2 are variables chosen to affect the signal to noise ratio and k_3 is an arbitrary bias on the initial condition, also chosen to affect the signal to noise.

Output Measurements

(1) $z(x,t) \doteq y(x,t;\underline{u}^*) + k_0\ N_0(t) \qquad x,t \in (0,1) \times (0,1)$

where $N_0(t)$ is a random telegraph signal with amplitude ± 1.0 and k_0 is a constant which alters the signal to noise ratio. It is assumed that $N_0(t)$, $N_1(t)$, $N_2(t)$ are mutually independent random variables.

(2) Measurements were taken at 4 points of the spatial domain.

$$z(x^i,t) = y(x^i,t;\underline{u}^*) + k_0^i\ N_0^i(t),\ (i = 1,2,3,4)$$
$$x^1 = 0.2,\quad x^2 = 0.4,\quad x^3 = 0.6,\quad x^4 = 0.8.$$

The minimization of $J(\underline{v})$ is displayed in Figure 1 for both measurement processes A and B. The behaviour of one of the elements of $G_m(\underline{u})$, namely $G(u_1)$ is displayed in Figure 2. It was found that three iterations were sufficient to determine $\underline{u}$ for which $G_m(\underline{u}) = 0$ under measurement A, and five iterations solved case B.

D. Extensions to Parameter Identification

The conventional expedient of converting a linear parameter identification problem into a nonlinear state identification problem can be considered in the context of our results, providing the following approximations are employed:

(1) Linearize the resulting nonlinear state equations

(2) Reduce the result to cannonical parabolic form by introducing, where appropriate, "diffusion terms" which are removed in the limit, as suggested in (8). That is, we make the linear equations "quasi reversible".

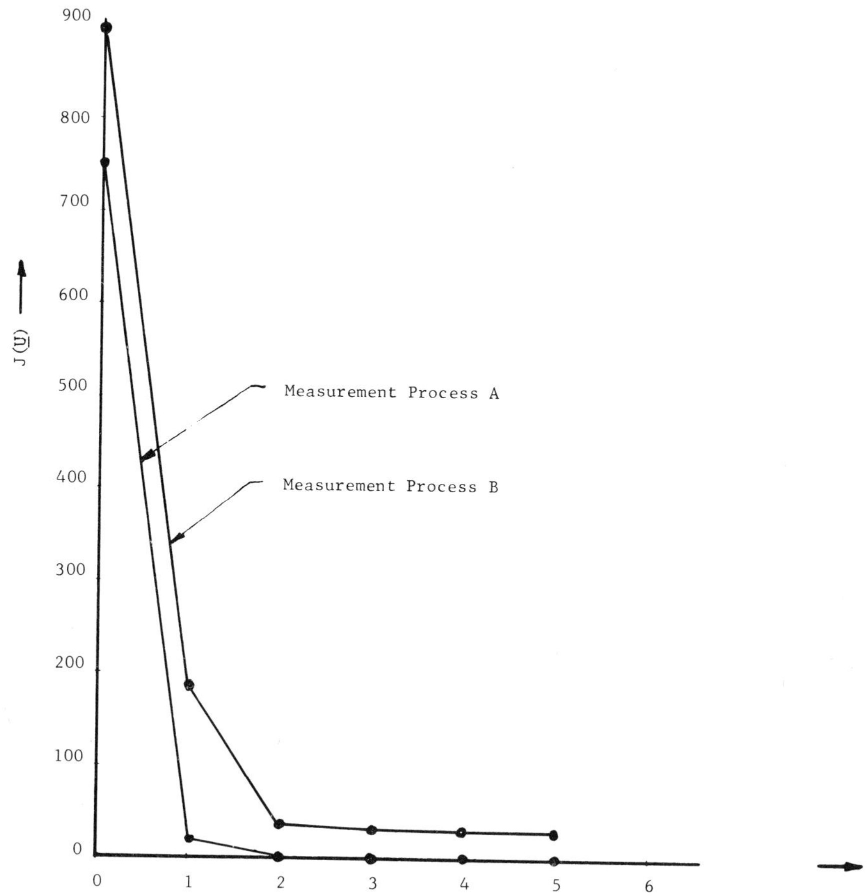

Figure 1: Minimization of the error functional.

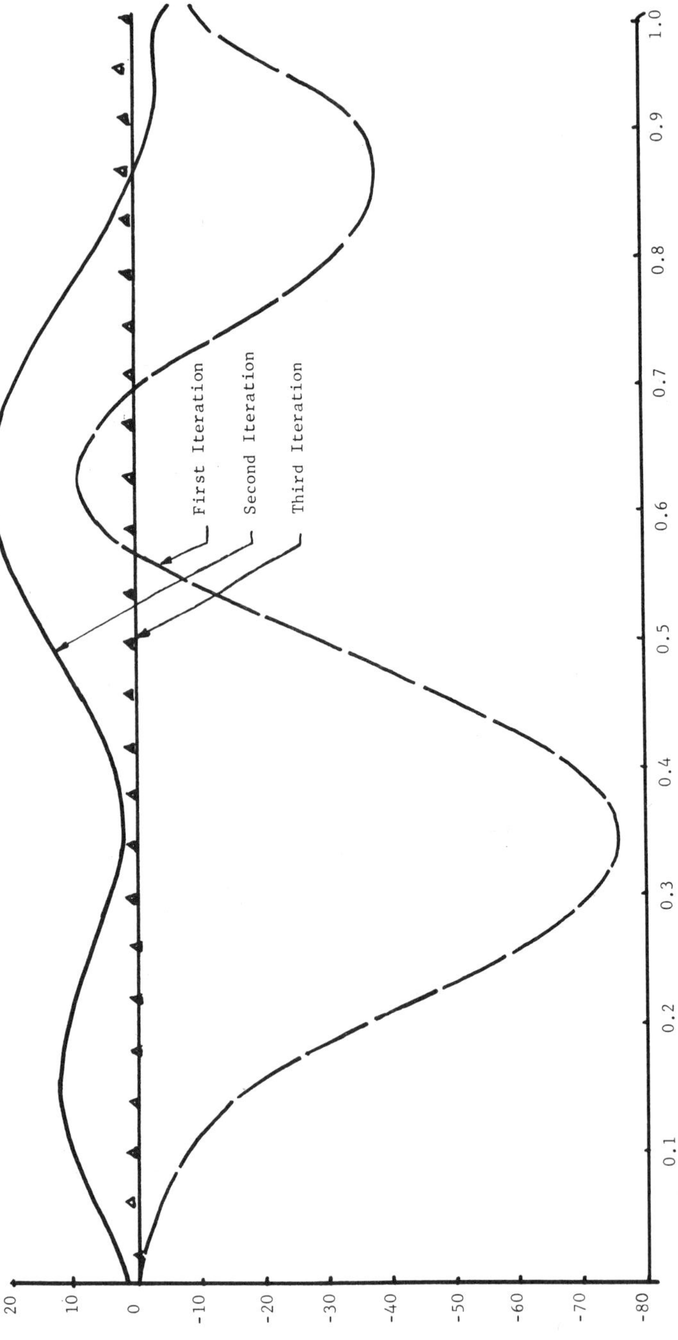

Figure 2: $G_M(U_1)$ under measurement process B with M = 8.

REFERENCES

(1) G.A.PHILLIPSON — "The State Identification of a Class of Distributed Systems", Ph.D. Thesis, Case Western Reserve University.

(2) J.L.LIONS, and G.STAMPACCHIA — "Variational Inequalities", Communications on Pure and Applied Mathematics,Vol.XX,(1967), pp. 493-519.

(3) A.V.BALAKRISHNAN,and J.L.LIONS — "State Estimation for Infinite Dimensional Systems", J.Comp. and System Sciences,Vol.1,(1967),pp. 391-403.

(4) L.S.LASDON, S.K.MITTER,and A.D.WAREN — "The Conjugate Gradient Method for Optimal Control Problems", IEEE Transactions on Automatic Control, Vol. AC-12,No.2,April 1967, pp. 132-138.

(5) J.TODD, Ed. — Survey of Numerical Analysis, New York, McGraw Hill, 1962.

(6) J.L.LIONS, — et.al., "Functional Analysis and Optimization", a two week short course, July 31-August 11, 1967 at U.C.L.A.

(7) G.A.PHILLIPSON,and S.K.MITTER — Numerical Solution of Optimal Control Problems for Distributed Parameter Systems, to be published.

(8) R.LATTES,and J.L.LIONS — "Methode de Quasi-Reversibilite' et Applications", Paris: Dunod, 1967.

ON PRIMAL AND DUAL METHODS FOR SOLVING DISCRETE OPTIMAL CONTROL PROBLEMS

E. Polak

Department of Electrical Engineering
and Computer Sciences
Electronics Research Laboratory
University of California, Berkeley

I. INTRODUCTION

Discrete optimal control problems can easily be seen to be nonlinear programming problems with considerable structure (1). In principle, therefore, they are solvable by nonlinear programming algorithms, such as the methods of feasible directions (2), (3). This may be called a primal approach since it deals with the problem without transformations. In practice, however, a primal approach may not be practical, since the dimension of the problem is invariably very large, necessitating the use of complex decomposition methods (4).

On the other hand, it has been known for some time (see (5), (6), (7), (8)), that optimal control problems with linear dynamics can be transcribed into low dimensional geometric problems which require a search in the co-state (i. e., Lagrange multiplier) space. This may be called a dual approach. Its great appeal lies in the fact that it exploits the structure of the optimal control problem to the utmost extent, to produce a very natural decomposition into a family of low dimensional problems.

This paper presents a few new algorithms of the dual type. These algorithms differ from previously published ones in that they apply to considerably more complex situations, use more efficient step size rules, and incorporate procedures for carrying out finite approximations compatible with convergence (i. e., they incorporate antijamming procedures). Computational difficulties are also discussed to some extent,

---

Research sponsored by the National Aeronautics and Space Administration under Grant NsG-354, Suppl. 5.

and in such a way as to make it possible for the expert to compare these difficulties with the ones arising in the use of primal methods.

The conclusion we are led to, and which is supported by some experimental work, is that when the number of state space constraints is small, dual methods can be considerably more efficient, but when the number of state space constraints is large, the efficiency of primal methods may be as great, or greater, as that of dual methods.

II. ALGORITHMS

As is well known, optimal control problems, with linear dynamics, convex cost functional, convex constraints on the control, and a finite number of strictly convex constraints on the state, are easily transcribable into a problem involving the separation of sets $\mathscr{C}(\alpha)$, of states reachable with cost α, from the state space constraints set Ω.

The Geometric Problem: We are given a map $\mathscr{C}(\cdot)$ from R^+ into the set of all subsets of R^n such that, (i) for every $\alpha \geq 0$, $\mathscr{C}(\alpha)$ is compact and convex; (ii) $\mathscr{C}(\cdot)$ is continuous in the Hausdorff metric; (iii) for every $0 \leq \alpha_1 \leq \alpha_2$, $\mathscr{C}(\alpha_1) \subset \mathscr{C}(\alpha_2)$.

We are also given a strictly convex, compact set Ω, and are required to find a $\hat{\alpha} \geq 0$, a vector $\hat{x} \in \Omega$, and a unit vector $\hat{s} \in R^n$ such that

$$\hat{\alpha} = \min \{\alpha \mid \mathscr{C}(\alpha) \cap \Omega \neq \phi, \ \alpha \geq 0\} \ ; \tag{1}$$

$$\{\hat{x}\} = \mathscr{C}(\hat{\alpha}) \cap \Omega \ ; \tag{2}$$

$$\langle x - \hat{x}, \hat{s} \rangle \leq 0 \quad \text{for all} \quad x \in \Omega \ ; \tag{3}$$

$$\langle x - \hat{x}, \hat{s} \rangle \geq 0 \quad \text{for all} \quad x \in \mathscr{C}(\hat{\alpha}) \ . \tag{4}$$

Assumption 1. In order to avoid the use of complicating projection operators, we shall assume that for every $\alpha > 0$ the set $\mathscr{C}(\alpha)$ has an interior.

Assumption 2. In order to assure the existence of a solution, we shall assume that for some $\alpha \in (0, \infty)$, Ω has points in the interior of $\mathscr{C}(\alpha)$.

Assumption 3. Let $\hat{\alpha}$ be defined by (1), then we assume that for every $0 < \alpha_1 < \alpha_2 \leq \hat{\alpha}$, $\mathscr{C}(\alpha_1) \neq \mathscr{C}(\alpha_2)$.

As we shall later see, the Geometric Problem can be solved by finding a unit vector $\hat{s}$ with suitable properties, which we shall now establish.

Definition 1. Let $S = \{s \in R^n \mid \|s\| = 1\}$, and let $v: s \to \Omega$ be the map defined by

$$<x - v(s), s> \leq 0 \quad \text{for all} \quad x \in \Omega \tag{5}$$

(Note that $v(\cdot)$ is a continuous map).

Definition 2. We shall say that a vector $\hat{s} \in S$ is optimal if for some $\hat{\alpha} \geq 0$, $v(\hat{s}) \in \mathcal{C}(\hat{\alpha}) \cap \Omega$ and

$$<x - v(\hat{s}), \hat{s}> \leq 0 \quad \text{for all} \quad x \in \Omega \tag{6}$$

$$<x - v(\hat{s}), \hat{s}> \geq 0 \quad \text{for all} \quad x \in \mathcal{C}(\hat{\alpha}) \tag{7}$$

We shall now present several algorithms for the solution of particular cases of the Geometric Problem.

CASE I: For every $\alpha \geq 0$, $\mathcal{C}(\alpha) = \Sigma(\alpha) \cap Q$, where Q is a convex polyhedron, and, for every $\alpha > 0$, $\Sigma(\alpha)$ is a strictly convex set. We also assume that if $0 \leq \alpha_1 < \alpha_2$, then $\Sigma(\alpha_1)$ is contained in the interior of $\Sigma(\alpha_2)$. (Note that by Assumption 2 the set Ω has points in the interior of Q).

To define an algorithm for the Case I, we shall need the following maps and sets.

Definition 3. For every $s \in S$ and every $v \in R^n$, let $P(v, s)$ denote the hyperplane

$$P(v, s) = \{x \in R^n \mid <x - v, s> = 0\} \tag{8}$$

(Note that $P(v(s), s)$ is a support hyperplane to Ω at $v(s)$, with outward normal s).

Proposition 1. Let $T \subset S$ be defined by

$$T = \{s \in S \mid <x - v(s), s> \geq 0 \quad \text{for all} \quad x \in \mathcal{C}(0)\} \tag{9}$$

Then the set T has the following properties: (i) If $\hat{s} \in S$ is optimal, then $\hat{s} \in T$; and, under the assumption of Case I, $v(\hat{s}) \in \mathcal{C}(c(\hat{s})) \cap P(v(\hat{s}), \hat{s})$, where $c: T \to R^1$ is defined below; (ii) There exists a $\alpha^* \in (0, \infty)$ such that

$$\mathcal{C}(\alpha^*) \cap P(v(s), s) \neq \varphi \quad \text{for all} \quad s \in T \tag{10}$$

(The last two statements are a consequence of Assumption 2)

Definition 4. Let $c: T \to R^1$ be defined by

$$c(s) = \min \{\alpha \mid \mathcal{C}(\alpha) \cap P(v(s), s) \neq \varphi, \ \alpha \geq 0\} \tag{11}$$

Definition 5. Let $w: T \to R^n$ be defined by

$$w(s) \in \mathcal{C}(c(s)) \cap P(v(s), s) \tag{12}$$

$$\|w(s) - v(s)\| = \min \{\|w - v(s)\| \mid w \in \mathcal{C}(c(s)) \cap P(v(s), s)\}$$

Proposition 2. Under the assumptions for Case I, for every $s \in T$, the set $\mathscr{C}(c(s)) \cap P(v(s), s)$ consists of exactly one point, $w(s)$. Consequently, $\hat{s} \in T$ is optimal if and only if $w(\hat{s}) = v(\hat{s})$.

Definition 6. For any two vectors $x, y \in R^n$, let $\pi(x, y)$ denote the operator which projects R^n, orthogonally, onto the subspace spanned by x, y. Let $p : R^n \times R^n \to R^1$ be defined by

$$p(x, y) = \min\{\alpha \mid \pi(x, y)(\mathscr{C}(\alpha)) \cap \pi(x, y)(\Omega) \neq \varphi, \ \alpha \geq 0\} \tag{13}$$

Definition 7. Let $a : T \to T$ be the search function defined by

$$a(s) \in \sigma(s) \triangleq \{s' \in T \mid s' = \lambda s + \mu(w(s) - v(s)), \lambda, \mu \in (-\infty, +\infty)\} \tag{14}$$

$$c(a(s)) = p(s, w(s) - v(s)), \tag{15}$$

with λ, μ in (14) chosen to minimize $\|a(s) - s\|$ over all $s' \in \sigma(s)$ for which (14) and (15) hold.

Remark 1. There may be more than one pair of values λ, μ for which (14) and (15) hold. Any one of these pairs may be taken to define $a(s)$ without affecting the convergence properties of the algorithm below, which we present in the form of an idealized computer program.

A Theoretical Algorithm. (16)

Step 1: Find a point $s_0 \in T$.

Step 2: Compute $a(s_0)$.

Step 3: If $a(s_0) = s_0$, stop; s_0 is optimal. Otherwise set $s_0 = a(s_0)$ and go to step 2.

Theorem 1. Let $s_0, s_1, s_2, \ldots$ be any sequence in T constructed by the algorithm (16) (i.e., $s_1, s_2, \ldots$ are the consecutive values assigned to s_0 in Step 3). Then either the sequence $\{s_i\}$ is finite and its last element is optimal, or it is infinite and every cluster point $\hat{s}$ in $\{s_i\}$ is optimal.

To prove this theorem we shall need the following result.

Lemma 1. Let T be a subset of R^n, let $c : T \to R^1$, and let $a : T \to T$ be a search function. Suppose that T contains "optimal" points which are characterized by the fact that $s \in T$ is optimal if and only if

$$c(a(s)) \leq c(s) \tag{17}$$

Also, suppose that either $c(\cdot)$ is continuous at all $s \in T$ which are not "optimal", or else $c(s)$ is bounded from above on T; and that for every $s \in T$, not "optimal", there exists a $\epsilon(s) > 0$ and a $\delta(s) > 0$ such that

$$c(a(s')) - c(s') \geq \delta(s) \text{ for all } s' \in T, \ \|s' - s\| \leq \varepsilon(s) \quad (18)$$

Let $\{s_i\}$ be a sequence in T constructed according to the rule

$$s_{i+1} = a(s_i), \quad i = 0, 1, 2, \ldots, \quad (19)$$

and satisfying

$$c(s_{i+1}) > c(s_i) \quad \text{for} \quad i = 0, 1, 2, \ldots \quad (20)$$

Then either $\{s_i\}$ is finite and its last element is "optimal", or it is infinite and every accumulation point of $\{s_i\}$ is "optimal".

Proof: Suppose that $\{s_i\}$ is finite and that s_r is its last element. Then we must have $c(a(s_r)) \leq c(s_r)$ for the sequence construction to stop. But then, by definition, s_r is optimal. Now suppose that $\{s_i\}$ is infinite and that $s_i \to s^*$ for $i \in K \subset \{0, 1, 2, \ldots\}$, where s^* is not optimal. Then there exist $\varepsilon^* > 0$, $\delta^* > 0$, and an integer $k \in K$ such that for all $i \geq k$, $i \in K$,

$$\|s_i - s^*\| \leq \varepsilon^* \quad (21)$$

and

$$c(s_{i+1}) - c(s_i) \geq \delta^* \quad (22)$$

Hence, for any two successive points s_i, s_{i+j}, i, $i+j \in K$, of the subsequence, we have, with $i \geq k$,

$$c(s_{i+j}) - c(s_i) = (c(s_{i+j}) - c(s_{i+j-1})) + \ldots + (c(s_{i+1}) - c(s_i)) \geq \delta^* \quad (23)$$

which contradicts the fact that $c(s_i) \to c^*$, either because $c(\cdot)$ is continuous at s^*, or because of (20) and the fact that $c(s)$ is bounded from above on T.

Proof of Theorem 1: First, note that (17) is satisfied by the maps $c(\cdot)$ and $a(\cdot)$, defined by (11), and (14), (15), respectively. Hence, if the sequence $\{s_i\}$ generated by the algorithm (16) is finite, its last element must be optimal.

We shall now show that the maps $c(\cdot)$ and $a(\cdot)$, under discussion, satisfy (18). Clearly, to show this it will suffice to show that the maps $c(\cdot)$ and $c(a(\cdot))$ are continuous at all non-optimal $s \in T$.

Continuity of $c(\cdot)$: Let s be any point in the interior of T and let δ be any number in $[0, c(s)]$. Then the sets $\mathcal{C}(c(s)-\delta)$ and $P(v(s), s)$ are strictly separated. Let $w' \in P(v(s), s)$ and $w'' \in \mathcal{C}(c(s)-\delta)$ be such that

$$\|w' - w''\| = \min\{\|x-y\| \mid x \in P(v(s), s),\ y \in \mathcal{C}(c(s)-\delta)\} \quad (24)$$

Let $w = (w' + w'')/2$. Then, by uniform continuity of $\langle \cdot - w, \cdot \rangle$ on $\Omega \times S$, it follows that there exists a $\epsilon' > 0$ such that for all $s' \in T$, with $\|s' - s\| \leq \epsilon'$, $P(w, s')$ separates $\mathcal{C}(c(s)-\delta)$ from Ω, and hence

$$c(s') \geq c(s) - \delta \quad \text{for all } s' \in T,\ \|s' - s\| \leq \epsilon' \quad (25)$$

Similarly, we can show that there exists a $\epsilon'' > 0$ such that

$$c(s') \leq c(s) + \delta \quad \text{for all } s' \in T,\ \|s' - s\| \leq \epsilon'' \quad (26)$$

Let $\epsilon = \min\{\epsilon', \epsilon''\}$, then

$$|c(s') - c(s)| \leq \delta \quad \text{for all } s' \in T,\ \|s' - s\| \leq \epsilon \quad (27)$$

which proves the continuity of $c(\cdot)$ at all points in the interior of T. Since an accumulation point of $\{s_i\}$ cannot be on the boundary of T ($s_i \in \{s \in T \mid c(s) > c(s_1) > 0\}$), we need not consider the behavior of $c(\cdot)$ on the boundary of T.

Continuity of $c(a(\cdot))$: First, by an argument similar to the one above, it can be shown that the map $p(\cdot,\cdot)$ defined by (13) is continuous at every pair of linearly independent vectors (x, y). Now, whenever s is not optimal, $w(s) - v(s) \neq 0$ and is orthogonal to s. Hence $c(a(\cdot))$, which is defined by

$$c(a(s)) = p(s, w(s) - v(s)),\quad s \in T \quad (28)$$

is continuous at every non-optimal $s \in T$ if $w(\cdot)$ is continuous at every non-optimal $s \in T$ (recall that $v(\cdot)$ is continuous on S).

Let $s^* \in T$ be non-optimal and let $\{s_i\}$ be any sequence in T converging to s. Then, setting $c_i = c(s_i)$, we have that $c_i \to c^* \triangleq c(s^*)$ and $\mathcal{C}(c_i) \to \mathcal{C}(c^*)$, by continuity of $c(\cdot)$ and of $\mathcal{C}(\cdot)$. Now, let w^* be an accumulation point of $\{w(s_i)\}$, i.e., $w(s_i) \to w^*$ for $i \in K \subset \{0, 1, 2, \ldots\}$. Then $w(s_i) \in \mathcal{C}(c_i)$, and therefore $w^* \in \mathcal{C}(c^*)$. Also, since $w(s_i) \in P(v(s_i), s_i)$,

$$\langle w(s_i) - v(s_i), s_i \rangle = 0 \quad \text{for} \quad i = 0, 1, 2, \ldots \quad (29)$$

Consequently, since $s_i \to s^*$, $v(s_i) \to v(s^*)$, and $w(s_i) \to w^*$ for $i \in K$, we must have $\langle w^* - v(s^*), s^* \rangle = 0$, i.e., $w^* \in P(v(s^*), s^*)$. Thus,

$$w^* \in \mathcal{C}(c(s^*)) \cap P(v(s^*), s^*) \quad (30)$$

Since Ω has points in the interior of Q, for every $s \in T$, $P(v(s), s)$ has points in the interior of Q. Furthermore, $\Sigma(c^*)$ is a strictly convex set. Hence $\mathscr{C}(c^*) \cap P(v(s^*), s^*)$ consists of only one point $w(s^*)$. Consequently, $w^* = w(s^*)$ and $w(\cdot)$ is continuous at s^*. This completes our proof.

An algorithm such as (16) cannot be implemented in practice because neither $v(s)$ nor $p(s, w(s) - v(s))$ can be calculated by means of a finite number of operations. In order to make a transition from the theoretical algorithm (16) to a practical algorithm, it is necessary to examine the effect that approximations to these functions may have on the convergence of the algorithm.

First note that

$$p(s, w(s)-v(s)) = \max\{c(s') \mid s' \in T,\ s' = \lambda s + \mu(w(s) - v(s)),\ \lambda, \mu \in (-\infty, +\infty)\} \tag{31}$$

i.e., $a(s)$, as defined by (14), (15), is computed by maximizing the function $c(\cdot)$ on the curve $\sigma(s)$ which is the intersection of T with the two dimensional subspace spanned by s and $w(s)-v(s)$.

Proposition 3. Let $\tilde{a}: T \to T$ by any map such that for every $s \in T$, $\tilde{a}(s) \in \sigma(s)$, and

$$c(\tilde{a}(s)) - c(s) \geq \beta(c(a(s)) - c(s)) \tag{32}$$

for any fixed $\beta \in (0, 1]$. Then, if $\tilde{a}(\cdot)$ is substituted for $a(\cdot)$ in the algorithm (16), the convergence properties of this algorithm are not altered, i.e., Theorem 1 still holds.

The significance of the above proposition is in the indication that, in practice, the search of a maximum $c(s')$, $s' \in \sigma(s)$, can be reduced to the examination of a few values only, with s' restricted to the segment $\{s' \in \sigma(s) \mid s' = \mu(s)(\lambda s + (1-\lambda(w(s)-v(s)));\ \lambda \in [0, 1],\ \mu(s) = \|\lambda s + (1-\lambda)(w(s)-v(s))\|^{-1}\}$.

This leaves us with the evaluation of $c(s)$, $w(s)$ and $v(s)$. As will be seen from our examples, given $v(s)$, $c(s)$ and $w(s)$ can be computed, without much difficulty, by finite step procedures, in a number of interesting cases. However, this is not generally true for $v(s)$. The following definition shows the type of approximation which we may use for $v(s)$, and which automatically results in approximations to $c(s)$, $w(s)$ and $a(s)$, without upsetting the convergence properties of the resulting modification of Algorithm (16).

Definition 8. For every $\epsilon > 0$ and $s \in S$, let $V_\epsilon(s) \subset R^n$ be defined by

$$V_\epsilon(s) = \{v_\epsilon(s) \mid \|v_\epsilon(s) - v(s)\| \leq \epsilon \text{ and } \langle x - v_\epsilon(s), s \rangle \leq 0 \text{ for all } x \in \Omega\} \quad (33)$$

In order to describe a realistic algorithm, we shall need, in addition, the following.

Definition 9. Let $U \subset R^n \times S$ be such that for every $(v, s) \in U$ there exists a $\alpha \in [0, \infty)$ such that $\mathcal{C}(\alpha) \cap P(v, s) \neq \varphi$. We then define the maps $\tilde{c}: U \to R$ and $\tilde{w}: U \to R^n$ as follows:

$$\tilde{c}(v, s) = \min\{\alpha \mid \mathcal{C}(\alpha) \cap P(v, s) \neq \varphi, \alpha \geq 0\} \quad (34)$$

$$\{\tilde{w}(v, s)\} = \mathcal{C}(c(v, s)) \cap P(v, s) \quad (35)$$

A Realistic Algorithm: (36)

Suppose that a $\epsilon > 0$ and a $s_0 \in T$ are given.

Step 1: Set $\epsilon_0 = \epsilon$.

Step 2: Compute a point $v_{\epsilon_0}(s_0) \in V_{\epsilon_0}(s_0)$.

Step 3: Compute $\tilde{c}(v_{\epsilon_0}(s_0), s_0)$, $\tilde{w}(v_{\epsilon_0}(s_0), s_0)$ and the curve $\tilde{\sigma}(v_{\epsilon_0}(s_0), s_0)$ which is the intersection of T with the two dimensional subspace spanned by s_0 and $\tilde{w}(v_{\epsilon_0}(s_0), s_0) - v_{\epsilon_0}(s_0)$.

Step 4: For each $s' \in \tilde{\sigma}(v_{\epsilon_0}(s_0), s_0)$, compute a vector $v_{\epsilon_0}(s')$ in $V_{\epsilon_0}(s')$ and then find a vector $s_1 \in \tilde{\sigma}(v_{\epsilon_0}(s_0), s_0)$ such that

$$\tilde{c}(v_{\epsilon_0}(s_1), s_1) = \max\{\tilde{c}(v_{\epsilon_0}(s'), s') \mid s' \in \tilde{\sigma}(v_{\epsilon_0}(s_0), s_0)\} \quad (37)$$

Step 5: If $\tilde{c}(v_{\epsilon_0}(s_1), s_1) - \tilde{c}(v_{\epsilon_0}(s_0), s_0) > \epsilon_0$, set $s_0 = s_1$ and go to step 1.

If $\tilde{c}(v_{\epsilon_0}(s_1), s_1) - \tilde{c}(v_{\epsilon_0}(s_0), s_0) \leq \epsilon_0$, set $\epsilon_0 = \epsilon_0/2$ and go to step 2.

Theorem 2. Let $\{s_i\}$ be any infinite sequence in T constructed by the Algorithm (36) (i.e., $s_1, s_2, \ldots$ are the consecutive values assigned to s_0 in step 5), then any cluster point of $\{s_i\}$ is optimal.

We omit a proof of this theorem since it can easily be established by modifying slightly the proof of Theorem 1.

Remark 2: Obviously, the computation of the point s_1 in step 4 of Algorithm (36) cannot be carried out in a finite number of steps. However, Proposition 3 lends support to the heuristic conclusion that even if the maximization in (37) is carried out over a fairly small number of points $s' \in \tilde{\sigma}(v_{\epsilon_0}(s_0), s_0)$, the algorithm will still converge in the sense of Theorem 2. Note that in practice one would have to add a stopping rule of the form: stop if $\epsilon_0 \leq \epsilon'$. A detailed example of the use of Algorithm (36), embodying certain additional features and heuristics can be found in (8).

CASE II. For every $\alpha \geq 0$, $\mathscr{C}(\alpha) = \Sigma(\alpha) \cap Q$, where Q is a convex polyhedron and $\Sigma(\alpha) = \delta(\alpha)C$, with C a convex polyhedron containing the origin in its interior, and $\delta : R^+ \to R^+$, a continuous, strictly monotonic increasing function. (Again, because of Assumption 2, Ω has points in the interior of Q).

It is easy to see that in this case the map $c(\cdot)$ defined by (11) is continuous, but that the map $w(\cdot)$ defined by (12) is not. Hence, with the following exception, the Algorithm (16), or its modifications such as (36), can no longer be used with certainty of success.

Theorem 3. Suppose that the function $w(\cdot)$ defined by (12) is continuous at every non-optimal $s \in T$. If $\{s_i\}$ is a sequence in T generated by the Algorithm (16), then either $\{s_i\}$ is finite and its last element is optimal, or else it is infinite and every cluster point in $\{s_i\}$ is optimal.

The above theorem is an obvious extension of Theorem 1. The following result gives a sufficient condition for this theorem to apply.

Proposition 4. Suppose that for every non-optimal $s \in T$, $\mathscr{C}(c(s)) \cap P(v(s), s)$ consists of a single vertex of $\mathscr{C}(c(s))$, then $w(\cdot)$ is continuous at every non-optimal $s \in T$.

Once $\mathscr{C}(c(s)) \cap P(v(s), s)$ contains more than one point, the evaluation of w(s) becomes rather laborious. Therefore, rather than look for heuristics as a means of ensuring convergence of algorithms using the map $w(\cdot)$, it becomes preferable to introduce the following, obviously continuous map into the construction of algorithms for Case II.

Definition 10. Let $z : T \to R^n$ be defined by

$$\begin{aligned} & z(s) \in \mathscr{C}(c(s)) \\ & \|z(s) - v(s)\| = \min\{\, \|z - v(s)\| \mid z \in \mathscr{C}(c(s))\,\} \end{aligned} \qquad (38)$$

We now get the following straightforward extensions of the

results presented under the heading of Case I.

Theorem 4. Let $b: T \to T$ be a search function defined by (14), (15), with b taking the place of a and z taking the place of w. If $b(\cdot)$ is used instead of $a(\cdot)$ in Algorithm (16), then Theorem 1 remains valid under the assumptions of Case I and also becomes valid under the assumptions of Case II.

In order to modify the Algorithm (36), we introduce the following map.

Definition 11. Let U and $\tilde{c}(\cdot,\cdot)$ be defined as in (34). We then define the map $\tilde{z}: U \to R^n$ by

$$\begin{aligned} &\tilde{z}(v, s) \in \mathcal{C}(\tilde{c}(v, s)) \\ &\|\tilde{z}(v, s) - v(s)\| = \min\{\|s - v(s)\| \mid z \in \mathcal{C}(\tilde{c}(v, s))\} \end{aligned} \tag{39}$$

Theorem 5. Suppose that the map $\tilde{z}(\cdot,\cdot)$ replaces the map $\tilde{w}(\cdot,\cdot)$ in the Algorithm (36). Then Theorem 2 remains valid under the assumptions of Case I and also becomes valid under the assumptions of Case II.

This concludes our theoretical development. We shall now give two examples to illustrate the level of difficulty involved in evaluating the functions $c(\cdot)$, $w(\cdot)$, $z(\cdot)$, and we shall then indicate a procedure for computing points in the set $V_\epsilon(s)$.

III. EVALUATION OF c(s), w(s) AND z(s).

Example 1. A number of minimum energy, discrete optimal control problems, with or without state space constraints, transcribe, upon elimination of the dynamics equations, into the following form.

$$\text{minimize } \{ \sum_{i=1}^{N} u_i^2 \mid \sum_{i=1}^{N} u_i r_i \in \Omega, \ |u_i| \le 1 \} \tag{40}$$

where $r \in R^n$, and Ω is a compact, strictly convex subset of R^n. If, for $\alpha \ge 0$, we now define

$$\mathcal{C}(\alpha) = \{x \mid x = \sum_{i=1}^{N} u_i r_i, \ \sum_{i=1}^{N} u_i^2 \le \alpha^2, \ |u_i| \le 1\} \tag{41}$$

we find that the assumptions of Case 1 are satisfied, provided the set $\{r_i\}$ contains n linearly independent vectors, and Ω has points in the interior of the set $Q = \{x \mid x = \sum_{i=1}^{N} u_i r_i; |u_i| \le 1\}$.

Now, for any $s \in T$, we have

$$c(s) = \min\{\sum_{i=1}^{N} u_i^2 \mid \langle \sum_{i=1}^{N} u_i r_i - v(s), s\rangle = 0, \ |u_i| \leq 1\} \qquad (42)$$

To evaluate (42), we apply the optimality conditions stated in (1), according to which $c(s)$ corresponds to controls $u_i(s)$ and a multiplier $\lambda(s) < 0$ satisfying

$$u_i(s) = \text{sat}(\lambda(s) \langle s, r_i\rangle) \quad \text{for} \quad i = 1, 2, \ldots, N \qquad (43)$$

$$\sum_{i=1}^{N} \langle s, r_i\rangle \ \text{sat}(\lambda(s)\langle s, r_i\rangle) = \langle v(s), s\rangle \qquad (44)$$

It is clear that $\lambda(s)$ can be easily obtained from the piece-wise linear expression (44) to yield, through (43),

$$c(s) = (\sum_{i=1}^{N} u_i^2(s))^{1/2}; \quad w(s) = \sum_{i=1}^{N} u_i(s) r_i \qquad (45)$$

Thus, the calculation of $c(s)$, $w(s)$ is quite easy. To obtain $z(s)$, however, we would have to minimize a quadratic form subject to linear and quadratic constraints, which makes z unattractive for use in algorithms for minimum energy problems.
Example 2. Analogously to minimum energy problems, minimum fuel, discrete optimal control problems reduce to

$$\text{minimize}\{\sum_{i=1}^{N} |u_i| \mid \sum_{i=1}^{N} u_i r_i \in \Omega, \ |u_i| \leq 1\} \qquad (46)$$

with the same assumptions as those following (40). Now, for $\alpha \geq 0$, we define

$$\mathcal{C}(\alpha) = \{x \mid x = \sum_{i=1}^{N} u_i r_i, \ \sum_{i=1}^{N} |u_i| \leq \alpha, \ |u_i| \leq 1\} \qquad (47)$$

i. e., this is a Case II type problem. Now, for $s \in T$,

$$c(s) = \min\{\sum_{i=1}^{N} |u_i| \mid \langle \sum_{i=1}^{N} u_i r_i - v(s), s\rangle = 0, \ |u_i| \leq 1\} \qquad (48)$$

Let $\xi(\cdot)$ be a function defined on the nonzero reals by $\xi(x) = 0$ if $|x| < 1$, and $\xi(x) = \text{sgn}\, x$ if $|x| \geq 1$. Also, for

$\lambda \leq 0$, let $J(\lambda) \subset \{1, 2, \ldots, N\}$ be defined by $J(\lambda) = \{i \mid |\lambda < s, r_i>| = 1, i \in \{1, 2, \ldots, N\}\}$. Then, from the optimality conditions[1] in (1), it follows that $c(s)$ must correspond to controls $u_i(s)$ and a multiplier $\lambda(s) < 0$ such that

$$u_i(s) = \xi(\lambda(s) < s, r_i >) \quad \text{for all} \quad i \in \bar{J}(\lambda(s)) \tag{49}$$

$$\sum_{i \in J(\lambda(s))} u_i(s) < s, r_i > + \sum_{i \in \bar{J}(\lambda(s))} \xi(\lambda(s) < s, r_i >) = < v(s), s > \tag{50}$$

Noting that the expression

$$\sum_{i \in J(\lambda)} |u_i| + \sum_{i \in \bar{J}(\lambda)} |\xi(\lambda < s, r_i >)|, \quad \lambda \leq 0, \quad |u_i| \leq 1 \tag{51}$$

is piecewise constant and monotonic increasing in $(-\lambda)$, and that it is bounded from above by N, we conclude that $\lambda(s)$ is the smallest value of $(-\lambda)$ for which a discontinuity occurs in (51) and (50) is satisfied. Thus $\lambda(s)$ and $c(s)$ are finally obtained by solving a number of low dimensional linear programs.

To compute $w(s)$ and $z(s)$ we now solve

$$\min\{ \|w - v(s)\|^2 \mid w = \sum_{i \in J(\lambda(s))} u_i r_i + \sum_{i \in \bar{J}(\lambda(s))} \xi(\lambda(s) < s, r_i >) r_i$$

$$|u_i| \leq 1 \text{ for } i \in J(\lambda(s)), < w - v(s), s > = 0 \} \tag{52}$$

$$\min\{ \|z - v(s)\|^2 \mid z = \sum_{i=1}^{N} u_i r_i, \ |u_i| \leq 1, \ \sum_{i=1}^{N} u_i \leq c(s) \} \tag{53}$$

Both (52) and (53) are solvable by standard quadratic programming algorithms.

IV. EVALUATION OF $v_\epsilon(s)$.

We shall now consider the problem of computing points $v_\epsilon(s)$ in the set $V_\epsilon(s)$, defined by (33). Usually, the set Ω is described by inequalities, i.e.,

$$\Omega = \{x \in R^n \mid q^i(x) \leq 0, \ i = 1, 2, \ldots, m\} \tag{54}$$

where the $q^i : R^n \to R^1$ are strictly convex, continuously differentiable functions.

When the $q^i(\cdot)$ are quadratic forms and $v(s)$ is not on an edge, i.e., there is exactly one $i \in \{1, 2, \ldots, m\}$ such that $q^i(v(s)) = 0$, then $v(s)$ can be calculated exactly and without difficulty. This is done by solving the m systems of equations, $q^i(v) = 0$, $\nabla q^i(v) = \lambda_i s$, $i = 1, 2, \ldots, m$, for m values v_i, only one of which is feasible and hence is the desired point $v(s)$. When $v(s)$ is on an edge, one can give reasonably simple approximation procedures such as the one in (8).

In general, a point $v_\epsilon(s)$ can be computed as follows. Apply a feasible directions algorithm based on linear programming (2) to the problem

$$\text{maximize}\,\{ \langle s, x\rangle \mid q^i(x) \leq 0, \ i = 1, 2, \ldots, m\} \tag{55}$$

to obtain a sequence of points $x_j \in \partial\Omega$, $j = 0, 1, 2, \ldots$. Stop the calculation when an x_k has been found such that

$$\rho\epsilon \geq -\min\{y \mid y + \langle s, h\rangle \geq 0;\ y - \langle \nabla q^i(x_k), h\rangle \geq 0,\ i \in I_{\rho\epsilon}(x_k);\ |h_i| \leq 1\} \tag{56}$$

where $\rho > 0$ is a suitably chosen number and $I_{\rho\epsilon}(x_k) = \{i \mid q^i(x_k) + \rho\epsilon \geq 0,\ i \in \{1, 2, \ldots, m\}\}$. Then set $v_\epsilon(s) = x_k + \epsilon s$. (Note that the feasible directions algorithm solves a problem of the form (56) at each x_j it produces and hence the above stop rule involves no extra work).

V. CONCLUSIONS

Since in the algorithms presented in this paper, $v_\epsilon(s)$ has to be calculated quite frequently, it is clear that this calculation becomes a dominant factor in determining the speed of these algorithms. When m, the number of inequalities in (54) is small, the calculation of $v_\epsilon(s)$ is sufficiently simple to preserve an appreciable advantage for the algorithms presented in this paper with respect to primal methods (such as feasible directions). When m becomes large, the decomposition effect is reduced, and it is no longer clear whether primal or dual methods are to be preferred and the matter must be settled experimentally, taking also into account the effectiveness of available heuristics to accelerate these methods.

REFERENCES

1. M. Canon, C. Cullum, and E. Polak, "Constrained Minimization Problems in Finite Dimensional Spaces," J. SIAM Control, vol. 4, pp. 528-547, 1966.

2. G. Zoutendijk, "Methods of Feasible Directions: A Study in Linear and Nonlinear Programming," Elsevier, Amsterdam, 1960.

3. D. M. Topkis, A. Veinott, Jr., "On the Convergence of Some Feasible Direction Algorithms for Nonlinear Programming," J. SIAM Control, vol. 5, No. 2, p. 268, May 1967.

4. G. B. Dantzig, "Linear Control Processes and Mathematical Programming," J. SIAM Control, vol. 4, No. 1, pp. 56-60, 1966.

5. L. W. Neustadt, "Synthesizing Time Optimal Control Systems," Journal of Mathematical Analysis and Applications, vol. 1, pp. 484-493, 1960.

6. J. H. Eaton, "An Iterative Solution to Time-Optimal Control," Journal of Mathematical Analysis and Applications, vol. 5, pp. 329-344, 1962.

7. R. O. Barr and E. G. Gilbert, "Some Iterative Procedures for Computing Optimal Controls," Third Congress of the International Federation of Automatic Control, London 20-25, Paper No. 24. D, June 1966.

8. E. Polak and M. Deparis, "An Algorithm for Minimum Energy Control," University of California, Electronics Research Laboratory, Berkeley, California, ERL Memorandum M225, 1 November 1967.

ON THE ACCELERATION OF CONVERGENCE OF ALGORITHMS FOR SOLVING OPTIMAL CONTROL

Boris N. Pshenichnii
Institute of Cybernetics, Kiev, USSR

In recent years computational techniques for solving optimal control problems have been developed extensively. The number of papers in this field is so large that now it is difficult to list even the most important of them. However, the majority of them is characterized by the application of the steepest descent method or some of its various modifications taking into account the constraints. In this way it is possible to give the methods of solution of a broad class of optimal control problems. But, unfortunately, the speed of convergence of all of these methods is very slow. The speed of convergence can be estimated by means of a geometrical series whose ratio is almost always close to unity. Therefore, the computation time necessary to obtain an appropriate approximation is very long.

Hence there is an urgent need for finding such methods and algorithms which would enable us to accelerate substantially the rate of convergence. Recently there have appeared many papers (1)-(11) in which some algorithms for minimizing functions of finite number of variables or for solving systems of algebraic equations, possessing super-linear or quadratic convergence are proposed.

In the majority of these papers (1)-(9) the idea of conjugate gradients (4) is used. Many kinds of modifications of this method are proposed, which allow the computational process to be organized in more convenient way. Apparently the most convenient is the modification proposed by Fletcher and Powell (2) and based on the idea of Davidon (1). The fundamental advantage of the algorithm proposed by Fletcher and Powell lies in the fact that it is necessary to compute only first derivatives of a function and the function itself. Moreover, this algorithm is stable, i.e., convergent for any arbitrary initial point. This is so because at every step the angle between the direction of movement and that of gradient is obtuse. A disadvantage of this method is that it requires the accurate minimization of the function along a given direction. If it is not accomplished, it can violate the whole process. At the same time such a seemingly simple problem as minimization of a function along a given direction can be solved only at the expence of computing of a great number of values of the function and of its gradient. It requires a large amount of computer time in such cases as optimal control or boundary problems, where computing of a value of the function requires the solution of a Cauchy problem for source system of differential equations. In general, it has to be stressed that the problem of choosing the length of the step in the gradient type algorithms has not been sufficiently investigated. The nice exceptions in that respect are the works of Davidon (9(and Goldstein (11), (20), where some algorithms for the choice of the length of the step along given direction are proposed.

The different approach toward the acceleration of convergence is given by Newton's method. In applications to minimization problems this approach is reduced to the solution of the system of equations obtained by setting the gradient equal to zero. But direct application of Newton's method requires computing of second derivatives, which, as a rule, is very difficult. For that reason the paper by Goldstein (11) is of great interest. The computation of second derivatives was substituted here by computation of finite differences. Moreover, such a modification of the method is given, which for convex functions provides super-linear convergence for any arbitrary initial point. Note that Goldstein's method can be substantially improved by combining it with the secant method proposed by Wolfe (10) and developed in detail by Meyergreus.

This paper is devoted to investigating the possibilities of applications of the methods with accelerated convergence for solving optimal control problems.

In the first part an algorithm (17) will be presented. The idea of this algorithm is close to that of conjugate gradients, but it does not require the choice of the length of the step according to the condition of minimum along the direction. This makes it possible to reduce the number of computations of the values of the function and its derivatives. At the same time for convex functions the algorithm is convergent for any arbitrary initial point, and a quadratic form is minimized in a finite number of steps.

In the second part of the paper it is shown how the algorithms with accelerated convergence can be applied for solving time optimal control problem for linear systems. Note, that time optimal problem was already investigated by McFadden and Gilbert in (16), where a method of acceleration of convergence taking advantage of the specific nature of the problem was applied.

The control problems of linear systems possess the particular property that their solution can be reduced to the problem of minimization of a function of finite number of variables (15). Therefore, any of the algorithms listed above can be applied for solving these problems.

Nonlinear systems represent much more complicated problems. Up to now the only known method of reducing these problems to the finite dimensional case is to formulate an appropriate boundary value problem on the basis of Pontryagin's maximum principle and to choose the missing boundary conditions on the left side. Such an approach was proposed as soon as the maximum principle was formulated. But, since the right-hand sides of differential equations are discontinuous functions, the obtained boundary value problems are of such a type that cannot be solved by means of known methods. Without sufficient justification this method was applied by Jsayev and Sonin (18)-(19).

In the third part of the paper we present a method of computing the derivatives of the right-hand end of a trajectory with respect to initial data in the case where right-hand sides of differential equations are functions with discontinuities of the first kind. It is a step toward the solution of boundary value problems resulting from the maximum principle.

In general, we have to note, that application of the methods with accelerated convergence to the optimal control problems is not a well-investigated field, and this paper does not pretend to present any conclusions. On the contrary this is but a start and the main idea is rather to call attention to the importance of the problems. In particular no computational results are presented in this paper.

1. In this section the following notation will be used: small

latin letters x, y, ... etc., will denote n-dimensional column vectors. Capital latin letters will denote matrices. An asterisk superscript will denote transpose; hence x^* is a row vector. Therefore, x^*y denotes inner-product, while yx^* is a matrix.

We shall investigate the problem of minimization of quadratic function

$$\varphi(x) = c + a^*x + \tfrac{1}{2}x^*\mathcal{G}x \tag{1}$$

where $x \in E^n$, $\mathcal{G}$ is symmetric positive definite matrix. The gradient of this function is given by

$$g(x) = a + \mathcal{G}x \,.$$

Further on we shall denote by g_k the gradient of $g(x)$ at the point x_k.

We shall investigate the following process:

$$r_k = M_k z_k \,, \qquad z_k = M_k^* g_k \,, \tag{2}$$

$$x_{k+1} = x_k - \lambda_k r_k \,, \tag{3}$$

$$y_k = g_{k+1} - g_k \,, \tag{4}$$

$$M_{k+1} = M_k - \frac{r_k y_k^*}{r_k^* y_k} \,, \tag{5}$$

$$\mathcal{G}_{k+1} = \mathcal{G}_k - \lambda_k \frac{r_k r_k^*}{r_k^* y_k} \,, \tag{6}$$

$$k = 0, 1, \ldots, n-1$$

Along with the initial conditions: $x = x_o$, M_o- identity matrix, $_o$- zero matrix.

It is assumed that during the whole process the system is not degenerate, i.e., $r_k^* y_k \neq 0$.

The investigation of the system will be reduced to proving several simple properties.

Property 1. $y_k = -\lambda_k \mathcal{G} r_k$.

It is obvious.

Property 2. $r_i^* y_j = 0$ for $i \neq j$, $0 \leq i \leq n-1$.
We shall give the proof by induction. Let

$$r_i^* y_j = 0 \,, \qquad i \neq j \,, \qquad 0 \leq i, j \leq k \tag{7}$$

We shall show that $r_{k+1}^* y_j = 0$ for $j = 0, 1, \ldots, k$. Indeed, from (5) and (2) we have

$$M_{k+1} = I - \sum_{i=0}^{k} \frac{r_i y_i^*}{r_i^* y_i},$$

$$r_{k+1} = z_{k+1} - \sum_{i=0}^{k} \frac{r_i (y_i^* z_{k+1})}{(r_i^* y_i)},$$

$$r_{k+1}^* y_j = z_{k+1}^* y_j - \sum_{i=0}^{k} \frac{(z_{k+1}^* y_i)(r_i^* y_j)}{(r_i^* y_i)},$$

hence taking into account (7)

$$r_{k+1}^* y_j = z_{k+1}^* y_j - z_{k+1}^* y_j = 0 . \tag{8}$$

Further, from Property 1 and from (8) we obtain

$$r_i^* y_{k+1} = -\lambda_{k+1} r_i^* \mathcal{G} r_{k+1} = \frac{\lambda_{k+1}}{\lambda_i} (-\lambda_i \mathcal{G} r_i)^* r_{k+1} = \frac{\lambda_{k+1}}{\lambda_i} y_i^* r_{k+1} = 0.$$

which completes the proof of Property 2.

Corollary. $r_i^* \mathcal{G} r_j = 0, \; i \neq j, \; 0 \leq i, \; j \leq n-1$.

It follows immediately from Properties 1 and 2.

Property 3. $\mathcal{G}_n = \mathcal{G}^{-1}$

Indeed, from (6) we get

$$\mathcal{G}_n = -\sum_{k=0}^{n-1} \lambda_k \frac{r_k r_k^*}{r_k^* y_k} .$$

Hence taking into account Property 2 we have

$$\mathcal{G}_n y_j = -\lambda_j r_j$$

From Property 1

$$\mathcal{G}^{-1} y_j = -\lambda_j r_j$$

Since the vectors y_j, $j=0,1,\ldots,n-1$ are linearly independent (they are biorthogonal to r_j) the proof of Property 3 follows from the last two equations.

Property 4. If at every step the value of λ_k is chosen to to minimize $\varphi(x_k - \lambda r_k)$, i.e., if it has the form

$$\lambda_k = \frac{g_k^* r_k}{r_k^* r_k} , \qquad (9)$$

then x_n is the solution of our minimization problem. We shall omit the proof of this Property. It can be easily obtained from the previous one.

Let us formulate now the algorithm. One iteration can be written in the following form

0. $M_0 := I, \quad z_0 := 0, \quad x : x_0$.
1. $r_k = M_k M_k^* g_k$,

   $x_{k+1} = x_k - \lambda_k r_k$,

   $y_k = g_{k+1} - g_k$,

   $$M_{k+1} = M_k - \frac{r_k y_k^*}{r_k^* y_k} ,$$

   $$z_{k+1} = z_k - \lambda_k \frac{r_k^* g_{k+1}}{r_k^* y_k} r_k ,$$

   $k=0,1,\ldots,n-1$.
2. $\tilde{x} = x_n - \sigma z_n$.

Thus by one iteration we understand the complete fulfillment of Stages 0-2. Stage 1 contains n elementary steps.

Theorem 1. If $\varphi(x)$ is given by (1), then $\tilde{x}$ obtained after first iteration with $\sigma = 1$ and an arbitrary $\lambda_k \neq 0$ is the solution of the optimization problem.

Proof. We shall show, that

$$z_n = \mathcal{G}^{-1} g_n .$$

The theorem follows from this equality. Indeed, if this equality is satisfied, then

$$\tilde{x} = x_n - \mathcal{G}^{-1} g_n = x_n - \mathcal{G}^{-1}(a + \mathcal{G} x_n) = -\mathcal{G}^{-1} a$$

and

$$g(\tilde{x}) = a + \mathcal{G}\tilde{x} = 0 .$$

From Property 3 we have

$$\mathcal{G}^{-1} g_n = \mathcal{G}_n g_n = -\sum_{k=0}^{n-1} \lambda_k \frac{r_k(r_k^* g_n)}{r_k^* y_k}. \qquad (10)$$

On the other hand

$$g_n = g_{n-1} + y_{n-1} = g_{k+1} + y_{k+1} + \dots + y_{n-1}.$$

Therefore according to Property 2

$$r_k^* g_n = r_k^* g_{k+1}.$$

Substituting in (10) we get

$$\mathcal{G}^{-1} g_n = -\sum_{k=0}^{n-1} \lambda_k \frac{r_k(r_k^* g_{k+1})}{r_k^* y_k}.$$

But it is easy to see that after one iteration we obtain exactly the same formula for z_n.

Thus the Theorem is proved.

Let now $\varphi(k)$ be an arbitrary continuously differentiable function, and $g(x)$ its gradient.

It is easy to see that, at least formally, all stages of the above algorithm can be applied. Naturally, now we can not expect that the process converges after one iteration.

Let us exame what can be assured.

We shall choose the length of the step λ_k and σ according the following rule. We put $\lambda^0 = 1$ and we shall divide successively this value by two so long as the following inequality is satisfied

$$f(x_k - \lambda r_k) - f(x_k) \leq -\lambda \frac{r_k^* g_k}{2}.$$

The value of λ obtained in this way we choose as λ_k. In the same manner we choose σ which satisfies the inequality

$$f(\widetilde{x}) - f(x_n) \leq -\sigma \frac{z_n^* g_n}{2}.$$

One can show that such a choice of the step is always possible. In the case of convex function possessing second derivatives it leads to finding minimum and for an arbitrary function to a local minimum.

Under some additional assumptions on the function the algorithm is quadratically convergent if from some stage on the step λ is constant and sufficiently small and σ is equal to unity.

Since the proof of this property is troublesome we shall not give it here. We shall show only that it is satisfied in one dimensional case. Indeed, a simple consideration shows that in one dimensional case given algorithm is equivalent to the following one

$$x_{k+1} = x_k - \left[\frac{\dot{\varphi}(x_k - \lambda\varphi(x_k)) - \dot{\varphi}(x_k)}{-\lambda\dot{\varphi}(x_k)} \right] \dot{\varphi}(x_k) ,$$

where $\dot{\varphi}(x)$ is the derivative of $\varphi(x)$ with respect to x. But it is well known Stepensen's algorithm (22) quadratic convergence of which was proved.

2. Let us now consider the possibility of application of the described algorithm for solving optimal control problems of linear systems. To do this we have to reduce these problems to the problem of minimization of a function of finite number of variables. The possibility of such a reduction was already shown in the works by Neustadt, Eaton and Pshenichniy (12)-(15). Before we discuss the subject we shall cite the following theorem, which is very useful in problems of optimization.

Theorem 2. Let $\mu(x, y)$ be a function continuous with respect to x and y and let exist a continuous gradient $\partial_x\mu(x, y)$ with respect to x.

Then the function

$$\varphi(x) = \max_{y \in \mathcal{D}} \mu(x, y) ,$$

where $\mathcal{D}$, is a compact set, is differentiable in any direction at any point x and

$$\frac{\partial\varphi(x)}{\partial e} = \max_{y \in \mathcal{D}(x)} (e_1 \partial_x \cdot u(x, y)$$

$$\mathcal{D}(x) = \{ y: y \in \mathcal{D}, \mu(x, y) = \varphi(x) \} .$$

If for some region of x the set $\mathcal{D}(x)$ consists of one point y(x) only, then it that region $\varphi(x)$ is continuously differentiable,

$$\partial_x \varphi(x) = \partial_x \mu(x, y(x)) ,$$

and y(x) is continuously dependent on x. The proof of that theorem can be found in (23).

Remark. By definition

$$\frac{\partial \varphi(x)}{\partial e} = \lim_{\lambda \to +0} \frac{\varphi(x+\lambda e) - \varphi(x)}{\lambda} .$$

Formula (x, y) denotes inner-product.

Now let the plant be described by the system of equations

$$\begin{aligned} \dot{x} &= \mathcal{A} x + \varphi(u) , \\ u &\in U , \end{aligned} \tag{11}$$

where $x \in E^n$, $\mathcal{A}$ is an $n \times n$-matrix and $\varphi(u)$ is a continuous vector-function of $u \in E^r$. The set U is a compact subset of E^r. The initial condition x^0 is given. We are looking for such an admissible control function u(t) (i.e., a measurable function u(t), such that $u(t) \in U$ for every t) for which the corresponding trajectory of the system (11) reaches the set M in minimal time.

We shall assume that the following conditions are fulfilled.

1. For every $\psi \neq 0$ the formula

$$(\psi(t), \varphi(u(t, \psi))) = \max_{u \in U} (\psi(t), \varphi(u))$$

defines the function $u(t, \psi)$ uniquely for all $t \geq 0$, except at most finite numbers of point on every finite interval. The function $\psi(t)$ is given here by

$$\begin{aligned} \dot{\psi}(t) &= -\mathcal{A}^* \psi(t) , \\ \psi(o) &= \psi_1 \end{aligned}$$

or what is equivalent by

$$\begin{aligned} \psi(t) &= \Phi^*(-t)\psi , \\ \Phi(t) &= e^{\mathcal{A}t} . \end{aligned}$$

2. The set M is convex and compact. Moreover, maximum of (ψ, z) with respect to $z \in M$ is assumed at unique point $z(\psi)$. T erefore, by Theorem 2 (for $\psi \neq 0$) $z(\psi)$ is a continuous function of ψ and

$$\partial_{\psi}\mathcal{H}(\psi) = z(\psi) ,$$

where

$$\mathcal{H}(\psi) = \max_{z \in M} (\psi, z) .$$

Let us recall now briefly the algorithm for solving the stated problem, which was given in (12)-(14) for the case where M consists of one point.

Let ψ be chosen and let $x(t, \psi)$ be the solution of System (11) corresponding to $u(t, \psi)$. We put

$$f(\psi, t) = (\psi(t), x(t, \psi)) + \mathcal{H}(-\psi(t)) .$$

Using Cauchy formula

$$x(t, \psi) = \Phi(t) x^{o} + \Phi(t) \int_{o}^{t} \Phi(-\tau) \varphi(u(\tau: \psi)) d\tau ,$$

after simple transformations we obtain

$$f(\psi, t) = (\psi, x^{o}) + \int_{o}^{t} \max_{u \in U} (\psi, \Phi(-\tau)\varphi(u))d\tau + \mathcal{H}(-\psi(t)) . \quad (12)$$

Taking advantage of Theorem 2 we get

$$\partial_{\psi} f(\psi,t) = x^{o} + \int_{o}^{t} \Phi(-\tau)\varphi(u(\tau, \psi))d\tau - \Phi(-t) z(-\psi(t)) =$$

$$= \Phi(-t)[x(t, \psi) - z(-\psi(t))] , \quad (13)$$

$$\partial_{t} f(\psi,t) = \max_{u \in U} (\psi(t), \mathcal{A} z(-\psi(t)) + \varphi(u)) .$$

Let us denote by $M(t\ x^{o})$ the set of all points admissible from x^{o} by system (11) at the time t, i.e., the set

$$M(t, x^{o}) = \left\{ z: z = \Phi(t) x^{o} + \Phi(t) \int_{o}^{t} \Phi(-\tau)\varphi(u(\tau))d\tau, u(\tau) \in U \right\} .$$

This set is compact and convex (24). By formula (12) we have

$$f(\psi, t) = \max_{z \in M(t, x^{o})} (\psi(t), z) + \mathcal{H}(-\psi(t)) .$$

Therefore, if the sets $M(t, x^{o})$ and M are not disjoint, i.e., if there is a point $z^0 \in M(t, x^0) \cap M$, then

$$f(\psi, t) \geq (\psi(t), z^o) + \mathscr{W}(-\psi(t)) = \max_{z \in M} (\psi(t), z^0 - z) \geq 0 .$$

Thus, if F is the minimal time in which the system is transferred from x^0 to M, then

$$f(\psi, F) \geq 0 . \tag{14}$$

Let us suppose now that in the process of iteration we have already found the value of the vector ψ^k and the time $t^k \leq F$, and that

$$f(\psi^k, t^k) = 0$$

There are two possibilities.

$$\partial_\psi f(\psi^k, t^k) = \Phi(-t^k)\left[x(t^k, \psi^k) - z(-\psi^k(t^k))\right] = 0 .$$

In this case

$$x(t^k, \psi^k) = z(-\psi^k(t^k)) \in M$$

and the problem is solved. Now let

$$\partial_\psi f(\psi^k, t^k) \neq 0$$

and let the vector e^k be such that

$$\left(e^k, \partial_\psi f(\psi^k, t^k)\right) = \left(e^k, \Phi(-t^k)\left[x(t^k, \psi^k) - z(-\psi^k(t^k))\right]\right) > 0 .$$

T erefore for small $\lambda > 0$ we have

$$f(\psi^k - \lambda e^k, t^k) = -\lambda \left(e^k, \partial_\psi f(\psi^k, t^k)\right) + 0(\lambda) < 0 .$$

Hence, it follows that $t^k < F$ and in the interval $[t^k, \bar{t}]$ there is a root of the equation

$$f(\psi^k - \lambda e^k, t) = 0 . \tag{15}$$

We choose λ in such a way that the value of this root is maximal and we put

$$\psi^{k+1} = \psi^k - \lambda e^k ,$$

and as t^{k+1} we choose the root of Equation (15) belonging to the interval $[t^k, \bar{t}]$.

In the same manner as in (14) we can show that if we put

$$e^k = \Phi(-t^k)\left[x(t^k, \psi^k) - z(-\psi^k(t^k))\right] = \partial_\psi f(\psi^k, t^k) ,$$

then the process is convergent in the sense that $t^k \to \bar{t}$ and

$$\| x(t^k, \psi^k) - z(-\psi^k(t^k)) \| \to 0 .$$

Now, let us note that in the new point ψ^{k+1}, t^{k+1}

$$\partial_t f(\psi^{k+1}, t^{k+1}) \geq 0 ,$$

since

$$f(\psi^k - \lambda e^k, t) < 0$$

for $t^k < t < t^{k+1}$. Let us suppose that

$$\partial_t f(\psi^{k+1}, t^{k+1}) > 0 . \tag{16}$$

Therefore, in the neighborhood of this point there is defined the function $t(\psi)$ given in the implicit form by the equation

$$f(\psi, t) = 0 . \tag{17}$$

The gradient of the function can be expressed by

$$\partial_\psi t(\psi) = - \frac{\partial_\psi f(\psi, t(\psi))}{\partial_t f(\psi, t(\psi))} . \tag{18}$$

Hence it follows that at the points ψ^{k+1}, t^{k+1}, where the inequality (16) takes place, our process is simply the gradient method of maximization of the function $t(\psi)$. Unfortunately, it does not necessarily imply the convergence of the process, for in general the function $t(\psi)$ is discontinuous.

But, if we make an important assumption that there exists such a $t_o < \bar{t}$, that for $t(\psi) \geq t_o$ the function $t(\psi)$ is continuously differentiable, then after finite number of steps our process transfers into process of maximization of the function $t(\psi)$. Moreover, by (18) and (13) at the maximum point we have

$$x(t(\psi^o), \psi^o) - z(\psi^o(t^o)) = 0 ,$$

and $t(\psi^o) = F$, because $t(\psi) \leq F$, i.e., we obtain the solution of our problem. Moreover, since the function $t(\psi)$ is continuously differentiable and its gradient can be computed using (18) and (13), the methods with accelerated convergence can be applied. With this we finish our investigations of time optimal problems and we start to consider the next problem.

Now, let the system be described by the same equations (11), but let the interval $[0, T]$ be fixed. We are looking for such an admissible control which minimize $x_1(T)$, where x_1 is the first coordinate of the vector x, under the condition, that

$$x_i(T) = x_i^1, \qquad 2 \leq i \leq m,$$

where $m \leq n$. We assume, that condition 1 given at the beginning of this chapter is satisfied.

Let

$$F(\psi) = \max_{z \in M(T, x^o)} (\psi, z - z^o), \tag{19}$$

$$z_o = \{0, x_{21}^1, \ldots, x_m^1, 0, \ldots, 0\}.$$

It was shown in (15) that considered problem is equivalent to minimization of a convex functional $F(\psi)$ in the subspace

$$\psi_1 = -1, \quad \psi_{m+1} = \ldots = \psi_n = 0. \tag{20}$$

If $u(t, \psi)$ is given by

$$(\psi(t), \varphi(u(t, \psi))) = \max_{u \in U} (\psi(t), \varphi(u)), \quad \psi(t) = \Phi^*(T-t)\psi,$$

and $x(t, \psi)$ is the corresponding trajectory, then it is easy to show that

$$F(\psi) = (\psi, x(T, \psi) - z^o).$$

Moreover, $x(T, \psi)$ is the unique point of $M(T, x^o)$ at which the maximum of right-hand side of equation (19) is assumed.

It follows from Theorem 2 that

$$\partial_\psi F(\psi) = x(T, \psi) - z^o.$$

Hence at the point ψ^o, where the minimum of $F(\psi)$ over subspace (20) is assumed, the conditions

$$x_i(T, \psi) = x_i^1 , \qquad 2 \leq i \leq m$$

must be satisfied.

Moreover, one can see that the gradient of $F(\psi)$ can be computed and therefore also in this case the optimal control problem is reduced to the problem of minimization of a function of finite number of arguments ψ_i, $i=2,\dots,m$.

3. Now, let us consider nonlinear problems. In particular we shall investigate the following one. Let the system be described by the system of equations

$$\begin{aligned} \dot{x}_i &= f_i(x,u), \qquad i=1,\dots,n \\ x &= \{x_1, x_2, \dots, x_n\}, \quad u = \{u_1, \dots, u_n\} \end{aligned} \tag{21}$$

The vectors u belong to a compact set $U \subset E^r$. We are looking for such an admissible function (i.e., such a measurable function $u(t)$, that $u(t) \in U$ for every t), which in the given time T transfers the system (21) from the initial state x^o to the terminal x^1 and which minimizes the functional

$$x_0(T) = \int_o^T f_o(x(t), u(t))\, dt$$

In the sequel we shall assume that the functions $f_i(x,n)$, $i=0,1,\dots,n$ are twice continuously differentiable with respect to x and u.

According to maximum principle (21) for $u^o(t)$ to be optimal it is necessary that there exist a continuous vector function $\psi(t) = \{\psi_o(t), \psi_1(t), \dots, \psi_n(t)\}$ such that the following conditions are fulfilled ($x^o(t)$ denotes the trajectory corresponding to $u^o(t)$):

$$\begin{aligned} \dot{x}_i(t) &= f_i(x^o(t), u^o(t)), \qquad i=0,1,\dots,n, \\ \dot{\psi}_i(t) &= -\sum_{j=0}^{n} \frac{\partial f_j(x^o(t), u^o(t))}{\partial x_i}\, \psi_j(t), \qquad i=0,1,\dots,n \end{aligned} \tag{22}$$

and if

$$\mathscr{H}(\psi, x, u) = \sum_{i=0}^{n} \psi_i f_i(x, u) ,$$

then

$$\mathscr{H}(\psi(t), x^o(t), u^o(t)) = \max_{u \in U} \mathscr{H}(\psi(t), x^o(t), u) \tag{23}$$

Moreover,

$$\psi_o(t) = \text{const} \leq 0 .$$

We shall assume that $\psi_o(t) < 0$ and therefore we can put $\psi_o(t) = -1$.

Let us denote

$$M(\psi, x) = \max_{u \in U} \mathscr{H}(\psi, x, u) \tag{24}$$

We shall assume that for every x and ψ the maximum of (24) is assumed at the unique point $u(\psi, x)$. The exceptions can be the points belonging to the disjoint surfaces

$$\varphi_k(x, \psi) = 0 \qquad k=1, \ldots, e \tag{25}$$

We shall assume that the functions $\varphi_k(x, \psi)$ are smooth. By Theorem 2 $u(\psi, x)$ is a continuous function of ψ and x for all points $\{x, \psi\}$ which do not belong to the surfaces φ_k.

We assume additionally that at such points $u(\psi, x)$ is a continuously differentiable function and if $\{x^o, \psi\}$ are such that

$$\varphi_k(x^o, \psi^o) = 0 \tag{26}$$

then $u(\psi, x)$ is convergent to some limit $u^o \in U$ for $x \to x^o$, $\psi \to \psi^o$ if all the points $\{x, \psi\}$ lie on the same side of the surface (25). Hence the function $u(\psi, x)$ is defined everywhere with exception of the surfaces (25) where it is discontinuous.

Therefore, it is easy to see that the optimal trajectory satisfying the conditions (22), (23) is the solution of the following boundary value problem

$$\dot{x}_i = \frac{\partial \mathscr{H}(\psi, x, u(\psi, x))}{\partial \psi_i} ,$$

$$i=0, 1, 2, \ldots, n ,$$

$$\dot{\psi}_i = -\frac{\partial \mathcal{H}(\psi, x, u(\psi, x))}{\partial x_i} \tag{27}$$

$$i=0,1,\ldots,n\ ,$$

$$x_0(0) = 0, \quad x(0) = x^0, \quad x(T) = x^1, \quad \psi_0 = -1\ .$$

where the right-hand side functions of (27) has discontinuities of the first kind along the surfaces (25).

Theorem 3. The system (27) can be described in the canonical form

$$\begin{aligned} \dot{x}_i &= \frac{\partial M(\psi, x)}{\partial \psi_i}\ , \\ \dot{\psi}_i &= -\frac{\partial M(\psi, x)}{\partial x_i}\ , \\ i&=0,1,\ldots,n\ . \end{aligned} \tag{28}$$

Proof: Indeed by Theorem 2 everywhere except (25) we have

$$\frac{\partial M(\psi, x)}{\partial \psi_i} = \frac{\partial \mathcal{H}(\psi, x, u(\psi, x)}{\partial \psi_i}$$

$$\frac{\partial M(\psi, x)}{\partial x_i} = \frac{\partial \mathcal{H}(\psi, x, u(\psi, x))}{\partial x_i}$$

Remark. Equation (28) is a usual, canonical form of Euler equation known from classical calculus of variations. Thus it was shown that this equation is also true in much more general case of optimal control problem. Summing up the results stated above, we can say, that the problem of finding of an extremal of our problem was reduced to the boundary value problem for the system (28) with discontinuous right-hand sides and with the following boundary conditions

$$x_0(0) = 0, \quad x(0) = x^0, \quad x(T) = x^1, \quad \psi_0 \equiv -1\ .$$

In what way can we solve this boundary value problem? Note, that since the point $x(0) = x^0$ is fixed, the right-hand side of the trajectory depends only on the initial value of the vector

$$\psi(0) = \{-1, \psi_1, \ldots, \psi_n\}\ .$$

Therefore, if we consider x(T) as known functions of ψ_i, $i=1,\ldots,n$ (for fixed ψ_i these functions can be computed by means of solving Cauchy problem for the system (28)), then our problem is reduced to the solution of the system of equations

$$x_i(T,\psi_1,\ldots,\psi_n) = x_i^1 ,$$
$$i = 1,\ldots,n$$

with respect to ψ_i.

The solution of the system can be obtained by Newton method, or it can be reduced to the minimization of the function

$$\sum_{i=1}^{n} (x_i(T,\psi_1,\ldots,\psi_n) - x_i^1)^2 .$$

Anyway it is necessary to find the derivatives of $x_i(T,\psi_1,\ldots,\psi_n)$ with respect to ψ_i. It follows to apply the methods with accelerated convergence, both that described in this paper as well as the others given in (1) - (10). The difficulties of the problem are due to the fact that the right-hand sides of Equations (28) are functions with discontinuities of the first kind. Therefore, the last part of the paper will be devoted to the investigations of the problem of possibilities of computing of derivatives of the end of the trajectory with respect to initial conditions, in the case where right-hand sides of the differential equations are discontinuous (25).

Let be given the system of differential equations

$$\dot{y} = f(y) ,$$
$$y = \{y_1,\ldots,y_n\} , \qquad 0 \le t \le T . \tag{29}$$

The vector-function f(y) is continuously differentiable with respect to y, everywhere except the surface $\varphi(y) = 0$ where it has the points of discontinuity of the first kind.

Therefore

$$f(y) = \begin{cases} f_1(y) & \text{for } \varphi(y) < 0 , \\ f_2(y) & \text{for } \varphi(y) > 0 , \end{cases}$$

where $f_i(y)$, $i=1,2$, are vector functions continuously differentiable everywhere. We shall assume also that the function $\varphi(y)$ is smooth.

Let y_0 be an arbitrary point such that $\varphi(y_0) < 0$. By $x'(y^0, t)$ we shall denote the solution of the equation

$$\dot{y} = f_1(y), \quad y(o) = y^0 .$$

If for some time t,

$$\varphi(x^1(y^0, t)) = 0 ,$$

and

$$(\partial_y \varphi(y), f_2(y))\big|_{y = x'(y^0, t_1)} > 0 \tag{30}$$

then for $t > t_1$ sufficiently small there exists the solution of the system

$$\dot{y} = f_2(y) , \quad t \geq t_1$$

$$y(t_1) = x^1(y^0, t_1) ,$$

which we shall denote by $x^2(x^1(y^0, t_1), t)$. This solution is entirely contained in the region $\varphi(y) \geq 0$.

Therefore the solution of system (29) with initial condition y^0 we can describe by the formula

$$x(y^0, t) = \begin{cases} x^1(y^0, t) & 0 \leq t \leq t_1 \\ x^2(x^1(y^0, t_1), t) & t \geq t_1 \end{cases}$$

Let $T > t_1$ be such that $x(y^0, T)$ is defined. We shall consider the dependence of $x(y^0, T)$ on y^0. To do that, we note that if

$$(\partial_y \varphi(y), f_1(y))\big|_{y = x^1(y^0, t_1)} > 0 \tag{31}$$

then for every y belonging to some neighborhood of y^0 the solutions $x^1(y, t)$ are defined and the function $t(y)$ is defined as the solution of the equation

$$\varphi(x^1(y, t)) = 0 . \tag{32}$$

Since $f_1(y)$ is a continuously differentiable function, then it is known that $x^1(y, t)$ is continuously differentiable function of y in the neighborhood of y^0. The differential of $x^1(y, t)$ in the direction e can be computed by means of solving the systems of equations in variations

$$\frac{d\overline{x_i}}{dt} = \sum_{i=1}^{n} \frac{\partial f_1(x^1(y,t))}{\partial y_i} \overline{x_i}\,, \quad i=1,\ldots,n \tag{33}$$

with the initial condition $\overline{x}(0) = e$. And we have

$$\frac{\partial x^1(y^o,\overline{t})}{\partial e} = \overline{x}(e,\overline{t})\,,$$

where

$$\frac{\partial x^1(y^o,\overline{t})}{\partial e} = \lim_{\lambda \to +0} \frac{x^1(y^o+\lambda e,\overline{t}) - x^1(y^o,\overline{t})}{\lambda}\,,$$

and $\overline{x}(e,t)$ denotes the solution of (33) at E, with initial condition $\overline{x}(0) = e$ and $y = y^o$.

Therefore, it follows that the function $t(y)$ is defined and continuously differentiable in the neighborhood of y^o. By the implicit function theorem we have

$$\frac{\partial t(y^o)}{\partial e} = - \left.\frac{(\partial_y \varphi(y),\ \overline{x}(e,t))}{(\partial_y \varphi(y), f_1(y))}\right|_{\substack{y=x^1(y^o,t(y^o)) \\ t=t(y^o)}} . \tag{34}$$

Now we are in the position to formulate the main result.

Theorem 4. Let for the initial condition y^o, $\varphi(y^o) < 0$ the solution of system (29) is defined on the interval $[0,T]$, and the conditions (30), (31) as well as $T > t(y^o)$ are satisfied. Then the right-hand end of the trajectory $x(y^o,T)$ is differentiable at the point y^o with respect to the initial conditions. The following procedure can be applied to obtain the value of the differential in the direction e. On the interval $[0,t(y^o)]$ we integrate the systems of equations in variations (33) with initial condition $\overline{x}(0) = e$ and we find the solution $\overline{x}(e,t(y^o))$ of the system at the time $t(y^o)$. Later on using (34) we compute the vector

$$e^1 = \overline{x}(e,t(y^o)) + \frac{\partial t(y^o)}{\partial e}\,[f_1(y)-f_2(y)]_{y=x^1(y^o,t(y^o))}\,.$$

Then on the interval $[t(y^o),T]$ we integrate the system of equations in variations:

$$\frac{d\overline{\overline{x}}_i}{dt} = \sum_{j=1}^{n} \frac{\partial f_2(x(y^o,t))}{\partial x_i} \overline{\overline{x}}_j\,, \tag{35}$$

with the initial condition $\overline{\overline{x}}(t(y^o)) = e^1$. The value $\overline{\overline{x}}(e^1, T)$ is equal to the value of the differential of $x(y^o, T)$ in the direction e.

The proof of the Theorem can be found in (25). Note that it can be easily generalized to the case where f(y) has more than one surface of discontinuity. Theorem 4 shows that under given, not very strong, assumptions the right-hand side end of the trajectory of the system of differential equations which right-hand sides are the functions with discontinuities of the first kind, is differentiable with respect to initial conditions. Moreover, the Theorem gives the method of computing of this differential.

Thus the application of Theorem 4 for system (28) makes it possible to reduce the corresponding boundary value problem to the problem of solving of the system of equations with respect to finite number of arguments. This by turns makes it possible to apply the methods with accelerated convergence.

To terminate we note that the system of equations in variations for (28) outside of the discontinuity surfaces can be described in the following form

$$\frac{d\overline{x_i}}{dt} = \sum_{j=0}^{n} \frac{\partial^2 M(\psi, x)}{\partial x_j \, \partial \psi_i} \overline{x}_j + \sum_{j=0}^{n} \frac{\partial^2 M(\psi, x)}{\partial \psi_j \, \partial \psi_i} \overline{\psi_j} ,$$

$$\frac{\partial \overline{\psi_i}}{\partial t} = - \sum_{j=0}^{n} \frac{\partial^2 M(\psi, x)}{\partial x_j \, \partial x_i} \overline{x}_j - \sum_{j=0}^{n} \frac{\partial^2 M(\psi, x)}{\partial \psi_j \, \partial \psi_i} \overline{\psi_j} .$$

Since

$$M(\psi, x) = \mathcal{H}(\psi, x, u(\psi, x)) ,$$

then under our assumptions concerning differentiability of $f_i(x, u)$ and $u(\psi, x)$ all needed differentials exist.

REFERENCES

1. Davidon, W. C., Variable Matric Method for Minimization, Argonne National Laboratory, Report No. ANL-5990, 1959.

2. Fletcher, R., and Powell, M. J. D., A Rapidly Convergent Descent Method for Minimization, Computer Journal, Vol. 6, No. 2, 1963.

3. Fletcher, R., and Reeves, C. M., Function Minimization by Conjugate Gradients, Computer Journal, Vol. 7, No. 2, 1964.

4. Hestenes, M. R., and Stiefel, E., Method of Conjugate Gradients for Solving Linear Systems, National Bureau of Standards, Report No. 1659, 1952.

5. Barness, I., Solving Non-linear Systems, Computer Journal, Vol. 8, No. 1, 1965.

6. Broyden, G., Quasi Newton Methods and Their Application to Function Minimization, Mathematics of Computation, Vol. 21, No. 99, 1967.

7. Daniel, J. W., Convergence of the Conjugate Gradient Method with Computational Convenient Modification, Numerische Mathematik, Band 10, Heft 2, 1967.

8. Dennis, I. E., Jr., On Newton Like Methods, Numerische Mathematik, Band 11, Heft 4, 1968.

9. Davidon, W. C., Variance Algorithm for Minimization, Computer Journal, Vol. 10, No. 4, 1968.

10. Wolfe, F., The Secant Method for Simultaneous Non-linear Equations, Comm. Assoc. Comp. Math., Vol. 2, No. 12, 1959.

11. Goldstein, A. A., and Price, Y. F., An Effective Algorithm for Minimization, Numerische Mathematik, Band 10, Heft 3, 1967.

12. Neustadt, L. W., Synthesizing Time Optimal Control Systems, J. Math. Anal. and Appl., Vol. 1, No. 4, 1960.

13. Eaton, Y. H., Iterative Solution of Time Optimal Control, J. Math. Anal. and Appl., Vol. 5, No. 12, 1962.

14. Pshenichniy, B. N., Numerical Method for Computing Time Optimal Control of Linear Systems, Z. Vycisl. Mat. i Mat. Fiz., Vol. 4, No. 1, 1964.

15. Pshenichniy, B. N., Linear Optimal Control Problems, J. SIAM on Control, Vol. 4, No. 4, 1966.

16. Fadden, E. J., and Gilbert, E. G., Computational Aspects of the Time-Optimal Control Problem. Computing Method in Optimization Problems, Ed. by Balakrishnan, A. V., and Neustadt, L. W., Academic Press, 1964.

17. Pshenichniy, B. N., On One Gradient Algorithm, Z. Vycisl. Mat. i Mat. Fiz., Vol. 8, No. 3, 1968.

18. Isayev, V. K., and Sonin, V. V., On One Modification of Newton Method for Numerical Solving of Boundary Value Problems, Z. Vycisl. Mat. i Mat. Fiz., Vol. 3, No. 6, 1963.

19. Isayev, V. K., Sonin, V. V., Computational Aspects of the Problem of Optimal Flight as Boundary Value Problem, Z. Vycisl. Mat. i Mat. Fiz., Vol. 5, No. 2, 1965.

20. Goldstein, A. A., On Steepest Descent, J. SIAM on Control, Ser. A, Vol. 3, No. I, 1965.

21. Poutryagin, L. S., Boltyanshii, V. G., Gamkrelidze, R. V., and Mishchenko, E. F., The Mathematical Theory of Optimal Processes, Interscience, New York, 1962.

22. Ostrowski, A. M., Solution of Equations and Systems of Equations, Academic Press, New York, 1966.

23. Pshenichniy, B. N., On Pursuing Problem, Kibernetika, No. 6, 1967.

24. Neustadt, L. W., The Existence of Optimal Controls in the Absence of Convexity Conditions, J. Math. Appl., Vol. 4, No. I, 1963.

25. Pshenichniy, B. N., Danilin, Yu. M., On Differentiability with Respect to Initial Conditions of the Solution of the System of Differential Equations with Discontinuous Right-Hand Sides. Theory of Optimal Solutions, Izd. IKAN USSR, No. 1, 1968.

A MODIFIED NEWTON-RAPHSON METHOD FOR DETERMINING STABILITY DERIVATIVES FROM FLIGHT DATA

Lawrence W. Taylor, Jr., and Kenneth W. Iliff
NASA Flight Research Center
Edwards, Calif.

INTRODUCTION

The systems identification problem of accurately and reliably determining the stability and control derivatives (coefficients of the differential equations of motion) of airplanes from flight data has been difficult and time consuming despite the considerable effort that has been devoted to this problem over the years. This is not to say that there is a lack of methods; on the contrary, many methods have been tried and most have been successful when the response data have been free of noise and well conditioned. Unfortunately, however, poor conditioning, instrumentation and measurement noise, and errors in the model of the airplane's dynamics are generally great enough to cause considerable error in the resulting estimates.

One of the methods that has continued to be used is based on special, simple formulas (1) which take advantage of particular parts of standard forms of response, the characteristics of which can be expressed in terms of a single or a few unknown coefficients. Although these formulas have been used with success, their disadvantages are many. For example, only some of the primary unknown coefficients of stability and control derivatives can be thus determined. In addition, the forms of response that can be analyzed are very restrictive, i.e., effect of control must be either dominant or negligible.

Another of the methods used has been "analog matching" (1, 2) or manual adjustment of the potentiometers of an analog computer used to compute a matching time history of the recorded response from flight. After a match is achieved, the potentiometer settings are equated to the desired coefficients. Unfortunately, the skill and technique of the operator is a factor in the resulting estimates. The variance of these estimates and the time and frustrating work required to produce them is less than satisfactory.

The regression methods of least squares (3) and of Shinbrot (4) involve no manual operation nor are they limited in the coefficients that can be obtained, but experience has indicated the variance of estimated coefficients to be excessive.

It seems reasonable to expect a fit of the solution of the equations of motion to give more constraint and, therefore, more accurate estimates than a fit of the differential equations of motion per se, as with least squares. This would suggest a quadratic cost of the difference between the computed solution and measured response. Unfortunately, although the equations of motion are linear in the state and control variables, the problem of minimizing the difference is nonlinear in the unknown coefficients, thereby requiring some form of iterative solution (5).

It has been the authors' experience that the straight gradient technique has been much too slow in converging to be of use for this problem. Consequently, a modified form of the Newton-Raphson method (5) has been developed that rapidly converges to minimize the weighted mean square fit error. The complexity and computation time involved in using the unmodified method has been reduced considerably by using only the first gradient of the difference to approximate the second gradient of the cost. This approximation improves as the solution is reached. The problem of failing to achieve convergence for poor starting values of the unknown coefficients has been alleviated by first using the measured response to compute the gradient instead of the calculated response. It has not been necessary to reduce the step size or weaken in any other way the basic Newton-Raphson method.

This paper presents the formulation of least squares and the Newton-Raphson method. The results are compared and discussed. The work reported was done jointly by the authors and Dr. A. V. Balakrishnan of the University of California at Los Angeles. Example solutions are included that show not only the quality of the fitted solution but also a comparison of the estimated coefficients with values obtained by other techniques.

STATEMENT OF THE PROBLEM

The model most often used to describe airplane dynamics can be expressed as a system of linear, constant-coefficient differential equations of the usual form and notation (6)

$$\dot{x} = Ax + Bu$$

where

$$A = \begin{bmatrix} L_p & L_r & L_\beta & 0 \\ N_p & N_r & N_\beta & 0 \\ \alpha_0 & -1 & Y_\beta & Y_\varphi \\ 1 & 0 & 0 & 0 \end{bmatrix}$$

$$u = \begin{bmatrix} \delta_a \\ \delta_r \\ 1 \end{bmatrix} \quad x = \begin{bmatrix} p \\ r \\ \beta \\ \varphi \end{bmatrix} \quad \dot{x} = \begin{bmatrix} \dot{p} \\ \dot{r} \\ \dot{\beta} \\ \dot{\varphi} \end{bmatrix}$$

$$B = \begin{bmatrix} L_{\delta_a} & L_{\delta_r} & L_0 \\ N_{\delta_a} & N_{\delta_r} & N_0 \\ Y_{\delta_a} & Y_{\delta_r} & Y_0 \\ 0 & 0 & 0 \end{bmatrix}$$

The elements of the A and B matrices, and x and u vectors are defined in the list of symbols. A 1 appears in the u vector as a convenient means of expressing the constant bias terms.

Measures of the state and its time derivative are contaminated with noise, i.e.,

$$z = x + n_1$$

and

$$\dot{z} = \dot{x} + n_2$$

where x is the true state vector, n_1 and n_2 are the contaminating noise vectors, and z and $\dot{z}$ are the measured state and measured state derivative. The control input vector u is considered to be free of noise. Note that $\dot{z}$ is simply a label and not a differential operation on z.

The problem addressed in this paper is: given z, $\dot{z}$, and u, determine certain unknown elements in the matrices A and B. In the vocabulary of airplane dynamics these coefficients of the linearized equations of motion are termed stability and control derivatives, which is a reference to the Taylor's series expansion of the aerodynamic forces and moments.

LEAST-SQUARES METHOD

Let us first consider the minimization of the following expression which involves only the i th component of the noise n_2. The noise n_1 which contaminates the measured state will be assumed to be zero for the present, as

$$J = \int_0^T {n_2}_i^2(t)dt$$

where

$${n_2}_i(t) = \dot{z}_i(t) - \dot{x}(t) = \dot{z}_i - A_i z(t) - B_i u(t)$$

It is convenient to express the vectors z and u and the coefficients to be determined in terms of single vectors, as

$${n_2}_i = \dot{z}_i - c^T \begin{pmatrix} z \\ u \end{pmatrix}$$

We can then write

$$\int_0^T {n_2}_i^2 dt = \int_0^T \dot{z}_i^2 dt - 2\int_0^T \dot{z}_i \begin{pmatrix} z \\ u \end{pmatrix}^T c\,dt + \int_0^T c^T \begin{pmatrix} z \\ u \end{pmatrix}\begin{pmatrix} z \\ u \end{pmatrix}^T c\,dt$$

Setting the gradient with respect to c equal to zero, we get

$$\nabla_c \int_0^T {n_2}_i^2 dt = 0 - 2\int_0^T \dot{z}_i \begin{pmatrix} z \\ u \end{pmatrix} dt + 2\int_0^T \begin{pmatrix} z \\ u \end{pmatrix}\begin{pmatrix} z \\ u \end{pmatrix}^T dt\,c$$

Solving for c, we get the familiar least-squares estimate

$$c = \left[\int_0^T \begin{pmatrix} z \\ u \end{pmatrix}\begin{pmatrix} z \\ u \end{pmatrix}^T dt\right]^{-1} \int_0^T \dot{z}_i \begin{pmatrix} z \\ u \end{pmatrix} dt$$

The least-squares method was applied to flight data for the X-15 airplane. The resulting values for the coefficients were used to compute a time history of the state vector for comparison with the measured response from flight (see fig. 1). The fit of $\dot{p}$, $\dot{r}$, and $\dot{\beta}$ is good, but other variables have drifted apart. This is especially true of φ, p, and r. This is the expected result of fitting only $\dot{p}$, $\dot{r}$, and $\dot{\beta}$ as is done using least squares. It would be more desirable to minimize the difference in the time histories shown. It will be shown that, although it can be done, the identification problem becomes nonlinear, requiring some form of iteration technique.

GRADIENT METHOD

Let us next consider the minimization of the following expression with respect to the vector c of unknown elements in A, B, and x(o):

$$J = \int_0^T n_1^T(t) D_1 n_1(t)dt + \int_0^T n_2^T(t) D_2 n_2(t)dt$$

where

$$n_1 = z - x(A, B, x(o))$$

$$n_2 = \dot{z} - Ax - Bu$$

x is the solution of $\dot{x} = Ax + Bu$

The gradient of J with respect to the vector c can be expressed in terms of the gradient of x as follows:

$$\nabla_c J = -2\int_0^T n_1^T D_1 \nabla_c x dt - 2\int_0^T n_2^T D_2 \nabla_c (Ax + Bu)dt$$

The gradient of x is defined as

$$\nabla_c x = \begin{bmatrix} \frac{\partial p}{\partial c_1} & \frac{\partial p}{\partial c_2} & \frac{\partial p}{\partial c_3} & \cdots & \frac{\partial p}{\partial c_M} \\ \frac{\partial r}{\partial c_1} & \frac{\partial r}{\partial c_2} & & & \frac{\partial r}{\partial c_M} \\ \frac{\partial \beta}{\partial c_1} & \frac{\partial \beta}{\partial c_2} & & & \frac{\partial \beta}{\partial c_M} \\ \frac{\partial \varphi}{\partial c_1} & \frac{\partial \varphi}{\partial c_2} & & & \frac{\partial \varphi}{\partial c_M} \end{bmatrix}$$

The elements of the gradient of x can be determined in the following way. If the state equation is differentiated with respect to a_{ij}, for example, we get

$$\frac{\partial \dot{x}}{\partial a_{ij}} = \frac{\partial A}{\partial a_{ij}} x + A\frac{\partial x}{\partial a_{ij}} + \cancelto{0}{\frac{\partial B}{\partial a_{ij}}} u + B\cancelto{0}{\frac{\partial u}{\partial a_{ij}}} = A\frac{\partial x}{\partial a_{ij}} + A_{a_{ij}} x$$

where $A_{a_{ij}}$ and $B_{b_{ij}}$ equal the null matrix the same size as A and B, respectively, except for the i-j th element which cquals 1. The i-j th element corresponds to that element in A or B with respect to which the gradient is taken.

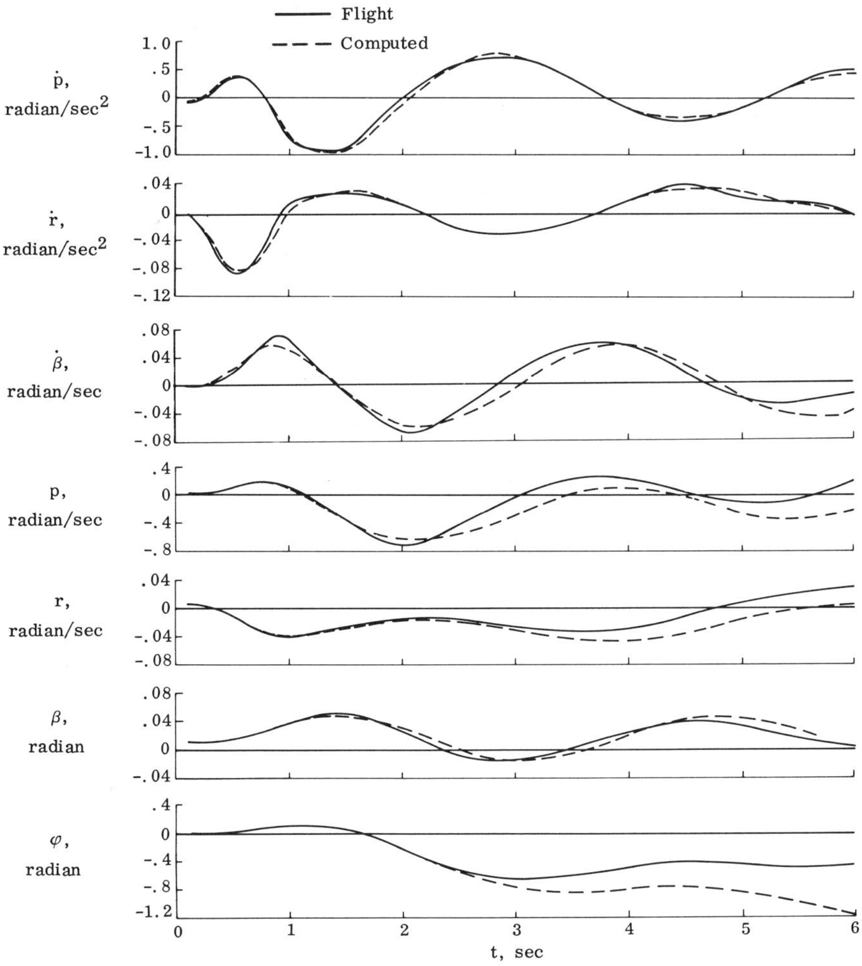

Fig. 1. Comparison of Time Histories Measured in Flight and Computed By Using Least-Squares Coefficients.

The solution for $\frac{\partial x}{\partial a_{ij}}$ can be expressed as

$$\frac{\partial x}{\partial a_{ij}}(t) = \int_0^t e^{A(t-\tau)} A_{a_{ij}} x(\tau) dt$$

A similar procedure for coefficients in B gives

$$\frac{\partial x}{\partial b_{ij}}(t) = \int_0^t e^{A(t-\tau)} B_{b_{ij}} u(\tau) dt$$

A similar procedure is used for elements of the initial conditions x(o)

$$\frac{\partial x}{\partial x_i(o)}(t) = e^{At} \begin{pmatrix} 0 \\ \vdots \\ 1 \\ 0 \end{pmatrix} i$$

To obtain a gradient solution that minimizes J, the following recursive relations are used:

$$A_{n+1} = A_n + \epsilon \nabla_A J$$

$$B_{n+1} = B_n + \epsilon \nabla_A J$$

The value of ϵ can be chosen in many different ways. Although theoretically each iteration will reduce the cost or fit error, in practice the reductions become almost infinitesimal. Unfortunately, although the fit error is reduced considerably before it stalls, the corresponding values of the unknown coefficients were not determined with sufficient accuracy.

NEWTON-RAPHSON METHOD

Without changing the statement of the problem or the function to be minimized, let us make the following observation: For small changes in the values of the coefficients to be determined, the changes in x are nearly linear, that is,

$$x(t) \approx x_0(t) + \nabla_c x(t) \Delta c$$

The expressions for the difference between the measured and the true values become linear, thus enabling the solution for Δc to be expressed as

$$\Delta c = \left[\int_0^T \nabla_c{}^T \begin{pmatrix} x \\ \dot{x} \end{pmatrix} \begin{bmatrix} D_1 & 0 \\ 0 & D_2 \end{bmatrix} \nabla_c \begin{pmatrix} x \\ \dot{x} \end{pmatrix} dt \right]^{-1} \int_0^T \nabla_c{}^T \begin{pmatrix} x \\ \dot{x} \end{pmatrix} \begin{bmatrix} D_1 & 0 \\ 0 & D_2 \end{bmatrix} \begin{pmatrix} n_1 \\ n_2 \end{pmatrix}$$

Although the difference in notation might disguise the fact, the preceding solution is the same as that obtained with the Newton-Raphson method if the term involving the second gradient times the noise is neglected as suggested by Balakrishnan in reference 5. The savings in computation are considerable. Application of the Newton-Raphson method to the example discussed required only four iterations. This represents a computation time of about 7 minutes on the SDS 9300 digital computer. It is clear from the authors' experience that the Newton-Raphson method is superior to the gradient method both in terms of iteration and computation for the application under discussion.

Figure 2 shows the computed state time histories compared with the measured time histories for the X-15 airplane. The corresponding weighted mean square fit error is 0.2 percent of that for least squares. Most of the reduction is due to the improved fit of φ. The fits of p and r are also improved.

Figure 3 shows the comparison between the values of the coefficients obtained for the X-15 airplane from wind-tunnel tests and by applying the least-squares and Newton-Raphson methods. It is difficult to assess the two methods on the basis of the differences shown, however, because of the uncertainties in the wind-tunnel values.

One should note that an important advantage of the Newton-Raphson method compared with the least-squares method is that it is not necessary that all components of the state variables and their time derivatives be measured. The corresponding element in the weighting matrix is simply set equal to zero for the missing data. Other advantages include a single set of values for several data sets and an estimate of the variance of the values obtained.

COMPARISON OF VARIANCES OF VARIOUS METHODS

Because of the uncertainties in the wind-tunnel values of the coefficients, it has been impossible to conclude which method results in the most accurate estimates of the coefficient values. A statistical model was constructed and used to indicate the relative values of variance in the estimates obtained using the least-squares, Shinbrot, and Newton-Raphson methods. Specifically, a time history was computed using wind-tunnel values of the derivatives with noise added to represent measured flight data. The power spectral density of the noise was made to approximate the fit error. A set of five time histories, which differed only in the specific noise added, was analyzed. Estimates of the variance and average value of the coefficients that result from applying least-squares, modified least-squares, Shinbrot's, and Newton-Raphson methods are shown in figure 4. Modified least squares refers to a combination of the usual least squares and one in which the equations of motion are integrated. Figure 4 shows that the Newton-Raphson method gives the value closest to the actual value for every coefficient. Although the variance is indicated to be greater, the greatly reduced bias makes the Newton-Raphson method superior to all others considered for the example shown.

CONCLUDING REMARKS

The problem of determining stability derivatives or coefficients of the state equations from measured state time histories of airplanes has been reviewed.

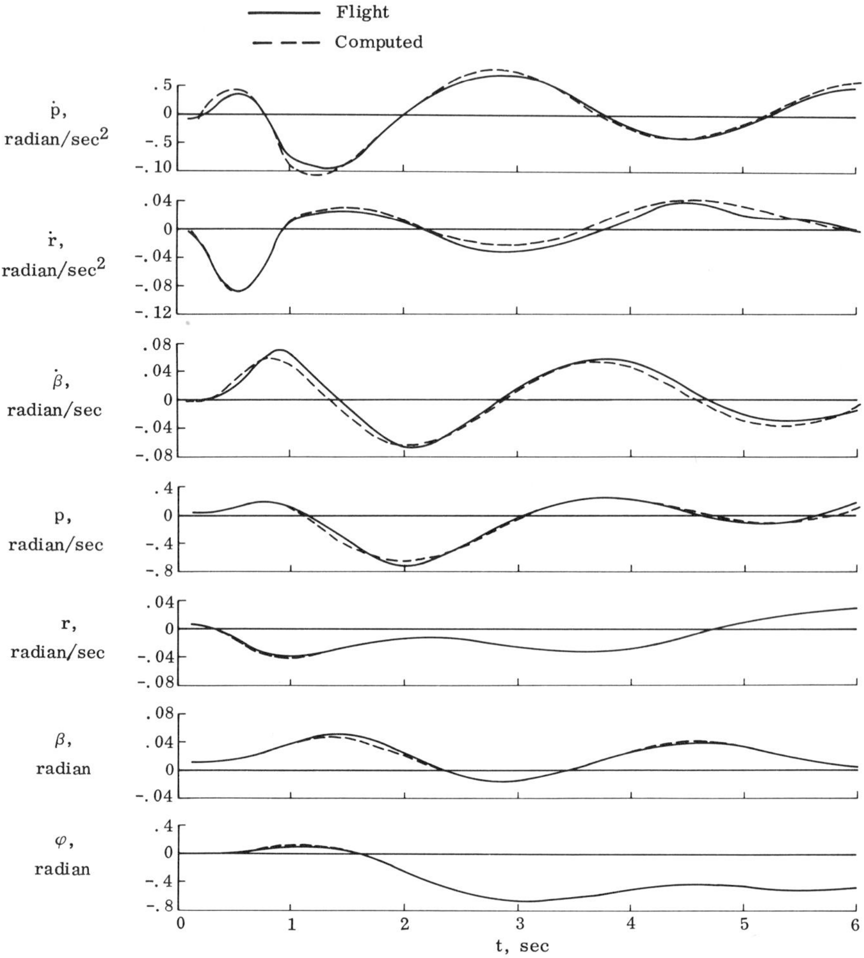

Fig. 2. Comparison of Time Histories Measured in Flight and Computed By Using Newton-Raphson Coefficients.

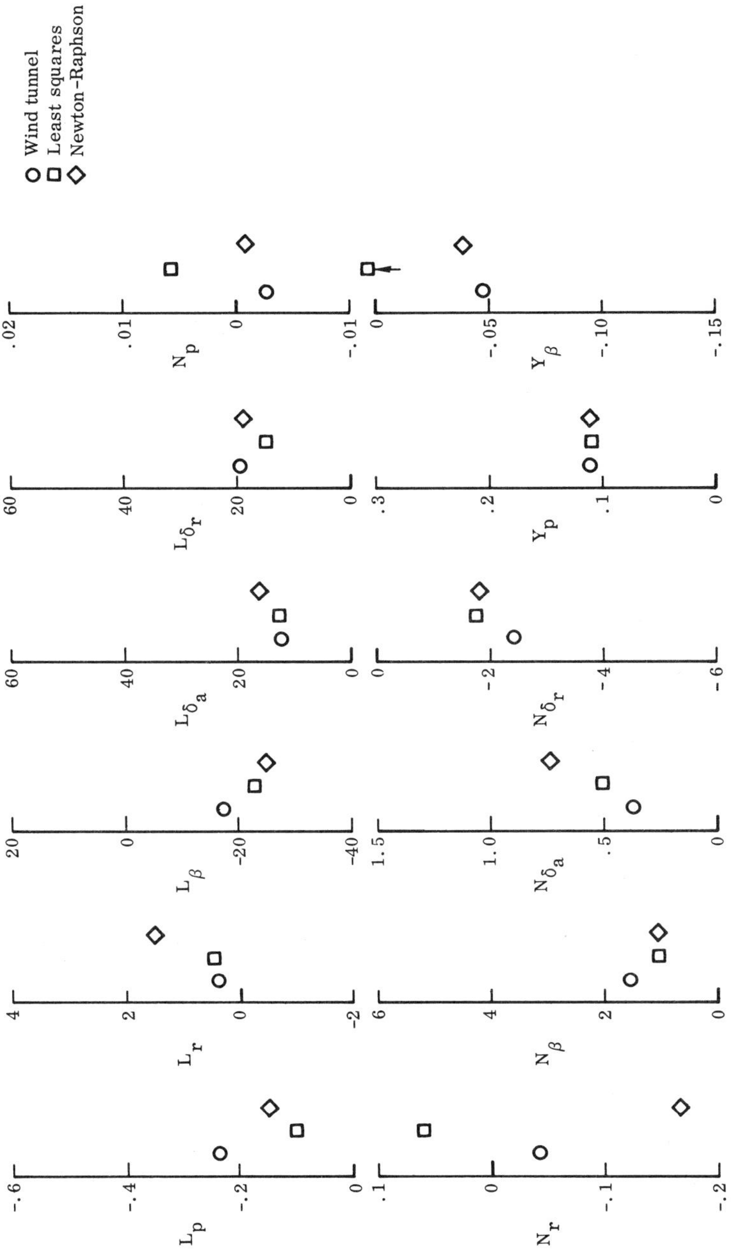

Fig. 3. Comparison of Coefficients Determined From Least-Squares and Newton-Raphson Methods and Wind-Tunnel Tests.

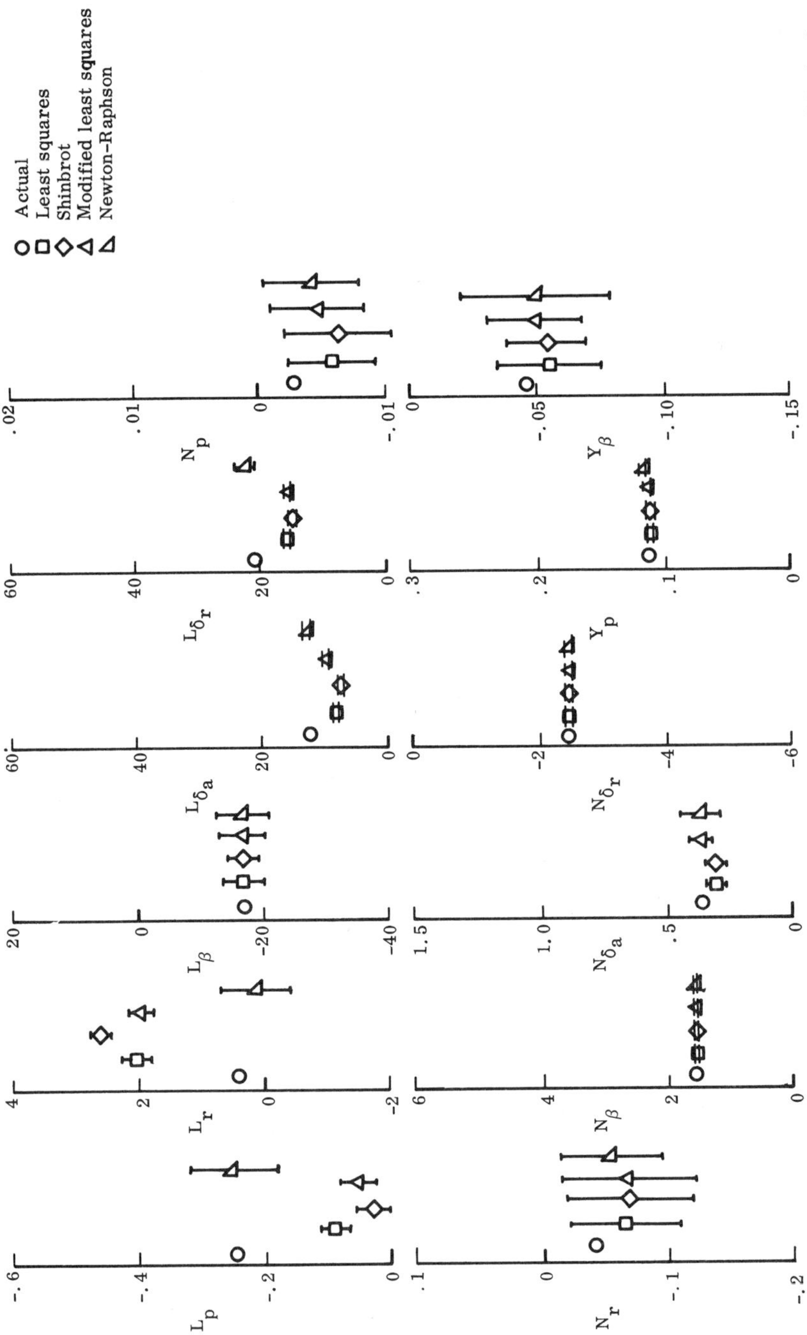

Fig. 4. Comparison of Results Using Least-Squares, Modified Least-Squares, Shinbrot, and Newton-Raphson Methods of Obtaining Stability Derivatives With the Actual Values Used for Calculating the Time History Records.

The same set of flight data was analyzed using a gradient method to find the set of coefficients that would minimize the mean square error in the measured state and that computed using only the control input. Difficulties in convergence were encountered.

A Newton-Raphson method was used with success to solve the convergence problem. One important advantage of the Newton-Raphson method compared with the least-squares method is that it is not necessary that all components of the state variables and their time derivatives be measured.

The coefficients obtained by using the Newton-Raphson method were used to compute a time history. The corresponding weighted mean square fit error was 0.2 percent of that for the method of least squares.

A statistical model was used to determine experimentally the variance of values for the coefficients using the least-squares, Shinbrot, modified least-squares, and Newton-Raphson methods of identification. The Newton-Raphson method was superior to all other methods for the example considered.

Automatic determination of stability and control derivatives through the use of this technique results in savings in manpower, time, and computer (analog) usage. Other advantages include a single set of values for several data sets and an estimate of the variance of the values obtained.

The method has a potential use in many other systems identification problems.

SYMBOLS

A	stability matrix $(P \times P)$
$A_{a_{ij}}$	null matrix except for i-j th element which equals 1 $(P \times P)$
B	control matrix $(P \times Q)$
$B_{b_{ij}}$	null matrix except for i-j th element which equals 1 $(P \times Q)$
c	vector of unknown coefficients
D	weighting matrix
J	cost or weighted mean square fit error
L	rolling moment divided by the moment of inertia about the X-axis, radians/second^2
N	yawing moment divided by the moment of inertia about the Z-axis, radians/second^2
n	noise vector
P	number of state variables
p	roll rate, radians/second
Q	number of control variables
r	yaw rate, radians/second
T	total time, seconds
t	time, seconds
u	control vector $(\delta_a, \delta_r, 1)(Q \times 1)$

x	computed state vector (p, r, β, φ)(P × 1)
Y	side force divided by mass and velocity, radians/second
z	measured state vector (P × 1)
α_o	angle of attack of the principal X-axis, radians
β	sideslip angle, radians or degrees
Δ	increment
δ_a	aileron deflection, radians or degrees
δ_r	rudder deflection, radians or degrees
ϵ	relaxation coefficient
τ	auxiliary time variable, seconds
φ	bank angle, radians or degrees
$\nabla_c(\cdot)$	gradient of $(\cdot)$ with respect to c

Subscripts

i	i th row or component
M	number of unknown coefficients
$\delta_a, \delta_r, p,$ r, β, φ	partial derivatives
o	a nominal condition

A dot over a quantity denotes the time derivative.

REFERENCES

1. Wolowicz, Chester H.: Considerations in the Determination of Stability and Control Derivatives and Dynamic Characteristics From Flight Data. AGARD Rep. 549 - Part 1, 1966.

2. Rampy, John M.; and Berry, Donald T.: Determination of Stability Derivatives From Flight Test Data by Means of High Speed Repetitive Operation Analog Matching. FTC-TDR-64-8, Air Force Flight Test Center, May 1964.

3. Howard, J.: The Determination of Lateral Stability and Control Derivatives From Flight Data. Canadian Aeronautics and Space Journal, March 1967, pp. 127-134.

4. Shinbrot, Marvin: On the Analysis of Linear and Nonlinear Dynamical Systems From Transient-Response Data. NACA TN 3288, 1954.

5. Balakrishnan, A. V.: Communication Theory. McGraw-Hill, 1968.

6. Anon.: Dynamics of the Airframe. Rept. AE-61-4II, Northrop Corp., Norair Div., Sept. 1952.

On Some Transportation Problems

Milan Vlach
Charles University
Department of Applied Mathematics
Prague, Czechoslovakia

Let $k, n (k \leq n), p_1, p_2, \ldots, p_n$ be natural numbers, let S_k^n be the set of all subsets (combinations) $\{j_1, j_2, \ldots, j_k\}$ of k elements formed from the set $N = \{1, 2, \ldots, n\}$, and let

$$\left\| a^{\{j_1, j_2, \ldots, j_k\}}_{i_{q_1} i_{q_2} \ldots i_{q_{n-k}}} \right\|$$

be given $p_{q_1} \times p_{q_2} \times \ldots \times p_{q_{n-k}}$ non-negative $(n-k)$-dimensional matrices $\{j_1, j_2, \ldots, j_k\} \in S_k^n$, $\{q_1, q_2, \ldots, q_{n-k}\} = N \setminus \{j_1, j_2, \ldots, j_k\}$. The n-index transportation problem of the type k – in the sequel T_k^n-problem – is formulated as follows: It is to state whether the set R_k^n of all $p_1 \times p_2 \times \ldots \times p_n$ non-negative n-dimensional matrices

$$X = \left\| x_{i_1 i_2 \ldots i_n} \right\|$$

satisfying for all $\{j_1, j_2, \ldots, j_k\}$ the conditions

$$\left\| \sum_{i_{j_1}=1}^{p_{j_1}} \sum_{i_{j_2}=1}^{p_{j_2}} \cdots \sum_{i_{j_k}=1}^{p_{j_k}} x_{i_1 i_2 \dots i_n} \right\| = \left\| a^{j_1, j_2, \dots, j_k}_{i_{q_1} i_{q_2} \dots i_{q_{n-k}}} \right\|$$

is non-empty, and if it be so, whether in R_k^n exist - and if exist, then to find at least on of them - - matrices $\hat{X}$ such that a given real function f on R_k^n attains its minimum on R_k^n at $\hat{X}$. A T_k^n-problem is a linear one if

$$f\,(X) = \sum_{i_1=1}^{p_1} \sum_{i_2=1}^{p_2} \cdots \sum_{i_n=1}^{p_n} c_{i_1 i_2 \dots i_n} x_{i_1 i_2 \dots i_n}$$

where $C = c_{i_1 i_2 \dots i_n}$ is given. Members of R^n are called feasible solutions and $\hat{X}$'s are called optimal solutions.

Remarks. In the case k=n it is sufficient to consider only T_1^1-problems; linear T_1^1-problems are trivial; some non-linear T_1^1-problems can be solved by dynamic programming (1) ; linear T_1^2-problem represents the Hitchock distribution problem, linear T_{n-1}^n-problem the general transportation problem (2) , T_1^3-problem the solid transportation problem (3) ; the capacitated transportation problem and some other problems can be formulated as T_1^3--problems (4) , (5) .

To obtain necessary conditions and in some cases also sufficient conditions for the existence of a feasible solution to the T_k^n-problem, we use the following theorem (6). Let G be a non-empty finite set and let α , β be real functions on the family of all subsets of G. For each subset A of G we define the sequences of functions $\{M_i\}_{i=0}^{\infty}$,

$\{ m_i \}_{i=0}^{\infty}$ as follows:

$$M_0(A) = \alpha(A) \;, \quad m_0(A) = \beta(A)$$

$$M_{i+1}(A) = \max \left\{ \max_{\substack{A' \cup A'' = A \\ A' \cap A'' = \emptyset}} \left[M_i(A') + M_i(A'') \right], \max_{B \subset G \setminus A} \left[M_i(A \cup B) - m_i(B) \right] \right\}$$

$$m_{i+1}(A) = \min \left\{ \min_{\substack{A' \cup A'' = A \\ A' \cap A'' = \emptyset}} \left[m_i(A') + m_i(A'') \right], \min_{B \subset G \setminus A} \left[m_i(A \cup B) - M_i(B) \right] \right\}$$

Theorem. If $\alpha(\emptyset) = \beta(\emptyset) = 0$ and $-\infty \leqq \alpha(A) < +\infty$, $-\infty < \beta(A) \leqq +\infty$ for $A \subset G$ and if there is an additive function φ on the family of all subsets of G such that $A \subset G \Rightarrow \alpha(A) \leqq \varphi(A) \leqq \beta(A)$, then for each subset A of G the limits $\lim_{i \to \infty} M_i(A)$, $\lim_{i \to \infty} m_i(A)$ exist and $\lim_{i \to \infty} M_i(A)$ $\lim_{i \to \infty} m_i(A)$.

If we put $G = P_1 \times P_2 \times \ldots \times P_n$ where $P_i = \{1, 2, \ldots, p_i\}$, $i = 1, 2, \ldots, n$ and define

$$\alpha(\emptyset) = \beta(\emptyset) = 0$$

$$\alpha(A) = \beta(A) = a_{i_{q_1} i_{q_2} \ldots i_{q_{n-k}}}^{\{j_1, j_2, \ldots, j_k\}}$$

for those sets which have the form of cartesian product in suitable order of $P_{j_1}, P_{j_2}, \ldots, P_{j_k}$, $\{q_1\}, \{q_2\}, \ldots, \{q_{n-k}\}$

$$\alpha(A) = 0 \quad , \quad \beta(A) = M$$

for other subsets A of G, where M is sufficiently large numbers e.g. the sum of all elements of all matrices $\left\| a_{i_{q_1} i_{q_2} \dots i_{q_{n-k}}}^{\{j_1, j_2, \dots, j_k\}} \right\|$, then for each feasible solution X the function φ_x defined on the family of all subsets of G by

$$\varphi_x(A) = \begin{cases} \sum_{(i_1, i_2, \dots, i_n) \in A} x_{i_1 i_2 \dots i_n} & \text{if } A \neq \emptyset \\ 0 & \text{if } A = \emptyset \end{cases}$$

is additive and satisfies conditions $\alpha(A) \leq \varphi_x(A) \leq \beta(A)$ for each subset A of G and hence the theorem gives necessary conditions for the existence of a feasible to the T_k^n-problem.

Remarks. These conditions are also sufficient in the case of T_n^n-problem, T_{n-1}^n-problem and such a T_1^3-problem that at least one of the sets P_1, P_2, P_3 does not contain more than two elements (7). Unfortunately the author does not know whether these conditions are sufficient also in general case. For T_1^3-problem other conditions e.g. conditions stated by Haley (4) and conditions stated by Morávek and Vlach (8) follow from considered conditions. It is also worth noting that if all $a_{i_{q_1} i_{q_2} \dots i_{q_{n-k}}}^{\{j_1, j_2, \dots, j_k\}}$ are integers, then in the case of T_n^n-problems and

T^n_{n-1}-problems the existence of a feasible solutions implies the existence of an integer feasible solution. On the other hand there exists an integer T^3_1-problem that has non-integer feasible solution and that has no integer feasible solution.

Considering that even for not very large $n, p_1, p_2, \dots, p_n$ T^n_k-problems can be too large to be solved by standard methods, e.g. in the linear case by the simplex method, it is not useless to search other approaches. For instance the idea of branching and bounding (9) can be made to function in obtaining algorithms for T^n_{n-1}-problems and for special class of T^3_1-problems. Corresponding description and experimental results are presented in (10), (11), (12).

References

(1) Bellman, R., Dynamic Programming, Princeton University Press, 1957.

(2) Dwyer, P.S., and Galler, B.A., The Method of Reduced Matrices for a General Transportation Problem, Journal of the Association for Computing Mach., 4, 1957, pp. 303 - 318.

(3) Haley, K.B., The Solid Transportation Problem, Operations Research 10, 1962, pp. 448 - 463.

(4) Haley, K.B., The Multi-Index Problem, Operations Research 11, 1963, pp. 368 - 379.

(5) Schmid, K. Zurückführeeng eines Sortenproblems auf das dreidimensionale Transportproblem, Unternehneensforschung 10, 1966, pp. 32 - 41.

(6) Morávek, J., and Vlach, M., On Necessary Conditions for a Class of Systems of Linear Inequalities, Aplikace matematiky 13, 1968, pp. 299 - - 303.

(7) Haley, K.B., Note on the Letter by Morávek and Vlach, Operations Research 15, 1967, pp. 545 - - 546.

(8) Morávek,J., and Vlach,M., On the Necessary Conditions for the Existence of the Solution of the Multi-Index Transportation Problem, Operations Research 15, 1967, pp. 542 - 545.

(9) Little,J.D.C., Murty,K.G., Sweeney,D.W., and Karel,C., An Algorithm for the Travelling Salesman Problem, Operations Research, 11, 1963, pp. 972 - 990.

(10) Vlach,M., Řešení dopravního problému metodou větvení, Ekonomicko-matematický obzor 2, 1966, pp. 388 - 402.

(11) Vlach,M., Branch and Bound Method for Three - -Index Assignment problem, Ekonomicko-matematický obzor 3, 1967, pp. 181 - 191.

(12) Hájek,V., K metodě větvení a odhadů pro trojindexový přiřazovací problém, Ekonomicko-matematický obzor 4, 1968, pp. 233 - 245.

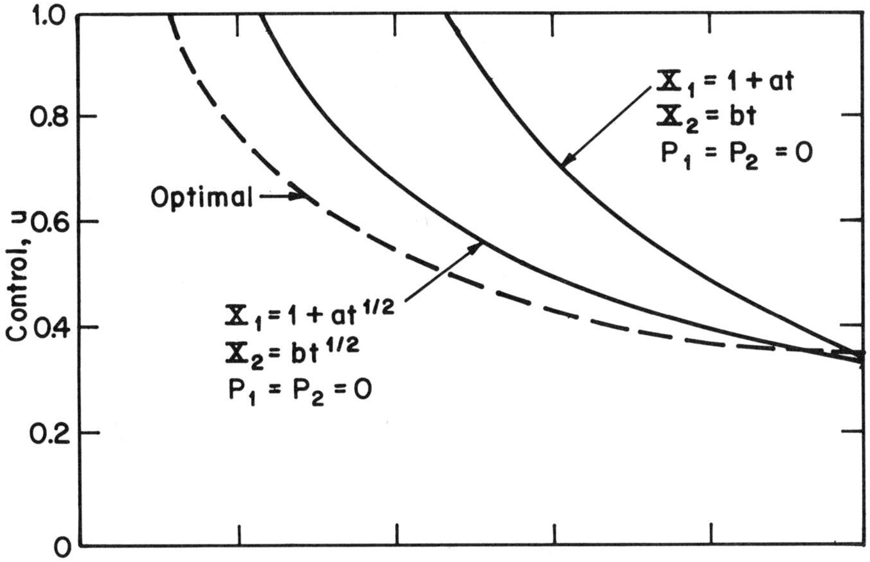

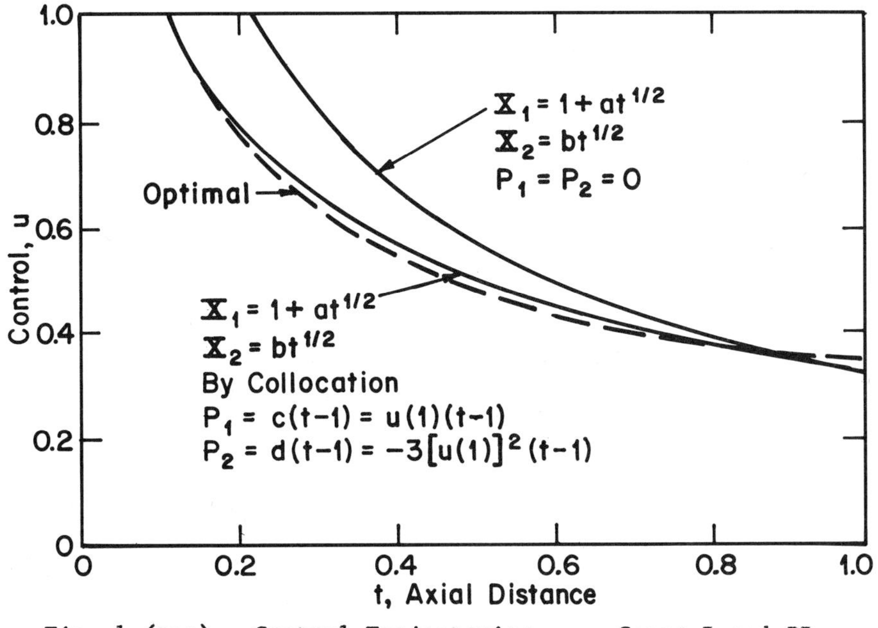

Fig. 1 (top) Control Trajectories Cases I and II

Fig. 2 (bottom) Control Trajectories , Collocation of Case II

Computation of a and b yields:

$$a = -.443$$
$$b = .280$$

The resulting near-optimal profile is shown on Fig. 1, and is seen to approximate $\hat{u}$ more closely than the preceding profile.

The performance index, $x_2(1)$ was evaluated for the two near-optimal control policies by numerically solving Eqs. (1) and (2) with u = U by a Runge-Kutta procedure. For Case I, a value of $x_2(1) = .267$ was obtained; and for Case II, $x_2(1) = 0.277$. This latter value is almost 97% of the optimum and indicates the effectiveness of the method.

Better agreement might be expected if more involved expressions for P_1 and P_2 are used:

$$P_1 = c\ (t - 1) \qquad (15a)$$

$$P_2 = d\ (t - 1) \qquad (15b)$$

Much of the benefit of these expressions can be obtained within the context of the state variable parameters a and b by applying the method of collocation to Eqs. (4) and (5). Here $\Psi_i = \delta\ (1 - t)$, the dirac delta function with argument $(1 - t)$. The constants c and d are thus selected to satisfy Eqs. (4) and (5) at the point t = 1. Specifically the approximation of Eq. (4) yields:

$$c = U(1) = \frac{X_1(1)}{6X_2(1)} = \frac{1 + a}{6b}$$

And the approximation of Eq. (5) yields:

$$d = -3\ [U\ (1)]^2 = -3 \left[\frac{1 + a}{6b}\right]^2$$

Hence the U approximation becomes, for Case II

$$U = \frac{1+at^{1/2}}{6bt^{1/2}} \left\{ \frac{1+ \left(\frac{1+a}{6b}\right) (1-t) + 3 \left(\frac{1+a}{6b}\right)^2 (1-t)}{1+1/3 \left(\frac{1+a}{6b}\right) (1-t) + 3 \left(\frac{1+a}{6b}\right)^2 (1-t)} \right\} \qquad (16a)$$

if this value ≤ 1

$U = 1$ if the value computed in (16a) > 1 (16b)

Although this approximation for $\hat{u}$ is more involved than the ones previously used, it still depends on only two parameters, a and b, and solution proceeds as before. The results are presented on Fig. 2, where it can be seen that the approximation U given by Eq. (16) closely fits the optimal control trajectory. The performance index, $x_2(1)$, obtained by using the approximate control profile of Eq. (15) is 0.267. That is, although better apparent agreement between the approximate and optimal control policy has been achieved, no improvement in performance has resulted. The application of collocation to this problem is a crude approximation and it is not alarming that performance was not improved.

Finally, Case III considered the Galerkin determination of all four parameters, a, b, c, and d, using the t^2 state variable trial functions and the approximate adjoint variable trajectories of Eq. (15). The values were computed by a minimization of the sum of the residual squared errors of the algebraic equations:

$$a = -0.415$$
$$b = 0.283$$
$$c = 0.239$$
$$d = -0.649$$

The resultant control trajectory is shown on Fig. 3 and is seen to be a quite reasonable approximation to the optimal. The performance index associated with this near-optimal profile, however, was not improved over the previous ones, suggesting a certain insensitivity in the region of the optimum. A comparison of the approximate adjoint variable trajectories with the optimal trajectories (4) is given in Fig. 4. The close agreement between the two indicates that Galerkin approximations to the differential equations are indeed justifiable.

Discussion

The primary advantage of the method is that it does not require the solution of differential equations. Direct approximation of the control policy in terms of unknown parameters, requires that the system differential equations be solved before parameter optimization can be accomplished. By satisfying the integral approximations, the differential equations have been reduced to non-linear algebraic equations in terms of the mixing coefficients.

$$X_1 = 1 + at^{1/2} = 1 - .415\, t^{1/2} \qquad P_1 = c(t-1) = .239(t-1)$$
$$X_2 = bt^{1/2} = .283\, t^{1/2} \qquad P_2 = d(t-1) = -.649(t-1)$$

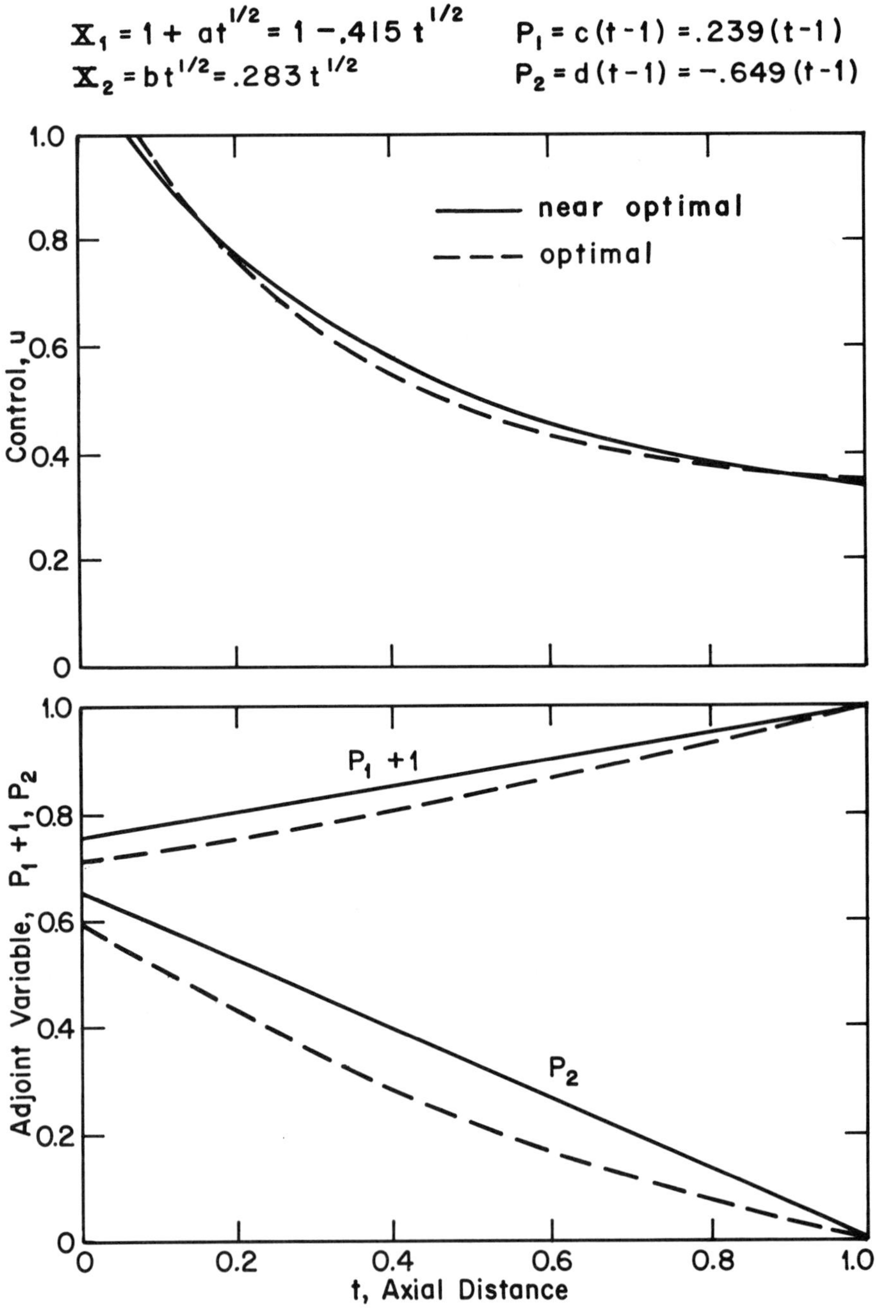

Fig. 3 (top)   and   Fig. 4 (bottom)   Case III

A second advantage of the method is that it allows a knowledge of the general shape of the state variable trajectories to be used to suggest trial functions. Often, this knowledge is available in physical situations; and the proposed method provides a procedure that incorporates this physical insight into the approximate solution of the problem. The expression for U in Eq. (16) is a two-constant form not likely to be suggested if one were obtaining a near-optimal solution by the technique of approximating the control profile. Yet, the fit between the U of Eq. (16) and the optimal profile is quite good, and U has been constructed in a straightforward fashion from simple trial functions.

The results from the reactor profile example indicate that the level of approximation is commensurate with the computational effort expended and that satisfactory results can be obtained with the procedure.

References

1. Bilous, O. and N.R. Amundson, "Optimum Temperature Gradients in Tubular Reactors", Chem. Eng. Sci., 5, 81, 115 (1956).

2. Aris, R., "Studies in Optimization II. Optimum Temperature Gradients in Tubular Reactors," Chem. Eng. Sci., 13, 18 (1960).

3. Denn, M.M. and R. Aris, "Greens Functions and Optimal Systems", Ind. Eng. Chem. 4, 7, 213, 248 (1965).

4. Schechter, R.S., "The Variational Method in Engineering", pp. 51-67, McGraw Hill (1967).

5. Lee, E. Stanley, "Quasilinearization and Invariant Imbedding," pp. 130-149, Academic Press (1968).

SOME ALGORITHMS FOR FINDING THE SHORTEST ROUTES THROUGH THE GENERAL NETWORKS

Jin Y. Yen

Graduate School of Business Administration

University of California

Berkeley, California

Summary: This paper presents a basic algorithm and its modification for finding all shortest routes and shortest distances from a fixed origin to all other nodes in N-node general networks in which the distances of the arcs can be negative. The algorithms respectively require only $\frac{1}{2}M(N-1)(N-2)$ and about $\frac{1}{4}M(N-1)(N-2)$, $1 < M \leqq N-2$, additions and comparisons -- equal to only about one half and one quarter of the number required by other best algorithms. The new algorithms are efficient for both hand and computer applications. In hand application especially, when N is large, the new algorithms can be expected to work much more efficient than other available algorithms.

The comparisons of the efficiencies of the newly proposed algorithms with Dreyfus' (4) -- namely, the best of other algorithms -- is also presented.

INTRODUCTION

The problem to find the shortest routes and the shortest distances from a fixed origin to all other nodes in a N-node general network (in which the distances of arcs can be negative) can be solved by algorithms proposed by Ford (6), Moore (9), Bellman (1), Floyd (5), Murchland (10), Dantzig (3), Dantzig, Blattner and Rao (2), Hu (7), Dreyfus (4), and others. The best of these algorithms -- namely, Dreyfus' algorithm -- requires about $M(N-1)^2$, $1 < M \leqq N-2$, additions and comparisons.

The purpose of this paper is to present a basic matrix algorithm (Algorithm 1) and its modification (Algorithm 2) for solving the above problem. The advantages of the algorithms are as follows.

(1) They solve the problem in general networks in which the distances of arcs can be symmetric, assymmetric, zero, positive, or negative -- provided there exists no non-positive loop.

(2) They require only N^2 memory addresses.

(3) They respectively require only $\frac{1}{2}M(N-1)(N-2)$ and about $\frac{1}{4}M(N-1)(N-2)$, $1 < M \leqq N-2$, additions and comparisons --

equal to only about one half and one quarter of the number required by other most efficient algorithms.

(4) They operate very simply in a N by N matrix, from which both shortest routes and shortest distances are to be found.

(5) They can simply be programmed for computer applications.

DEFINITION AND NOTATION

Consider in a N-node general network, let

(i), or (j), i,j=1,2,...,N, be the nodes where (1) is the origin,

(i,j), $i \neq j$, be the directed arcs from (i) to (j),

(1)-(j)-...-(i), $i \neq j \neq 1$, be the route from (1) to (i) passing through (j),...,

$d_{i,j} \gtreqless 0$, $i \neq j$, be the distances of (i,j). If (i,j) exists $d_{i,j}$ is a finite number; otherwise, $d_{i,j}$ is considered equal to infinity. Note that $d_{i,j}$ can take any real number except some numbers that generate non-positive loops in the network,

$D = [d_{i,j}]$ be the distance matrix of the network,

$f_i^{(k)}$, or $f_j^{(k)}$, i,j=1,2,...,N, be the tentative shortest distances from (1) to (i), or (j), at iteration k, k=1,2, ...,½N,

f_i, or f_j, i,j=1,2,...,N, be the shortest distances from (1) to (i), or (j).

FUNCTIONAL EQUATIONS

By the dynamic programming technique, $f_i^{(k)}$, or $f_j^{(k)}$, i,j=1,2,...,N, are the set of values that satisfy the following systems of recursive functions.

Algorithm 1.

$$f_i^{(0)} = d_{1,i}, \quad i=1,2,\ldots,N; \tag{1.1}$$

$$f_i^{(2k-1)} = \min_{1<j<i} \left[f_j^{(2k-1)} + d_{j,i},\ f_i^{(2k-2)} \right], \tag{1.2}$$

$$i=3,4,\ldots,N, \quad f_1^{(2k-1)}=0, \quad f_2^{(2k-1)}=f_2^{(2k-2)};$$

$$f_i^{(2k)} = \min_{N \geq j > i} \left[f_j^{(2k)} + d_{j,i},\ f_i^{(2k-1)} \right], \tag{1.3}$$

$i=N-1,N-2,\ldots,2,\ f_N^{(2k)}=f_N^{(2k-1)},\ f_1^{(2k)}=0.$

For $k=1,2,\ldots,\frac{1}{2}N$.

The iterative process of the algorithm is to be terminated when $f_i^{(2k)}=f_i^{(2k-1)}$, or $f_i^{(2k+1)}=f_i^{(2k)}$, for $i=1,2,\ldots,N$. If the algorithm does not terminate in N iterations it implies there exists at least a negative loop in the network. In such case, the solution to the problem cannot be defined.

Algorithm 2.

Note that when $f_j^{(2k)}=f_j^{(2k-1)}=f_j^{(2k-2)}$, for $j=1,2,\ldots,N$, $k=1,2,\ldots,\frac{1}{2}N$, the following equations hold.

$$f_i^{(2k-1)} \geqq \left[f_j^{(2k-1)}+d_{j,i},\ f_i^{(2k-2)}\right],\ i=3,4,\ldots,N,\ 1<j<i,\ k=2,3,\ldots$$

$$f_i^{(2k)} \geqq \left[f_j^{(2k)}+d_{j,i},\ f_i^{(2k-1)}\right],\ i=N-1,N-2,\ldots,2,\ N\geqq j>i,\ k=2,3,\ldots$$

Therefore, it is not necessary to compute the new $f_i^{(2k-1)}$ and $f_i^{(2k)}$ in the iterative process. Such that Algorithm 1 can be modified into Algorithm 2 to cut down a great number of computations as follows.

$$f_i^{(0)}=d_{1,i},\ i=1,2,\ldots,N; \tag{2.1}$$

$$f_i^{(1)}=\min_{1<j<i}\left[f_j^{(1)}+d_{j,i},\ f_i^{(0)}\right], \tag{2.2}$$
$$i=3,4,\ldots,N,\ f_1^{(1)}=0,\ f_2^{(1)}=f_2^{(0)};$$

$$f_i^{(2)}=\min_{N\geqq j>i}\left[f_j^{(2)}+d_{j,i},\ f_i^{(1)}\right],\ i=N-1,N-2,\ldots,2, \tag{2.3}$$
$$f_N^{(2)}=f_N^{(1)},\ f_1^{(2)}=0;$$

$$\begin{cases} f_i^{(2k-1)}=\min_{1<j<i}\left[f_j^{(2k-1)}+d_{j,i},\ f_i^{(2k-2)}\right],\ i=3,4,\ldots,N, \\ \qquad f_1^{(2k-1)}=0,\ f_2^{(2k-1)}=f_2^{(2k-2)}, \\ \text{if } f_j^{(2k-1)}\neq f_j^{(2k-2)}\neq f_j^{(2k-3)},\ 1<j<i; \qquad (2.4.1) \end{cases}$$

$$\left| \begin{array}{l} f_i^{(2k-1)}=f_i^{(2k-2)},\ i=3,4,\ldots,N,\ f_1^{(2k-1)}=0,\ f_2^{(2k-1)}=f_2^{(2k-2)}, \\ \quad \text{if } f_j^{(2k-1)}=f_j^{(2k-2)}=f_j^{(2k-3)},\ 1<j<i; \end{array} \right. \tag{2.4.2}$$

$$\left\{ \begin{array}{l} f_i^{(2k)}=\min\limits_{N\geq j>i}\left[f_j^{(2k)}+d_{j,i},\ f_i^{(2k-1)}\right],\ i=N-1,N-2,\ldots,2 \\ \qquad\qquad\qquad\qquad\qquad\qquad f_N^{(2k)}=f_N^{(2k-1)},\ f_1^{(2k)}=0, \\ \quad \text{if } f_j^{(2k)}\neq f_j^{(2k-1)}\neq f_j^{(2k-2)},\ N\geq j>i \qquad (2.5.1) \\ f_i^{(2k)}=f_i^{(2k-1)},\ i=N-1,N-2,\ldots,2,\ f_N^{(2k)}=f_N^{(2k-1)},\ f_1^{(2k)}=0, \\ \quad \text{if } f_j^{(2k)}=f_j^{(2k-1)}=f_j^{(2k-2)},\ N\geq j>i. \qquad (2.5.2) \end{array} \right.$$

For $k=2,3,\ldots,\frac{1}{2}N$.

Similar to Algorithm 1, the iterative process of Algorithm 2 is to be terminated when $f_i^{(2k)}=f_i^{(2k-1)}$, or $f_i^{(2k+1)}=f_i^{(2k)}$, for $i=1,2,\ldots,N$.

PROOF

In proof, it is to shown that the iterative process of the basic algorithm converges in finite steps and the solution thus obtained is unique and optimal.

Let us define: in a route, "(i) is to the right of (j) if i>j" -- denote it by $(i)\succ(j)$; and "(i) is to the left of (j) if i< j" -- denote it by $(i)\prec(j)$.

Since 1) there exists no non-positive distance loop in the network as assumed, and 2) the positive distance loop will increase the length of a route with additional distance, the optimal routes from (1) to (i), i=2,3,...,N, can be written as follows.

$$\left|\underbrace{(1)\prec(2^*)\prec(3^*)\prec\ldots\prec(N_1^*)}_{\text{1st homogeneous block}}\right|\left.\underbrace{\succ(N_1+1^*)\succ(N_1+2^*)\succ\ldots\succ(N_2^*)}_{\text{2nd homogeneous block}}\right|\prec$$

$$\ldots\ \left|\underbrace{(N_{M-1}+1^*)\ \ldots\ (N_M^*)}_{\text{M-th homogeneous block}}\right| \tag{3.0}$$

where (2^*), (3^*), ... , (N_M^*) are either the particular member of (2), (3), ... , (N), or empty; and, $1< M\leq N-1$.

In 1st homogeneous block, since the nodes are $(1)\prec(2^*)\prec(3^*)\prec\ldots\prec(N_1^*)$, the unique and optimal distances from

(1) to (2*),(3*),...,(N_1*) -- as shown by Parikh (11) -- are

$$f_i = \min_{1 \leq j<i} \left[f_j + d_{j,i} \right] = \min_{1<j<i} \left[f_j + d_{j,i},\ d_{1,i} \right],$$
$$i=2^*,3^*,\ldots,N_1^*, \tag{3.1}$$

which is contained in (1.2) for k=1 as

$$f_i^{(1)} = \min_{1<j<i} \left[f_j^{(1)} + d_{j,i},\ f_i^{(0)} \right],\ i=3,4,\ldots,N;\quad f_1^{(1)}=0,\ f_2^{(1)}=f_2^{(0)}. \tag{3.2}$$

Therefore, the unique and optimal distances from (1) to (2*), (3*),...,(N_1*) are determined in Iteration 1.

In 2nd homogeneous block, since 1) f_i, i=2*,3*,...,N_1*, are already determined in Iteration 1, and, 2)(N_1*) $\succ$ (N_1+1*)$\succ$ (N_1+2*)$\succ$ ... $\succ$ (N_2*), the unique and optimal distances from (1) to (N_1+1*),(N_1+2*),...,(N_2*) are

$$f_i = \min_{\substack{j=2^*,3^*,\ldots,N_2^* \\ j>i}} \left[f_j + d_{j,i} \right],\ i=N_1+1^*,N_1+2^*,\ldots,N_2^* \tag{3.3}$$

which is contained in (1.3) for k=1 as

$$f_i^{(2)} = \min_{N>j>i} \left[f_j^{(2)} + d_{j,i},\ f_i^{(1)} \right],\ i=N-1,N-2,\ldots,2;\quad f_N^{(2)}=f_N^{(1)},\ f_1^{(2)}=0 \tag{3.4}$$

Therefore, the unique and optimal distances from (1) to (N_1+1*),(N_1+2*),...,N_2* are determined in Iteration 2.

. . .

As shown by (3.0), since M, the number of homogeneous blocks, is bounded by N-1, the successive approximation of the shortest distances from (1) to (i), i=2,3,...,N, terminates in no more than N-1 iterations.

Therefore, the iterative process of the algorithm converges in finite steps and the solution thus obtained is unique and optimal.

THE ILLUSTRATION OF MATRIX ALGORITHM

Now the matrix algorithms are developed from the functional equations for efficient hand application as well as for illustration. The following example is self-explanatory.

Let a 5-node general network have the distance matrix D as the following.

	1	2	3	4	5
1	0	3	-1	2	2
2	1	0	1	2	0
3	4	3	0	4	3
4	1	-1	0	0	1
5	0	2	1	2	3

D matrix

	1	2	3	4	5
1	0	3	-1	2	2
2	1	3	1	2	0
3	4	3	-1	4	3
4	1	-1	0	2	1
5	0	2	1	2	2

D^0, D^1 matrix

	1	2	3	4	5
1	0	3	-1	2	2
2	1	~~3~~ 1	1	2	0
3	4	3	-1	4	3
4	1	-1	0	2	1
5	0	2	1	2	2

D^2 matrix

Then the solution is to be obtained as follows.

Application of Algorithm 1.

Step 0. To write D to D^0.

Write D^0=D except write in pencil (as they will be erased later), $d_{i,i}^{(0)}=d_{i,i}$, i=1,2,3,4,5.

The reason for rewriting D is that it is useless to leave zeroes on the diagonal elements to indicate the zero-distances of self-loops. Instead, one can use these precious spaces to write $f_i^{(k)}$. As one will see later, to use the diagonal elements to write $f_i^{(k)}$ will make the tabulations very simple and the computations very efficient.

Step 1. To determine the shortest distance from (1) to (i), i=2,3,4,5.

Iteration 1: Starting from i=3 toward i=5 compute the new diagonal values $d_{i,i}^{(1)}$,

$$d_{i,i}^{(1)}=\min_{1<j<i}\left[d_{j,j}^{(1)}+d_{j,i},\ d_{i,i}^{(0)}\right],\ i=3,4,5,\ d_{1,1}^{(1)}=0,\ d_{2,2}^{(1)}=d_{2,2}^{(0)}.$$

Replace $d_{i,i}^{(0)}$ with $d_{i,i}^{(1)}$ if $d_{i,i}^{(1)}<d_{i,i}^{(0)}$; otherwise, leave $d_{i,i}^{(0)}$ alone and denote it by $d_{i,i}^{(1)}$.

$d_{i,i}^{(1)}$, i=1,2,3,4,5, are obtained as follows.

$d_{1,1}^{(1)}=0$, $d_{2,2}^{(1)}=d_{2,2}^{(0)}=3$,

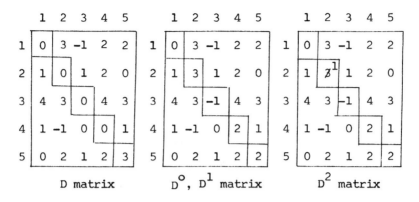

$d^{(1)}_{3,3}=\min\left[d^{(1)}_{2,2}+d_{2,3},\ d^{(0)}_{3,3}\right]=\min(3+1,-1)=-1,$
$d^{(1)}_{4,4}=\min\left[d^{(1)}_{2,2}+d_{2,4},\ d^{(1)}_{3,3}+d_{3,4},\ d^{(0)}_{4,4}\right]=\min(3+2,-1+4,2)=2,$
$d^{(1)}_{5,5}=\min\left[d^{(1)}_{2,2}+d_{2,5},\ d^{(1)}_{3,3}+d_{3,5},\ d^{(1)}_{4,4}+d_{4,5},d^{(0)}_{5,5}\right]$
$=\min(3+0,-1+3,2+1,2)=2.$

Note that 1) only the upper triangle elements enter into computations, and 2) the resulting matrix is D^1.

Iteration 2. Starting from i=4 toward i=2 compute the new diagonal values $d^{(2)}_{i,i}$,

$$d^{(2)}_{i,i}=\min_{1<j<i}\left[d^{(2)}_{j,j}+d_{j,i},\ d^{(1)}_{i,i}\right],\ i=4,3,2,\ d^{(2)}_{5,5}=d^{(1)}_{5,5},\ d^{(2)}_{1,1}=0.$$

Replace $d^{(1)}_{i,i}$ with $d^{(2)}_{i,i}$ if $d^{(2)}_{i,i}<d^{(1)}_{i,i}$; otherwise, leave $d^{(1)}_{i,i}$ alone and denote it by $d^{(2)}_{i,i}$.

$d^{(2)}_{i,i}$, i=5,4,3,2,1, are obtained as follows.

$d^{(2)}_{5,5}=d^{(1)}_{5,5}=2,$
$d^{(2)}_{4,4}=\min\left[d^{(2)}_{5,5}+d_{5,4},\ d^{(1)}_{4,4}\right]=\min(2+2,2)=2,$
$d^{(2)}_{3,3}=\min\left[d^{(2)}_{5,5}+d_{5,3},\ d^{(2)}_{4,4}+d_{4,3},\ d^{(1)}_{3,3}\right]=\min(2+1,2+0,-1)=-1,$
$d^{(2)}_{2,2}=\min\left[d^{(2)}_{5,5}+d_{5,2},\ d^{(2)}_{4,4}+d_{4,2},\ d^{(2)}_{3,3}+d_{3,2},\ d^{(1)}_{2,2}\right]$
$=\min(2+2,2-1,-1+3,1)=1,$

$d^{(2)}_{1,1}=0.$

Note that 1) only the lower triangle elements enter into computations, and 2) the resulting matrix is D^2.

Iteration 3. Similar to Iteration 1, compute $d^{(3)}_{i,i}$ and obtain D^3.

Iteration 4. Similar to Iteration 2, compute $d^{(4)}_{i,i}$ and obtain D^4.

Note that $d^{(4)}_{i,i}=d^{(3)}_{i,i}$, i=1,2,3,4,5. This implies that f_i, i=1,2,3,4,5, are determined in Iteration 3. Therefore, the algorithm terminates.

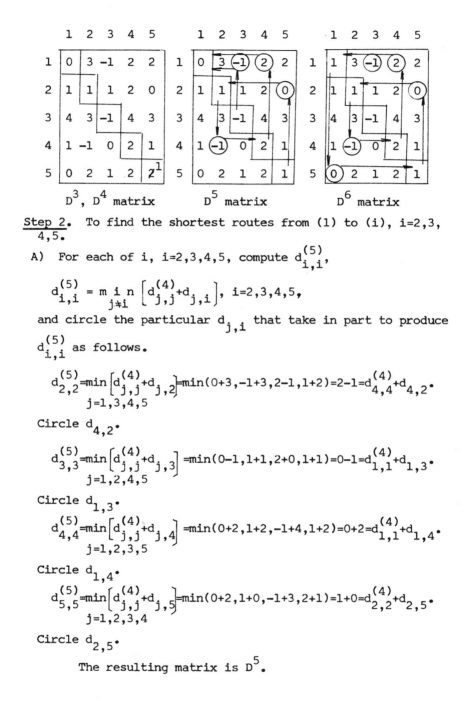

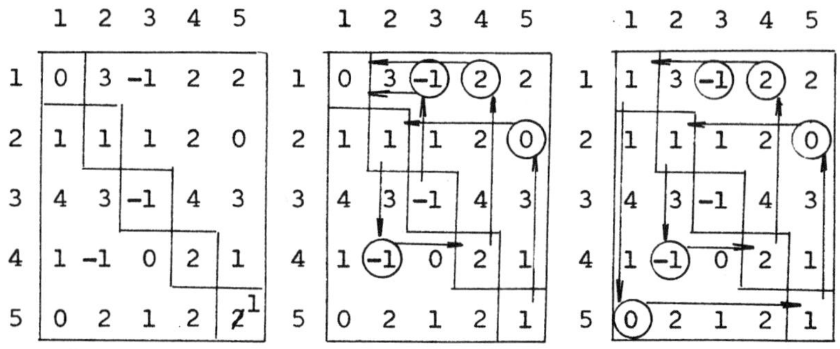

D^3, D^4 matrix $\qquad$ D^5 matrix $\qquad$ D^6 matrix

Step 2. To find the shortest routes from (1) to (i), i=2,3,4,5.

A) For each of i, i=2,3,4,5, compute $d_{i,i}^{(5)}$,

$$d_{i,i}^{(5)} = \min_{j \neq i} \left[d_{j,j}^{(4)} + d_{j,i} \right], \quad i=2,3,4,5,$$

and circle the particular $d_{j,i}$ that take in part to produce $d_{i,i}^{(5)}$ as follows.

$$d_{2,2}^{(5)} = \min_{j=1,3,4,5} \left[d_{j,j}^{(4)} + d_{j,2} \right] = \min(0+3,-1+3,2-1,1+2) = 2-1 = d_{4,4}^{(4)} + d_{4,2}.$$

Circle $d_{4,2}$.

$$d_{3,3}^{(5)} = \min_{j=1,2,4,5} \left[d_{j,j}^{(4)} + d_{j,3} \right] = \min(0-1,1+1,2+0,1+1) = 0-1 = d_{1,1}^{(4)} + d_{1,3}.$$

Circle $d_{1,3}$.

$$d_{4,4}^{(5)} = \min_{j=1,2,3,5} \left[d_{j,j}^{(4)} + d_{j,4} \right] = \min(0+2,1+2,-1+4,1+2) = 0+2 = d_{1,1}^{(4)} + d_{1,4}.$$

Circle $d_{1,4}$.

$$d_{5,5}^{(5)} = \min_{j=1,2,3,4} \left[d_{j,j}^{(4)} + d_{j,5} \right] = \min(0+2,1+0,-1+3,2+1) = 1+0 = d_{2,2}^{(4)} + d_{2,5}.$$

Circle $d_{2,5}$.

The resulting matrix is D^5.

B) Find the <u>tracks</u> for i, i=2,3,4,5, by connecting the of nodes as follows.

<u>Track</u> for i=2: $d^{(5)}_{2,2}$, $d_{4,2}$, $d^{(5)}_{4,4}$, $d_{1,4}$, $d^{(5)}_{1,1}$.

<u>Track</u> for i=3: $d^{(5)}_{3,3}$, $d_{1,3}$, $d^{(5)}_{1,1}$.

<u>Track</u> for i=4: $d^{(5)}_{4,4}$, $d_{1,4}$, $d^{(5)}_{1,1}$.

<u>Track</u> for i=5: $d^{(5)}_{5,5}$, $d_{2,5}$, $d^{(5)}_{2,2}$, $d_{4,2}$, $d^{(5)}_{4,4}$, $d_{1,4}$, $d^{(5)}_{1,1}$.

C) Find the shortest routes from (1) to (i), i=2,3,4,5, by tracing through the tracks as follows.

Shortest route from (1) to (2): (1)-(4)-(2).
Shortest route from (1) tO (3): (1)-(3).
Shortest route from (1) to (4): (1)-(4).
Shortest route from (1) to (5): (1)-(4)-(2)-(5).

Remark: When the shortest route and the shortest distance from (1) to itself through the network is desired, the following additional step finds the solution.

<u>Step 3</u>. To find the shortest distances and the shortest route from (1) to itself through the network.

A) Compute $d^{(6)}_{1,1}$,

$$d^{(6)}_{1,1}=\min_{j=2,3,4,5}\left[d^{(5)}_{j,j}+d_{j,1}\right]=\min(1+1,-1+4,2+1,1+0)=d^{(5)}_{5,5}+d_{5,1},$$

and circle $d_{1,5}$. Then, the shortest distance from (1) to itself is 1.

The resulting matrix is D^6.

B) Find the <u>track</u> for i=1 by connecting $d^{(6)}_{1,1}$, $d_{5,1}$, $d^{(6)}_{5,5}$, $d_{2,5}$, $d^{(6)}_{2,2}$, $d_{4,2}$, $d^{(6)}_{4,4}$, $d_{1,4}$, $d^{(6)}_{1,1}$.

C) Then the shortest route from (1) to itself is obtained by tracing through the <u>track</u> for i=1 as (1)-(4)-(2)-(5)-(1).

Note that in practice the above operations of the algorithm are to be performed in only one matrix. The time required to solved this problem by hand is only about two to three minutes, which is much shorter than the time required by other algorithms.

Application of Algorithm 2.

Algorithm 2 is to be carried out similarily to Algorithm 1 except the following technique is applied.

In Iterations 2k, k=1,2,..., if $d_{i,i}^{(2k)} < d_{i,i}^{(2k-1)}$, i=N-1, N-2,...,2, make a small circle mark in pencil with $d_{i,i}^{(2k)}$; otherwise, if $d_{i,i}^{(2k)} \geqq d_{i,i}^{(2k-1)}$ do not make any mark with $d_{i,i}^{(2k)}$. In Iterations 2k+1, k=1,2,..., if $d_{i,i}^{(2k+1)} < d_{i,i}^{(2k)}$, make a small triangle mark in pencil with $d_{i,i}^{(2k+1)}$; otherwise, if $d_{i,i}^{(2k+1)} \geqq d_{i,i}^{(2k)}$, do not make any mark with $d_{i,i}^{(2k+1)}$. Then from Iteration 3 on no computation for $d_{j,j}^{(m)}+d_{j,i}$, m=3,4,..., j=2,3,...,N, is necessary unless $d_{j,j}^{(m)}$ has at least a circle or triangle mark. In Iterations 2k+1, k=1,2,...,after all $d_{i,i}^{(2k+1)}$ are computed, erase all circle marks from $d_{i,i}^{(2k+1)}$; and, in Iterations 2k+2, k=1,2,..., after $d_{i,i}^{(2k+2)}$ are computed, erase all triangle marks with $d_{i,i}^{(2k+2)}$. Keep doing the above iterative process until no circle or triangle mark can be found on the diagonal. Then, $d_{i,i}$, i=2,3,...,N, are the shortest distances from (1) to (i), i=2,3,...,N.

EFFICIENCIES OF THE ALGORITHMS

The efficiency of a algorithm can be represented by its simplicity, accessibility, applicability, capacity, and speed. So far,these characteristics of the new algorithms are shown in the functional equations and the illustration as given above. The following is a table of comparison of the newly proposed algorithms with Dreyfus' algorithm -- namely, the best of other available algorithms.

	Dreyfus' algorithm	Algorithm 1	Algorithm 2
1. Method	Metric only	Metric and geometric	Metric and geometric
2. Hand application	Rather hard	Easy	Easy
3. To find the shortest routes	Rather hard	Easy	Easy
4. Memory addresses required	N^2	N^2	N^2
5. Maximum number of iterations required to terminate the algorithm	N-2	N-2	N-2
6. Actual number of iterations required to terminate the algorithm	M, $1<M\leq N-2$	M, $1<M\leq N-2$	M, $1<M\leq N-2$
7. Number of additions and comparisons required in each iteration	$(N-1)^2$	$\frac{1}{2}(N-1)(N-2)$	$\frac{1}{2}(N-1)(N-2)-L$, $0<L\leq\frac{1}{2}(N-1)(N-2)$
8. Maximum number of additions and comparisons required to terminate the algorithm	$(N-2)(N-1)^2$	$\frac{1}{2}(N-1)(N-2)^2$	About $\frac{1}{4}(N-1)(N-2)$ when N is large
9. Actual number of additions and comparisons required to terminate the algorithm	$M(N-1)^2$, $1<M\leq N-2$	$\frac{1}{2}M(N-1)(N-2)$, $1<M\leq N-2$	About $\frac{1}{4}M(N-1)(N-2)$ $1<M\leq N-2$ when N is large
10. Minimum efficiency as compared with Dreyfus' algorithm	-	About twice as efficient	About four times as efficicient when N is large

Table of comparison of the efficiencies of the new algorithm with Dreyfus' algorithm

ACKNOWLEDGEMENT

The author is very grateful to Professors Stuart E. Dreyfus, Jack D. Rogers and Yuh Sun for their reading of the manuscript and instructions.

REFERENCES

1. R.E. BELLMAN, "On a Routing Problem," Quart.Appl.Math. 16 87-90 (1958).
2. G. B. DANTZIG, W.C. BLATTNER AND M.R. RAO, All Shortest Routes from a Fixed Origin in a Graph, Technical Report No. 66-2, Operations Research House, Stanford University, Nov. 1966.
3. G. B. DANTZIG, All Shortest Routes in a Graph, Technical Report No. 66-3, Operations Research House, Stanford University, Nov. 1966.
4. S.E. DREYFUS, An Appraisal of Some Shortest Path Algorithms, paper presented at ORSA/TIMS Joint Meeting, San Francisco, April 30 - May 3, 1968.
5. R. W. FLOYD, "Algorithm 97, Shortest Path," Communication of the ACM, Vol. 5, No. 6, 345 (1962).
6. L. R. FORD, JR., Network Flow Theory, The RAND Corporation, P-923, August 1956.
7. T.C. HU, "Revised Matrix Algorithms for Shortest Paths," SIAM Journal of Mathematics, Vol. 15, No. 1, 207-218 (1967).
8. T. C. HU, "A Decomposition Algorithm for Shortest Paths in a Network," Opns. Res., Vol. 16, No. 1, 91-102 (1968).
9. E. F. MOORE, "The Shortest Path Through a Maze," Proc.Int. Symp. on the Theory of Switching, Part II, April 2-5, 1957. The Annals of the Computation Laboratory of Harvard University 30, Harvard University Press, 1959.
10. J. D. MURCHLAND, A New Method for Finding all Elementary Paths in a Complete Directed Graph, Transport Network Theory Unit, London School of Economics, Report LSE-TNT-22, Nov. 1966.
11. A. C. PARIKH, Some Theorems and Algorithms for Finding Optimal Paths over Graphs with Engineering Applications, unpublished Ph.D. theses, Purdue University, 1960.
12. J. Y. YEN, A Matrix Algorithm for Solving all Shortest Routes from a Fixed Origin in the Non-Negative Networks, paper to be presented at 15th International Meeting, The Institute of Management Sciences, Cleveland, Ohio, Sept. 11-13, 1968.

COMPUTATION OF NEAR-OPTIMAL TEMPERATURE PROFILES FOR A TUBULAR REACTOR: A STUDY OF TRAJECTORY APPROXIMATION

R.L. Zahradnik and Elliot S. Parkin
Department of Chemical Engineering
Carnegie-Mellon University
Pittsburgh, Pennsylvania

Introduction

It is possible to characterize optimal temperature profiles for tubular reactors by a number of variational formulations (1,2,3,4,5). The computation of these profiles invariably involves the solution on a given interval of a set of ordinary non-linear differential equations with boundary conditions specified at each end of the interval. Numerical solution procedures are required, generally involving iterative techniques. This paper presents a method for obtaining near-optimal profiles which involves computations that can be made either by hand or by computer solution of a set of algebraic equations.

In order to illustrate the use of the method, a near-optimal temperature profile in a tubular reactor is obtained for a specific reaction system. This problem has been discussed by several authors (4,5) and a reasonable experience with the computational requirements has been established, so that comparison can be made between this approach and the various other procedures.

Consider the following reactions to be carried out in a tubular chemical reactor:

$$A \underset{k_2}{\overset{k_1}{\rightleftarrows}} B \overset{k_3}{\rightarrow} C$$

It is desired to maximize the yield of B at the reactor outlet (t = 1) by selecting the temperature, T, (within assigned limits) as a function of normalized reactor length, t. Pure A is fed to the reactor and all reactions are first order, so that the describing differential equations may be written in terms of x_1 and x_2, the mole fractions of A and B respectively:

$$\frac{dx_1}{dt} = - k_1 x_1 + k_2 x_2 \qquad x_1 (0) = 1 \qquad (1)$$

$$\frac{dx_2}{dt} = k_1 x_1 - (k_2+k_3) x_2 \qquad x_2 (0) = 0 \qquad (2)$$

where k_1, k_2, and k_3 are temperature related rate constants of the reactions.

The analysis is simplified and the essence of the problem preserved by considering the special case where $\frac{1}{2} k_3 = k_2 = k_1^2 = u^2$. Also, since u and temperature are uniquely related, it is convenient to use the variable u instead of T to represent the control effort. The limits on temperature are taken to constrain u in the following normalized fashion:

$$0 \leq u \leq 1$$

The optimal policy is one which maximizes x_2 (1) and hence minimizes the Hamiltonian function, H:

$$\text{Min } H = - ux_1+3u^2x_2+p_1 (-ux_1+u^2x_2) + p_2 (ux_1-3u^2x_2)$$
$$\left\{ 0 \leq u \leq 1 \right\} \qquad (3)$$

for every t on the interval [0,1]. The following adjoint equations are obtained from the Hamiltonian:

$$\frac{dp_1}{dt} = u + p_1 u - p_2 u \qquad p_1 (1) = 0 \qquad (4)$$

$$\frac{dp_2}{dt} = - 3u^2 - p_1 u^2 + 3p_2 u^2 \qquad p_2 (1) = 0 \qquad (5)$$

It is easy to show that H is minimized by $\hat{u}$, selected as follows:

$$\hat{u} = \frac{x_1}{6x_2} \frac{(1 + p_1 - p_2)}{(1 + \frac{p_1}{3} - p_2)} \qquad \text{if this value} \leq 1 \qquad (6a)$$

$\hat{u} = 1$ if value computed in (6a) is > 1 (6b)

Solution of Eqs. (1),(2),(4), and (5) together with condition (6) defines the optimal temperature profile. A plot of this profile is presented in Fig. 1. The performance index, x_2 (1), attains a value of 0.287 for this control policy (4).

A Near-Optimal Computational Procedure

The contention of the present method is that the approximate solution of Eqs. (1),(2),(4), and (5), together with condition (6), defines a near-optimal control policy. The underlying idea of the method is the immediate approximation of each state and adjoint variable trajectory by means of a set of trial functions and mixing coefficients. The general forms of these approximations in terms of the variables of the optimal reactor profile are as follows:

$$x_1 \approx X_1 = X_1^*(t) + \sum_{i=1}^{n_1} a_i X_{1,i}(t) \tag{7}$$

$$x_2 \approx X_2 = X_2^*(t) + \sum_{i=1}^{n_2} b_i X_{2,i}(t) \tag{8}$$

$$p_1 \approx P_1 = P_1^*(t) + \sum_{i=1}^{n_3} c_i P_{1,i}(t) \tag{9}$$

$$p_2 \approx P_2 = P_2^*(t) + \sum_{i=1}^{n_4} d_i P_{2,i}(t) \tag{10}$$

where the starred quantities satisfy the specified boundary condition on the variable to be approximated. The individual summations extend to a sufficient number of terms(n_1, n_2, m_1, m_2) to describe adequately the variable to be approximated, and the individual sets of parameters $[a_i]$, $[b_i]$, $[c_i]$, and $[d_i]$ are called mixing coefficients. The various trial functions $X_{1,i}$ (t), $X_{2,i}$ (t), $P_{1,i}$ (t), and $P_{2,i}$ (t) satisfy the associated homogeneous boundary conditions on their respective variables and may be any convenient members of a complete set of functions.

The advantage of introducing approximations for the state variable profiles is that often the general shapes of the optimal state-variable trajectories are known beforehand, so that the trial functions may be selected to make the approximations correspond to these particular shapes. This advantage does not transfer to the adjoint variables, but this may not be too detrimental, as will be illustrated in the approximate solution to the reactor problem.

Substitution of the approximation functions into Eq. (3) reduces the Hamiltonian to a function of the control variable, the trial functions, and the mixing coefficients. Carrying out the indicated minimization of the Hamiltonian defines U, the near-optimal value of the control variable at any position t in terms of the trial functions and the mixing coefficients. A condition similar to condition (6) is obtained:

$$U = \frac{X_1}{6X_2} \quad \frac{(1 + P_1 - P_2)}{(1 + \frac{P_1}{3} - P_2)} \quad \text{if this value} \leq 1 \qquad (11a)$$

$$U = 1 \quad \text{if value computed in (11a)} > 1 \qquad (11b)$$

The mixing coefficients are selected to make the various approximations satisfy the system differential equations in some integral average sense. For example, Eq. (1) is replaced by the following n_1 algebraic equations where n_1 is the number of mixing coefficients in the x_1 approximation:

$$\int_0^1 \left\{ X_1 + UX_1 - U^2 X_2 \right\} \Psi_i dt = 0 \quad i=1,2,\ldots,n_1 \qquad (12)$$

Ψ_i may be any of a number of forms, depending upon which variation of the method of weighted residuals is used. If $\Psi_i = X_{1,i}(t)$, one of the trial functions, the method reduces to the Galerkin form. Similar sets of equations may be written to approximate Eqs. (2),(4), and (5). This results in $N = n_1 + n_2 + m_1 + m_2$ non-linear algebraic equations in terms of the N mixing coefficients.

Near-Optimal Computations for a Tubular Reactor

In order to illustrate the method, a number of specific approximations for the state and adjoint variables were considered. The first case used the following:

Case I

$$x_1 \approx X_1 = 1 + at \tag{13a}$$

$$x_2 \approx X_2 = bt \tag{13b}$$

$$p_1 \approx P_1 = 0 \tag{13c}$$

$$p_2 \approx P_2 = 0 \tag{13d}$$

This set of approximation functions includes only one trial function in each state variable approximation and none for the adjoint variables, which are effectively held constant at their boundary values. The solution of the non-linear algebraic equations for a and b resulting from the minimization of H and the application of the Galerkin method to Eqs. (1) and (2) was obtained by a Newton-Raphson technique on a digital computer, and yielded the following results:

$a = -0.422$
$b = 0.283$

In spite of the drastic treatment of the adjoint variable trajectory approximations, the near-optimal policy obtained in this way is close to the optimal one, as illustrated in Fig. 1. Case II illustrates the use of non-linear trial functions:

Case II

$$x_1 \approx X_1 = 1 + at^{1/2} \tag{14a}$$

$$x_2 \approx X_2 = bt^{1/2} \tag{14b}$$

$$p_1 \approx P_1 = 0 \tag{14c}$$

$$p_2 \approx P_2 = 0 \tag{14d}$$